HEALTHY FOOD

RENAL DIET COOKBOOK
FOR BEGINNERS

COOKBOOK

Caren Cooper

AN EASY AND ACCURATE GUIDE WITH 500 QUICK,
HEALTHY,AND KIDNEY-FRIENDLY RECIPES TO BETTER
MANAGE YOUR CHRONIC KIDNEY DISEASE WITHOUT
SACRIFICING FLAVOR.

The Table of
CONTENTS

Introduction

Are you, or do you know, someone who is suffering from kidney disease or illness? Are you tired of weekly dialysis, and you wish this suffering fades away? Then this book is for you.

Since the middle of the 20th century, the renal diet has been used when the famous scientist found some ideas and conclusions healthy and useful for kidneys. Since then, the diet has improved the health of kidney patients but also helps prevent kidney problems.

The Renal diet controls your consumption of sodium, protein, potassium, and phosphorous. A renal diet contributes to preventing renal failure. Below are a list of food/nutrients you should avoid preventing kidney-related problems:

Phosphate: Consumption of phosphate becomes dangerous when kidney failure reaches 80% and goes to the 4th/5th stage of kidney failure. So, it is better to lower your phosphate intake by counting the calories and minerals.

Potassium: After getting diagnosed, if your results show your potassium level is high in the blood, you should restrict your potassium intake. Baked and fried potatoes are very high in potassium. Leafy greens, fruit juices are high in potassium. You can still enjoy vegetables that are low in potassium.

Sodium: Adding salt is very important in our food, but when you are suffering from kidney problems, you have to omit or minimize your salt intake. Too much sodium intake can trigger high blood pressure and fluid retention in the body. You need to find substitutes that help season your food. Herbs and spices that are extracted from plants are a good option. Using garlic, pepper, mustard can increase the taste of your food without adding any salt. Avoid artificial "salts" that are low in sodium because they are high in potassium, which is also dangerous for kidney health.

Recipes from this cookbook are simple, delicious, and healthy. You can even use them as an inspiration to experiment and create your renal diet recipes. These samples can also be considered as snacks for you throughout the day.

This cookbook offers a low sodium diet, so it is essential to understand sodium intake. A low sodium renal diet can be achieved by adding potassium, low sodium intake, and adding fiber. Many people struggle with adding extra fiber to the diet, and many times it is treated as an unhealthy factor. But when added to the renal diet, you will soon understand the benefits.

If you're already used to the renal diet, you can work with the recipes from this cookbook. You can use the guide for more severe and careful renal diet beginners. If you want to live a happy, healthy renal diet, try these simple recipes for a better taste!

Chapter 1.
Understanding Kidney Disease

Kidney disease is becoming more prevalent in the United States, and so we need to learn as much about it as we can. The more we educate ourselves, the more we can do to take care of this important bodily system. If you've been diagnosed with chronic kidney disease (CKD), education can empower you to most effectively and purposefully manage the disease. Once you have a full understanding of what chronic kidney disease is, you can begin to take charge of your evolving health needs. Making healthy changes early in the stages of kidney disease will help determine how well you will manage your kidney health. I am here to guide you, every step of the way. Like any new process, it may seem intimidating at first. But this chapter provides the foundation for learning and will help you understand kidney disease as you begin your journey to healthier kidneys

What Do the Kidneys Do?

Our kidneys are small, but they do powerful things to keep our body in balance. They are bean-shaped, about the size of a fist, and are located in the middle of the back, on the left and right sides of the spine, just below the rib cage. When everything is working properly, the kidneys do many important jobs such as:
- Filter waste materials from the blood
- Remove extra fluid, or water, from the body
- Release hormones that help manage blood pressure
- Stimulate bone marrow to make red blood cells
- Make an active form of vitamin D that promotes strong, healthy bones

What Causes Kidney Disease?

There are many causes of kidney disease, including physical injury or disorders that can damage the kidneys, but the two leading causes of kidney disease are diabetes and high blood pressure. These underlying conditions also put people at risk for developing cardiovascular disease. Early treatment may not only slow down the progression of the disease, but also reduce your risk of developing heart disease or stroke.

Kidney disease can affect anyone, at any age. African Americans, Hispanics, and American Indians are at increased risk for kidney failure, because these groups have a greater prevalence of diabetes and high blood pressure.

When we digest protein, our bodies create waste products. As blood flows through the capillaries, the waste products are filtered through the urine. Substances such as protein and red blood cells are too big to pass through the capillaries and so stay in the blood. All the extra work takes a toll on the kidneys. When kidney disease is detected in the early stages, several treatments may prevent the worsening of the disease. If kidney disease is detected in the later stages, high amounts of protein in your urine, called macro albuminuria, can lead to end-stage renal disease.

The second leading cause of kidney disease is high blood pressure, also known as hypertension. One in three Americans is at risk for kidney disease because of hypertension. Although there is no cure for hypertension, certain medications, a low-sodium diet, and physical activity can lower blood pressure.

The kidneys help manage blood pressure, but when blood pressure is high, the heart has to work overtime at pumping blood. When the force of blood flow is high, blood vessels start to stretch so the blood can flow more easily. The stretching and scarring weakens the blood vessels throughout the entire body, including the kidneys. And when the kidneys' blood vessels are injured, they may not remove the waste and extra fluid from the body, creating a dangerous cycle, because the extra fluid in the blood vessels can increase blood pressure even more.

With diabetes, excess blood sugar remains in the bloodstream. The high blood sugar levels can damage the blood vessels in the kidneys and elsewhere in the body. And since high blood pressure is a complication from diabetes, the extra pressure can weaken the walls of the blood vessels, which can lead to a heart attack or stroke.
Other conditions, such as drug abuse and certain autoimmune diseases, can also cause injury to the kidneys. In fact, every drug we put into our body has to pass through the kidneys for filtration.

An autoimmune disease is one in which the immune system, designed to protect the body from illness, sees the body as an invader and attacks its own systems, including the kidneys. Some forms of lupus, for example, attack the kidneys. Another autoimmune disease that can lead to kidney failure is Good pasture syndrome, a group of conditions that affect the kidneys and the lungs. The damage to the kidneys from autoimmune diseases can lead to chronic kidney disease and kidney failure.

Treatment Plans for Chronic Kidney Disease (Ckd)

The best way to manage CKD is to be an active participant in your treatment program, regardless of your stage of renal disease. Proper treatment involves a combination of working with a healthcare team, adhering to a renal diet, and making healthy lifestyle decisions. These can all have a profoundly positive effect on your kidney disease—especially watching how you eat.

Working with your healthcare team. When you have kidney disease, working in partnership with your healthcare team can be extremely important in your treatment program as well as being personally empowering. Regularly meeting with your physician or healthcare team can arm you with resources and information that help you make informed decisions regarding your treatment needs, and provide you with a much needed opportunity to vent, share information, get advice, and receive support in effectively managing this illness.
Adhering to a renal diet. The heart of this book is the renal diet. Sticking to this diet can make a huge difference in your health and vitality. Like any change, following the diet may not be easy at first. Important changes to your diet, particularly early on, can possibly prevent the need for dialysis. These changes include limiting salt, eating a low-protein diet, reducing fat intake, and getting enough calories if you need to lose weight. Be honest with yourself first and foremost—learn what you need, and consider your personal goals and obstacles. Start by making small changes. It is okay to have some slip-ups—we all do. With guidance and support, these small changes will become habits of your promising new lifestyle. In no time, you will begin taking control of your diet and health.
Making healthy lifestyle decisions. Lifestyle choices play a crucial part in our health, especially when it comes to helping regulate kidney disease. Lifestyle choices such as allotting time for physical activity, getting enough sleep, managing weight, reducing stress, and limiting smoking and alcohol will help you take control of your overall health, making it easier to manage your kidney disease. Follow this simple formula: Keep toxins out of your body as much as you can, and build up your immune system with a good balance of exercise, relaxation, and sleep.

Chapter 2.
Different kind of Kidney failure

Doctors usually first suspect chronic kidney disease when their patients exhibit an increase in their blood creatinine levels. They will then seek to discover whether the kidney failure is acute, chronic, or acute superimposed on chronic. This may seem confusing, but these three terms have very simple descriptions:

1.   Acute: a condition experienced for a short period of time, but often to an intense degree.
2.   Chronic: a condition that persists for a long period of time or persistently.
3.   Acute superimposed on chronic: an acute disease that worsens renal function in a patient with chronic kidney disease.

Along with uncovering the duration of kidney failure, your doctor will search for the cause, as there are many potential causes. Sometimes, it is not easy to discover the duration of renal failure, and it might be easier first to discover the cause and then determine the duration from there.

Your doctor will test your urine, known as urinalysis. The purpose of this is to get the details on your urinary sediment, phosphate, creatinine, calcium, urea nitrogen, and electrolytes. They will also run a complete blood count, which is important as many people with kidney disease will experience reduced red blood cell production. Sometimes, to determine the cause of your disease, a doctor will run specific serologic tests in order to search for certain antibodies. The easiest way to differentiate chronic kidney disease from an acute kidney injury is with a medical history of abnormal urinalysis or elevated creatinine.

It becomes increasingly difficult to make a precise diagnosis when the renal function declines to values close to end-stage renal disease. In this case, the definitive diagnostic measure is a kidney biopsy. Yet, a doctor might not be able to perform a kidney biopsy when an ultrasound indicates the kidneys are small with excessive fibrous tissue. In this case, the risks of the procedure will outweigh the benefits. Your doctor will be able to examine the ultrasound to determine whether or not a renal biopsy is needed and if the benefits outweigh the risk or not.

There are five stages of chronic kidney disease, which doctors use to classify how damaged the kidneys have become, mark the progression of the disease, and indicate the severity of the side effects. A doctor will use the glomerular filtration rate (GFR) test in order to classify which stage a person is in.

Stage One

•   A person has normal GFR results (≥ 90 mL/min/1.73 m2) along with either persistent excessive albumin protein in the urine, structural kidney disease, or hereditary kidney disease. Kidney damage may also be viewable through an ultrasound, CT scan, X-ray with contrast, and an MRI.

Stage Two

•   GFR results 60 to 89 mL/min/1.73 m2. At this point, the person is unlikely to be experiencing symptoms from the disease. Therefore, if the disease is discovered this early, it is often only due to the treatment of another disease, such as diabetes or high blood pressure.

Stage Three A.

•   GFR results 45 to 59 mL/min/1.73 m2. A person may start to experience symptoms during stage three (either type A. or B.). These may include fatigue, lower back pain, shortness of breath, swelling, fluid retention, urination changes, muscle cramps, restless legs, or trouble sleeping. These symptoms are the same in both types of stage three.

Stage Three B.

•   GFR results 30 to 44 mL/min/1.73 m2

Stage Four

•   GFR results 15 to 29 mL/min/1.73 m2. Along with the symptoms in stage three, a person may experience additional symptoms in stage four. These symptoms can include nausea, vomiting, loss of appetite, taste changes, bad breath, difficulty concentrating, and nerve problems such as numbness and tingling.
Stage Five

•   GFR results <15 mL/min/1.73 m2. Along with the symptoms of the previous stages, a person in stage five (kidney failure) may experience itching, skin color changes, puffy eyes, and little to no urination.
Once your doctor knows the cause of your kidney disease, the duration, and stage of kidney disease, they will be able to devise an individual treatment plan. While kidney disease can be scary, if you follow the treatment plan and make beneficial lifestyle and diet changes, you can stop the progression of the disease and improve your prognosis in many cases. With a little knowledge, you no longer have to fear.

Chapter 3.
Kidney Failure Treatment

If you are unfortunate enough to experience kidney failure, then you have two options. You can look for a donor who might be able to donate one of their kidneys, or you may want to opt for dialysis.

Dialysis is an expensive and recurring process that you will need to do over and over again, depending on the condition of your kidneys.
Transplant, on the other hand, is mostly a one-time major expense, given that you are able to find a perfect match.

But regardless of the path you choose, there are thousands of people who have led a healthy and normal life, even with dialysis/kidney transplant. So, even if you are a victim, don't lose all your hopes just yet.

Let me talk a little bit about dialysis.

Dialysis is basically a process that helps to get rid of toxin and extra fluid build-up in your body through artificial means. However, an external machine won't really be able to do everything that your kidney can do, so even with dialysis, you might face some complications in the long run.

That being said, there are two types of dialysis.

Peritoneal Dialysis

This form of treatment tries to cleanse your blood by utilizing the lining of your abdominal area and cleansing solution known as "Dialysate." The best part about this dialysis is that it can easily be done at home, as long as you have a clean and private area.

Hemodialysis

This particular treatment is also known as "Hemo" and is the most common one for kidney failures. This form of dialysis utilizes a machine to filter and clean out your blood. It is recommended that you do this at a hospital; however, if you have the budget, then it is possible to do it at home, as well.
After dialysis is the kidney transplant.

Kidney Transplant

A kidney transplant, as the name implies, is essentially surgery that gives you a healthy kidney from a donor's body. It is possible to have a kidney donated from a live body or a donor who has already died but has donated their kidney for a good cause. As mentioned above, if you can get a healthy kidney, then it is possible to lead a completely normal life.
And lastly, you can try medical management.

Medical Management
If you have budget issues or j want to avoid dialysis or transplant altogether, then there are some medical solutions that you might look into to reduce the symptoms of kidney failure.
They won't completely reverse the effects, but they might let you stay healthy until your kidneys are unable to function anymore.

If you opt for medical management, then the first thing to do is consult with your physician, as they will be able to point you in the right direction.

They will create a care plan for you that will guide you on what you should do and what you should not do. Make sure always to keep a copy of the plan wherever you go and discuss the terms with your loved ones as well.
It should be noted that most individuals who tend to go for medical management opt for hospice care.

The primary aim of hospice care is to try and decrease your pain and improve the quality of your final days before you die.

In medical management, you can expect a hospice to:
•   Help you by providing you with a nursing home
•   Help your family and friends to support you
•   Try to improve the quality of your life as much as possible
•   Try to provide medications and care to help you manage your symptoms

But keep in mind that regardless of which path you take, always discuss everything with your doctor.

Learning to Deal with Kidney Failure
Learning that you are suffering from kidney failure might be a difficult thing to cope with. No matter how long you have been preparing for the inevitable, this is something that will come as a shock to you.

But, as mentioned earlier, just because you have started dialysis doesn't mean that everything that you hold dear has to come to an end!

It might be a little bit difficult at first to get yourself oriented to a new routine, but once you get into the groove, you'll start feeling much better.
Your nurses, loved ones, doctors, and co-workers will all be there to support you.
To make things easier, though, let me break down the individual types of problems that you might face and how you can deal with them.

Stress during Kidney Failure

When you are suffering from kidney failure, it's normal to be stressed out all the time. This might lead you to skip meals or even forgetting your medication, which might affect your health even more.

But you need to understand that life is full of hurdles and setbacks, and you really can't let them hold you back.

In that light, here are six tips to help you keep your stress under control:
•   Make sure to take some time to relax and unwind. Try to practice deep breathing, visualization, meditation, or even muscle relaxation. All of these will help you to stay calm and keep your body healthy.
•   Make sure to involve yourself in regular exercise. Take a hike, ride a bicycle or just simply take a jog. They all help. And if those aren't your thing, then you can always go for something more soothing, like tai chi or yoga.
•   When you are feeling too stressed, try to call up a friend or a beloved family member and talk to them. And if that's not helping, you can always take help from a psychiatrist/counselor.

•   Try to accept the things that are not under your control, and you can't change. Trying to enforce a change on something that is not within your reach will only make things worse for you. Better advice is to look for better ways of handling the situation instead of trying to change it.

•   Don't put too much pressure on yourself; try to be good to yourself and don't expect much. You are a human being, after all, right? You can make mistakes, so accept that. Just try your best.

•   And lastly, always try to maintain a positive attitude. Even when things go completely wrong, try to see the good instead of the bad and focus on that. Try to find things in all phases of your life that make you happy and that you appreciate, such as your friends, work, health, and family, for example. You have no idea how much help a simple change of perspective can bring.

And on the topic of working out.

Exercise

Apart from the special diet, such as the Renal Diet, physical activity is another way through which you can improve the quality of your life.

This might be a little bit tough to do if you are alone, but it is very much possible. However, you should keep in mind that working out alone won't help you; you must work out and follow a well-balanced, healthy diet.

Both of these combined will go to great lengths to help you lose weight and control your disease.

In fact, a study has shown that people who try to complete 10,1000 steps per day and work out for about 2½ hours every week while cutting down 500-800 calories per day and following a proper diet routinely have a 50% chance of reducing blood sugar to normal levels, which will further help you to stay healthy.

Common forms of exercise include:

•   Stair climbing

•   Tai Chi

•   Stretching

•   Yoga

•   Cycling

•   Walking

•   Swimming

And so on.

To perform these normal workouts, you don't have to join a gym or even buy any sort of expensive equipment! You can simply take a walk around your streets, do yoga at home, and so on.

Just make sure to consult with your doctor to find out which exercise is suitable for you and adjust them to your dialysis routine.

Anxiety and Depression

These two are possibly the most prominent issues that you are going to face. A feeling of depression might last for a long period of time if left unattended. Anxiety might come at the same time, but it won't last for long.

Either way, mood swings will occur that will suddenly make you sad.
However, you should know that it is completely normal to feel anxious or sad when you're going through such a huge change in life. This is even more prominent if you start taking dialysis, as it will require you to completely change your daily routine and follow a different type of diet.

During this adjusting phase, you'll feel many emotions, such as anger, fear, sadness, etc.

To summarize:

The symptoms of depression are:
•   Loss of interest
•   Loss of any appetite
•   Sleeping problems
On the other hand, symptoms of anxiety are:
•   Constant sweating
•   Quick breathing
•   Inconsistent heartbeat
•   Constant troubling thoughts

Regardless, the main thing to know is that you are not alone in this fight. Thousands of people have and are going through the same experience. Many people often feel left alone and lose the will to fight, but it doesn't have to be the same for you.
Help is always available! Try sharing with your family members, join support groups, talk to a social worker, etc.

It doesn't matter what your situation is; if you just reach out to the right person, then you will always find the help and support that you need

Chapter 4.
The Renal Diet and It Benefits

Dietary control, including protein, phosphorus, and sodium limitation, can impact perpetual renal patients by following conventional and nontraditional cardiovascular hazard factors.

Circulatory strain control might be supported by the decrease of sodium consumption and the vegan idea of the eating routine, which is significant for bringing down serum cholesterol and improving the plasma lipid profile.

Protein-limited eating regimens may have likewise calming and against oxidant properties.

The general principles of diet treatment for chronic kidney patients are as follows:
•   Limit protein intake to 0.8 gm/kg per kilogram per day for non-dialysis patients. Patients on dialysis need a greater amount of protein to compensate for the possible loss of proteins during the procedure. (1.0 to 1.2 gm/kg daily according to body weight)
•   Take enough carbohydrates to provide energy
•   Take normal amounts of oil—reduction of butter, pure fat, and oil intake.
•   Restriction of fluid and water intake in case of swelling (edema)
•   Dietary intake of sodium, potassium, and phosphorus limitation
•   Take adequate amounts of vitamins and trace elements. A high-fiber diet is recommended.

The details of the selection and modification of the diet for chronic kidney patients are as follows:

High-Calorie Intake

In addition to daily activities to maintain heat, growth, and body weight the body needs calories. Calories are taken with carbohydrates and fats. According to body weight, the daily normal calorie intake of patients suffering from chronic kidney disease is 35-40 kcal/kg. If caloric intake is insufficient, the body uses proteins to provide calories. Such protein distribution may cause harmful effects, such as improper nutrition and increased production of waste materials. Therefore, it is very important to provide sufficient calories to CKD patients. It is important to calculate the patient's daily calorie requirement based on the ideal body weight, not the current weight.

Carbohydrates
Carbohydrates are the primary source of calories required for the body. Diabetes and obesity patients should limit the number of carbohydrates. It is best to use complex carbohydrates that can be obtained from whole grains such as whole wheat or raw rice that can provide fiber. They should constitute a large part of the number of carbohydrates in the diet. The proportion of all other sugar-containing substances should not exceed 20% of the total carbohydrate intake, particularly in diabetic patients. As long as chocolate, hazelnut, or banana desserts are consumed in a limited amount, non-diabetic patients may be replaced with calories, fruit, pies, pastry, cookies, and protein.
Oils
Fats are a source of calories for the body and provide twice as many carbohydrates and proteins. Chronic kidney patients should limit the intake of saturated fat and cholesterol that may cause heart disease. In unsaturated fat, it is necessary to pay attention to the proportion of monounsaturated fat and polyunsaturated fat. Excessive uptake of omega-6 polyunsaturated fatty acids (CFAs) and a relatively high omega-6 / omega-3 ratio are detrimental, while the low omega-6 / omega-3 ratio has beneficial effects.

The use of vegetable oils instead of uniform oils will achieve this goal. Trans fat-containing substances such as potato chips, sweet buns, instant cookies, and pastries are extremely dangerous and should be avoided.

Restriction of Protein Intake

Protein is essential for the restoration and maintenance of body tissues. It also helps to heal wounds and fight infection. In patients with chronic renal failure who do not undergo dialysis, protein limitation is recommended to reduce the rate of decrease in renal function and postpone the need for dialysis and renal transplantation. (<0.8 gm/ kg daily according to body weight). However, excessive protein restriction should also be avoided due to the risk of malnutrition.

Anorexia is a common condition in patients with chronic kidney disease. Strict protein restriction, poor diet, weight loss, fatigue, loss of body resistance, and loss of appetite increase the risk of death. High proteins such as meat, poultry, and fish, eggs, and tofu are preferred. Chronic kidney patients should avoid high protein diets. Similarly, protein supplements or medications such as creatinine used for muscle development should be avoided unless recommended by a physician or dietician. However, as the patient begins dialysis, daily protein intake should be increased by 1.0 to 1.2 gm/kg body weight to recover the proteins lost during the procedure.

Fluid intake

Why should chronic kidney patients take precautions about fluid intake?

The kidneys are important in maintaining the correct amount of water in the body by removing excess liquid as urea. In patients with chronic kidney disease, the urea volume usually decreases as the kidney functions deteriorate. Reduction of urea excretion from the body causes fluid retention in the body, resulting in facial swelling, swelling of legs and hands, and high blood pressure. A build-up of fluid in the lungs causes shortness of breath and difficulty breathing. It can be life-threatening if not checked.
What precautions should chronic kidney patients take to control fluid intake?
The amount of fluid taken on a physician's advice should be recorded and monitored to prevent overloading or loss of fluid. The amount of water to be taken for each chronic kidney patient may vary, and this rate is calculated according to the urea excretion and fluid status of each patient.
What is the recommended amount of fluid for patients with chronic kidney disease?
Unlimited edema and water intake can be done in patients who do not have edema and can throw enough urea from the body. It is a common misconception that patients with kidney disease should take large amounts of water and fluids to protect their kidneys. The recommended amount of liquid depends on the patient's clinical condition and renal function.
Patients with edema who cannot appoint sufficient urea from the body should limit fluid intake. To reduce swelling, fluid intake within 24 hours should be less than the amount of urine produced by the daily body.

In patients with edema, the amount of fluid that should be taken daily should be 500 ml more than the previous day's urine volume to prevent fluid overload or fluid loss. This additional 500 ml of liquid will approximately compensate for the fluids lost by perspiration and exhalation.

Why should chronic kidney patients keep a record of their daily weight?

Patients need to record their weight daily to detect fluid increase or loss or to monitor fluid volume in their bodies. Bodyweight will remain constant if the instructions for fluid intake are strictly followed. Sudden weight gain indicates excessive fluid overload due to increased fluid intake in the body. Weight gain is a warning that the patient should make more rigorous fluid restriction. Weight loss is usually caused by fluid restriction and the use of diuretics.

Useful Tips for Restricting Fluid Intake

Reduce salty, spicy, or fried foods in your diet because these foods can increase your thirst and cause more fluid consumption.

Only for water when you are thirsty. Do not drink as a habit or because everyone drinks. When thirsty, consume only a small amount of water or try ice — sure, taking a little ice cube. Ice stays in the mouth longer than water to give a more satisfying result than the same amount of water. Remember to calculate the amount of liquid consumed. To calculate, freeze the amount of water allocated for drinking in the ice block.

To prevent dry mouth, gargle with water, but do not swallow the water. Dry mouth can also be reduced by chewing gum, sucking hard candies, lemon slices, or mint candies, and using a small amount of water to moisturize your mouth.

Always use small cups or glasses to limit fluid intake. Instead of consuming extra water for medication use, take your medicines while drinking water after meals.

High blood sugar in diabetic patients can increase the level of thirst. It is essential to keep blood sugar under tight control to reduce thirst.

Since the person's thirst increases in hot weather, measures to be in cooler environments may be preferred and recommended.

Chapter 5.
The Causes of Renal Failure

Renal disease, according to experts, requires early diagnosis and targeted treatment to prevent or delay both a condition of acute or chronic renal failure and the appearance of cardiovascular complications to which it is often associated.

In fact, hypertension and diabetes, not adequately controlled by drug therapy, prostatic hypertrophy, kidney stones or bulky tumors can promote onset as they reduce the normal flow of urine, increase the pressure inside the kidneys and limit functionality.
Or the kidney damage can be determined by inflammatory processes (pyelonephritis, glomerulonephritis) or by the formation of cysts inside the kidneys (polycystic kidney disease) or by the chronic use of some drugs, alcohol and drugs consumed in excess.

A fundamental role in alleviating the work of the already compromised kidneys is carried out by the diet which is, therefore, the first prevention. It must be studied with an expert nutritionist or a nephrologist in order to maintain or reach an ideal weight on the one hand and on the other to reduce the intake of sodium (salt), and the consequent control of blood pressure, and / or other substances (minerals), without creating malnutrition or nutritional deficiencies. Particular attention should also be paid to cholesterol, triglycerides and blood sugar levels.

Understanding what causes kidney failure goes a long way to deciding just what kind of treatment you should focus on. The most important factor that you should focus on is, of course, your diet. But as you focus on your diet, make sure that you are following your doctor's instructions, in the event of other complications. Let us look at a few of the common causes of kidney diseases.

Diabetes

We do know that diabetes is one of the leading causes of CKD. But we have yet to understand in detail why and how it can cause so much harm to the kidneys.
Time for a crash course in diabetes. What many may already know is that diabetes affects our body's insulin production rate. But what many may not know is the extent of damage that diabetes can cause to the kidneys.

High Blood Pressure

An important thing to remember here is that high blood pressure can be both a cause and symptom of CKD, similar to the case of diabetes.
So, what exactly is blood pressure? People often throw the term around, but they are unable to pinpoint exactly what happens when the pressure in the blood increases.

Autoimmune Diseases

IgA nephropathy and lupus are two examples of autoimmune diseases that can lead to kidney diseases. But just what exactly are autoimmune diseases?
They are conditions where your immune system perceives your body as a threat and begins to attack it.

We all know that the immune system is like the defense force of our body. It is responsible for guiding the soldiers of our body, known as white blood cells, or WBCs. The immune system is responsible for fighting against foreign materials, such as viruses and bacteria. When the system senses these foreign bodies, various fighter cells, including the WBCs, are deployed in order to combat the threat.

Typically, your immune system is a self-learning system. This means that it is capable of understanding the threat and memorizing its features, behaviors, and attack patterns. This is an important capability of the immune system since it allows the system to differentiate between our own cells and foreign cells. But when you have an autoimmune disease, your immune system suddenly considers certain parts of your body, such as your skin or joints, as foreign. It then proceeds to create antibodies that begin to

Symptoms of kidney disease?

If kidney disease progresses, then the blood level of end products of metabolism increases; this in turn, is the cause of feeling unwell. Various health problems may occur, such as high blood pressure, anemia (anemia), bone disease, premature cardiovascular calcification, discoloration, and change in the composition and volume of urine.
As the disease progresses, the main symptoms can be:
• 	Weakness, a feeling of weakness
• 	Trouble sleeping
• 	Lack of appetite
• 	Dry skin, itchy skin
• 	Muscle cramps especially at night
• 	Swelling in the legs
• 	Swelling around the eyes, especially in the morning
Diagnose With Kidney Disease
There are two simple tests that your family doctor can prescribe to diagnose a kidney disease.

Blood test: glomerular filtration rate (GFR) and serum creatinine level. Creatinine is one of those end products of protein metabolism, the level of which in the blood depends on age, gender, muscle mass, nutrition, physical activity, the foods taken before taking the sample (for example, a lot of meat was eaten), and some drugs. Creatinine is removed from the body through the kidneys, and if the work of the kidneys slows down, the level of creatinine in the blood plasma increases. Determining the level of creatinine alone is not sufficient for the diagnosis of chronic kidney disease since its value begins to exceed the upper limit of the norm only when GFR is decreased by half. GFR is calculated using a formula that includes four parameters which are; the creatinine reading, age, gender, and race of the patient. GFR shows the level at which the kidneys can filter. In the case of chronic kidney disease, the GFR indicator indicates the stage of the severity of kidney disease.

Urine analysis: the content of albumin in the urine is determined; also, the values of albumin and creatinine in the urine are determined by each other. Albumin is a protein in the urine that usually enters the urine in minimal quantities. Even a small increase in the level of albumin in the urine in some people may be an early sign of incipient kidney disease, especially in those with diabetes and high blood pressure. In the case of normal kidney function, albumin in the urine should not be more than 3 mg/mmol (or 30 mg/g). If albumin excretion increases even more, then it already speaks of kidney disease.

Chapter 6.
What you can Eat, What to Avoid

Foods You Need
There are many foods that work well within the renal diet, and once you see the available variety, it will not seem as restrictive or difficult to follow. The key is focusing on the foods with a high level of nutrients, which make it easier for the kidneys to process waste by not adding too much that the body needs to discard. Balance is a major factor in maintaining and improving long-term renal function.

Garlic

An excellent, vitamin-rich food for the immune system, garlic is a tasty substitute for salt in a variety of dishes. It acts as a significant source of vitamin C and B6, while aiding the kidneys in ridding the body of unwanted toxins. It's a great, healthy way to add flavor for skillet meals, pasta, soups, and stews.

Berries

All berries are considered a good renal diet food due to their high level of fiber, antioxidants, and delicious taste, making them an easy option to include as a light snack or as an ingredient in smoothies, salads, and light desserts. Just one handful of blueberries can provide almost one day's vitamin C requirement, as well as a boost of fiber, which is good for weight loss and maintenance.

Bell Peppers

Flavorful and easy to enjoy both raw and cooked, bell peppers offer a good source of vitamin C, vitamin A, and fiber. Along with other kidney-friendly foods, they make the detoxification process much easier while boosting your body's nutrient level to prevent further health conditions and reduce existing deficiencies.

Onions

This nutritious and tasty vegetable is excellent as a companion to garlic in many dishes, or on its own. Like garlic, onions can provide flavor as an alternative to salt, and provides a good source of vitamin C, vitamin B, manganese, and fiber, as well. Adding just one quarter or half of an onion is often enough for most meals, because of its strong, pungent flavor.

Macadamia Nuts

If you enjoy nuts and seeds as snacks, you many soon learn that many contain high amounts of phosphorus and should be avoided or limited as much as possible. Fortunately, macadamia nuts are an easier option to digest and process, as they contain much lower amounts of phosphorus and make an excellent substitute for other nuts. They are a good source of other nutrients, as well, such as vitamin B, copper, manganese, iron, and healthy fats.

Pineapple
Unlike other fruits that are high in potassium, pineapple is an option that can be enjoyed more often than bananas and kiwis. Citrus fruits are generally high in potassium as well, so if you find yourself craving an orange or grapefruit, choose pineapple instead. In addition to providing a high levels of vitamin B and fiber, pineapples can reduce inflammation thanks to an enzyme called brome lain.

Mushrooms

In general, mushrooms are a safe, healthy option for the renal diet, especially the shiitake variety, which are high in nutrients such as selenium, vitamin B, and manganese. They contain a moderate amount of plant-based protein, which is easier for your body to digest and use than animal proteins. Shiitake and Portobello mushrooms are often used in vegan diets as a meat substitute, due to their texture and pleasant flavor.

Foods you need to Avoid

Eating restrictions might be different depending upon your level of kidney disease. If you are in the early stages of kidney disease, you may have different restrictions as compared to those who are at the end-stage renal disease, or kidney failure. In contrast to this, people with an end-stage renal disease requiring dialysis will face different eating restrictions. Let's discuss some of the foods to avoid while being on the renal diet.

Dark-Colored Colas contain calories, sugar, phosphorus, etc. They contain phosphorus to enhance flavor, increase its life and avoid discoloration. Which can be found in a product's ingredient list. This addition of phosphorus varies depending on the type of cola. Mostly, the dark-colored colas contain 50–100 mg in a 200-ml serving. Therefore, dark colas should be avoided on a renal diet.

Canned Foods including soups, vegetables, and beans, are low in cost but contain high amounts of sodium due to the addition of salt to increase its life. Due to this amount of sodium inclusion in canned goods, it is better that people with kidney disease should avoid consumption. Opt for lower-sodium content with the label "no salt added". One more way is to drain or rinse canned foods, such as canned beans and tuna, could decrease the sodium content by 33–80%, depending on the product.

Brown Rice is a whole grain containing a higher concentration of potassium and phosphorus than its white rice counterpart. One cup already cooked brown rice possess about 150 mg of phosphorus and 154 mg of potassium, whereas, one cup of already cooked white rice has an amount of about 69 mg of phosphorus and 54 mg of potassium. Bulgur, buckwheat, pearled barley and couscous are equally beneficial, low-phosphorus options and might be a good alternative instead of brown rice.

Bananas are high potassium content, low in sodium, and provides 422 mg of potassium per banana. It might disturb your daily balanced potassium intake to 2,000 mg if a banana is a daily staple.

Whole-Wheat Bread may harm individuals with kidney disease. But for healthy individuals, it is recommended over refined, white flour bread. White bread is recommended instead of whole-wheat varieties for individuals with kidney disease just because it has phosphorus and potassium. If you add more bran and whole grains in the bread, then the amount of phosphorus and potassium contents goes higher.

Oranges and Orange Juice are enriched with vitamin C content and potassium. 184 grams provides 333 mg of potassium and 473 mg of potassium in one cup of orange juice. With these calculations, oranges and orange juice must be avoided or used in a limited amount while being on a renal diet.

Some of the high-potassium foods, likewise potatoes and sweet potatoes, could also be soaked or leached to lessen the concentration of potassium contents. Cut them into small and thin pieces and boil those for at least 10 minutes can reduce the potassium content by about 50%. Potatoes which are soaked in a wide pot of water for as low as four hours before cooking could possess even less potassium content than those not soaked before cooking. This is known as "potassium leaching," or the "double cook Direction."

If you are suffering from or living with kidney disease, reducing your potassium, phosphorus and sodium intake is an essential aspect of managing and tackling the disease. The foods with high-potassium, high-sodium, and high-phosphorus content listed above should always be limited or avoided. These restrictions and nutrients intakes may differ depending on the level of damage to your kidneys. Following a renal diet might be a daunting procedure and a restrictive one most of the times. But, working with your physician and nutrition specialist and a renal dietitian can assist you to formulate a renal diet specific to your individual needs. #

Renal Diet Shopping List

Vegetables:
- Arugula (raw)
- Alfalfa sprouts
- Bamboo shoots
- Asparagus
- Beans - pinto, wax, fava, green
- Bean sprouts
- Bitter melon (balsam pear)
- Broccoli
- Broad beans (boiled, fresh)
- Cactus
- Cabbage - red, swamp, Napa/
Suey Choy, skunk
- Carrots
- Calabash
- Celery
- Cauliflower
- Chayote
- Celeriac (cooked)
- Collard greens
- Chicory
- Cucumber
- Corn
- Okra
- Onions
- Pepitas
- (Green) Peas
- Peppers
- Radish
- Radicchio
- Seaweed
- Rapini (raw)
- Shallots
- Green lettuce (raw)
- Snow peas
- Dandelion greens (raw)
- Daikon
- Plant Leaves
- Drumstick
- Endive
- Eggplant
- Fennel bulb
- Escarole
- Fiddlehead greens
- Ferns
- Hearts of Palm
- Irish moss

- Hominy
- Jicama, raw
- Leeks
- Kale(raw)
- Mushrooms (raw white)
- Lettuce (raw)
- Mustard greens
- Squash
- Turnip
- Tomatillos (raw)
- Watercress
- Turnip greens
- Wax beans
- Water chestnuts (canned)
- Winter melon
- Wax gourd
- Zucchini (raw)

Fruits:
- Acerola Cherries
- Apple
- Blackberries
- Asian Pear
- Boysenberries
- Blueberries
- Cherries
- Casaba melon
- Clementine
- Chokeberries
- Crabapples
- Cloudberries
- Cranberries (fresh)
- Grapefruit
- Gooseberries
- Pomegranate
- Grapes
- Rambutan
- Quince
- Rhubarb
- Raspberries (fresh or frozen)
- Jujubes
- Golden Berry
- Kumquat
- Jackfruit
- Lingonberries
- Lemon
- Loganberries
- Lime

- Mandarin orange
- Peach
- Pineapple
- Pear
- Plum
- Strawberries
- Rose-apple
- Tangerine
- Tangelo
- Watermelon

Fresh Meat, Seafood, and Poultry:

- Chicken
- Beef and Ground Beef
- Goat
- Duck
- Wild Game
- Pork
- Lamb
- Veal
- Turkey
- Fish

Milk, Eggs, and Dairy:

Milk:

- Milk (½-1 cup/day)

Non-Dairy Milk:

- Almond Fresh (Original, Unsweetened, Vanilla)
- Almond Breeze (Original, Vanilla, Vanilla Unsweetened, Original Unsweetened)
- Silk True Almond Beverage (Unsweetened Original, Original, Vanilla, Unsweetened Vanilla)
- Good Karma Flax Delight (Vanilla, Original, Unsweetened)
- Rice Dream Rice Drink (Vanilla Classic, Non-Enriched Original Classic)
- Silk Soy Beverage (Original, Vanilla, Unsweetened)
- Natura Organic Fortified Rice Beverage (Original, Vanilla)
- PC Organics Fortified Rice Beverage

Other Dairy Products:

- Non-Hydrogenated Margarine (Salt-Free or Regular)
- Butter (Unsalted or Regular)
- Whipping Cream
- Sour Cream
- Whipped Cream

Chapter 7.
Lifestyle For Preventing Kidney Disease

Lifestyle for a Healthy Kidney
You would definitely vow to stick to a fitness routine at least once every year. However, if you have had some difficulties with the follow-through, you are definitely in good company. Yet there are so many motives for making the commitment and continuing with it again.

Everybody's got a different excuse to lose momentum. The bottom line is that it's never too late to start a workout routine if staying healthy is essential to you. And it takes less time than to navigate down the Facebook page; one may fit in a day's work out. Possibly, when you watch TV, you should do it. If you follow guidelines of organizations such as the ACE (American Council on Exercise) and CDC (Centers for Disease Control & Prevention).

A total of 150 minutes of exercise per week is what you need to boost your cardiac well-being and decrease your chance of all forms of other diseases. It is totally up to you when and how you fit these minutes into your daily routine.
But start now, and use these ideas to help make your workout part of exercise.
Set a SMART goal
A SMART purpose, according to ACE, is to be:
*   Specific
*   Measurable measurements
*   Achievable
*   Right
*   Time

Period (fulfilled with a deadline and completed in a specified period)
Having objectives helps to offer concentration and order to what you wish to do. Meeting targets is rewarding because it helps create excitement, exercise experts claim. Only pay particular attention to the portion of this equation that is "attainable."
Just an impossible target sets you up to struggle. Instead of forcing yourself to exercise every day for 30 minutes every day of the week because you can't even squeeze in 15 on other days, look at your calendar to find two days when you can raise your gym period to 30 minutes reasonably. All adds up to get you to your 150-minute week target.
Vowing to Take More Steps Each Day
For almost a decade, public health specialists at the CDC have been encouraging Americans to take 10,000 steps per day. The 10,000 level averages out at around 5 miles a day, and "healthy" are known to be those that exercise as far. Those that get in 12,500 steps a day are "very involved." Even if weight reduction is not your priority, you can try to improve your everyday mileage to attain or sustain overall healthy health.
Render Exercise a Way of Life, not a Fad
Some individuals make the error of going hard for exercise targets, but they slacken off after they have been reached. They use fitness as a means to a goal, not a way of living their lives. This will result in health conditions and weight gain. Failure to see health as a lifestyle option ensures that daily activity's long-term advantages would not be reaped. Sure, in the short term, exercising will help you reduce or retain weight. Yet lifelong gains are created by an active lifestyle. It will lower the risk of future health problems, including:
*   Elevated Blood Pressure
*   Diabetes Nausea
*   Cardiac Disorder
*   Obesity
Exercise leads to better well-being and wellness, so make it a priority-it's never too late.

For Kidney Failure, What Foods do you Eat?

This may be a little complicated at first to put together a good renal disease meal program, particularly if you don't know which foods you shouldn't eat with renal disease People also want to think too deeply on what they cannot feed that they get overwhelmed to the extent that they don't know how much you can consume on a renal diet versus what you can eat. The trick is to reflect on the key ingredients you can avoid while still reflecting on the several choices that you do have available.
Here are few explanations of kidney disorder foods that you can eat:

Foods Unprocessed

In the U.S., in particular, people appear to rely on packaged foods to make their meals. Such goods are full of additives that are really not safe for anybody, including an individual with renal disease. Huge quantities of salt and lots of other additives are loaded with packaged foods like canned cheese and macaroni meal helper sets and even plain rice dishes, which come in a package. As a common concept, you shouldn't consume anything if it arrives in a wooden box. You should instead depend on the natural foods that can help the body regenerate and fill you up. When you're about to make any changes, learning what you should consume on a kidney diet helps. Without the additional preservatives, discover methods to make your preferred dishes from scratch.

The Natural Produce

Sometimes, vegetables and fruit are considered natural medication for your health, so the produce department is always a perfect way to start while you search for groceries. It should always be in your cart or on your dining table, especially foods like bell peppers, onions, cabbage, and super-foods such as berries. Ensure that you're still paying care to your potassium consumption if you're in the latter stages of the kidney disease, which may reduce your development choices a little more. You may ask what foods produced not to consume with renal disease, but this depends on your process and diet limits. Check for more choices with our meal preparation solution: 21 Day Pre-Dialysis Kidney Disease Vegetarian Meal Schedule

The Appropriate Grains

Although your kidneys might not have processed some whole grain choices, you may always appreciate stuff like pasta and rice in moderation. To make it simpler for the kidneys to absorb your consuming meal byproducts due to potassium & phosphorus limits, sticking to the white varieties of these ingredients. You will appreciate the whole grain forms to raise fiber if you are not limited (Stage 3 / 4 CKD).

Spices and Herbs

To make meals taste nice, you do not need salt. If you sprinkle in numerous spices which are part of foods you may eat on a renal diet, you may begin to find that foods naturally tastes more delightful and have deeper flavors than you have ever thought possible. Go for new or dried herbs & spices (salt-free) to season your meals anytime you need anything special to dress up the recipes.
Lean Proteins
You might be or might not need to restrict the protein consumption, based on what process of renal disease you're in. However, it is recommended that most patients also have serving of lean protein at least once a day. Normally, fish, egg whites, poultry, and tofu are the top options. Fish is particularly good for you, as it gives your diet with good healthy omega 3s. To create great and satisfying meals, you can use any of these options, and the choices are only as restricted as your imagination.

Consider tacos, fajitas, casseroles, and much more, beginning with these excellent options for lean protein.

You will start to create a tasty and balanced renal disease meal schedule, beginning with any of these food groups & examples. Before creating new diet decisions or changing drastically what you consume for your renal illness, always consult a doctor.

Chapter 8.
How to Slow Kidney Disease

8 Strategic Steps to Slow Kidney Disease
Seek treatment for hypertension
The pressure is now considered the leading cause of chronic renal failure. According to nephrologist Nestor Schor, professor at Unifesp, the increase in blood pressure damages the blood vessels of the kidneys and may cause hypertensive nephropathy. "This way, the organ becomes overloaded, and little by little loses its filtering capacity," he explains. Taking care of hypertension is essential even when it is not the cause of chronic renal failure, as it becomes even more important in the advanced stage of the disease.
Control of diabetes

"Diabetes is the second leading cause of chronic renal failure," says nephrologist Lucio Roberto Requião Moura of Hospital Israelita Albert Einstein. This is because the disease triggers the so-called diabetic nephropathy, a change in kidney vessels that leads to a protein loss in the urine. Besides, diabetes favours atherosclerosis, the formation of plaque fat in the arteries that hinders the filtration work of the kidneys. Over time, more and more toxic substances are trapped in the body, which can lead to death. One way to detect the problem, therefore, is to do urine tests to find out if the protein is being eliminated. Those already diagnosed with diabetes need to be more aware of their kidney health.
Watch the weight
Overweight people (Discover their ideal weight) have a higher risk of developing hypertension and diabetes, which is reason enough not to let the scale hand rise, says nephrologist Lucio. Added to this is the fact that obesity alters the way blood reaches the kidneys by the influence of certain hormones, overloading the organ. More so, being overweight is a risk factor for high cholesterol and triglycerides.
Adapt your diet
When it comes to food, analyzing the underlying disease that triggered kidney failure is critical. If it is diabetes, for example, the diet should be the right diet for those with diabetes. If it is hypertension, then there should be reduced salt intake. "However, in general, it is recommended that the patient avoid excessive protein intake, especially of animal origin, which gives rise to toxic elements in the body that would make the kidneys work harder," explains nephrologist Nestor. In specific cases of insufficiency yet, there may be retention of potassium in the body. Patients with this problem need to prepare food in a way that causes them to release some of this nutrient. Vegetables, for example, need to be cooked.

Inquire about medications

Self-medication is dangerous even for healthy people. For those with kidney failure, however, use without proper medical evaluation can accelerate kidney deterioration. "The most dangerous are non- hormonal anti-inflammatory drugs," warns nephrologist Lucio. Therefore, explain your problem at the beginning of every medical appointment to avoid aggravating the disease.

Way to drink alcohol
Although no studies are proving the isolated relationship between alcohol intake and chronic renal failure, alcohol abuse compromises the functioning of the body as a whole. Thus, it is recommended to handle consumption. If you are having a drink, however, nephrologist Nestor advises opting for wine. "It contains antioxidants that can help eliminate concentrated toxins in the body.
Put out the cigarette.
"Cigarettes are responsible for worsening blood pressure levels and are still involved with hormonal changes that worsen kidney function," explains nephrologist Lucio. Also, smoking triggers a vasoconstriction effect, decreasing the volume of blood filtered by the kidneys. In this case, there is no moderation option. The patient must end the addiction.
Practice exercises
The last recommended care for chronic kidney failure sufferers is regular exercise. "It prevents diabetes, hypertension, obesity, among other problems, and improves circulation and kidney function," says nephrologist Nestor. According to him, any activity is already better than physical inactivity. Still, it is always recommended to seek training that pleases the patient so that he does not feel discouraged over time.

Chapter 9.
Learning To Deal With Kidney Failure

During kidney disease, this is extremely important. They can advise you about sodium, phosphorous, and potassium content of favorite foods and recommend reducing your sodium intake. Your diet will be tailored to you, considering the stage of kidney disease you're in and any other illnesses or diseases you suffer from.
Keep a Food Diary:
You should track what you're eating and drinking to stay within the guidelines and recommendations given to you. Apps such as My Fitness Pal make this extremely easy and even track many of the minerals and levels in foods, including sodium, protein, etc. There are also apps specifically made for kidney disease patients to track sodium, phosphorous, and potassium levels.

Read Food Labels:

Some foods have hidden sodium in them, even if they don't taste salty. You will need to cut back on the amount of canned, frozen, and processed foods you eat. Check your beverages for added sodium.

Check food labels to avoid:

Potassium chloride, Tetrasodium phosphate, Sodium phosphate, Trisodium phosphate, Tricalcium phosphate, Phosphoric acid, Polyphosphate, Hexametaphosphate, Pyrophosphate, Monocalcium phosphate, Dicalcium phosphate, Aluminum phosphate, Sodium tripolyphosphate, Sodium polyphosphate.
Flavor foods with spices and herbs rather than shop-bought dressings and condiments: These add flavor and variety to your meals and are not packed with sodium; spices also have many health benefits. Stay away from salt substitutes and seasonings that contain potassium. Use citrus fruits and vinegar for dressings and to add flavor.

Keep up your appointments with your Doctor or Nephrologist:

Let your doctor know if you notice any swelling or changes in your weight.

Monitor drink and fluid intake:

You have probably been told you need to drink up to eight glasses of water a day. This is true for a healthy body, but for people experiencing the later stages of CKD, these fluids can build up and cause additional problems. The restriction of fluids will differ from person to person. Things to take into consideration are swelling urine output and weight gain. Your weight will be recorded before dialysis begins, and once it's over. This is done to determine how much fluid to remove from your body. If you are undergoing hemodialysis, this will be recorded approximately three times a week. If you are undergoing peritoneal dialysis, your weight is recorded every day. If there is a significant weight gain, you may be drinking too many fluids.

Measure portion sizes:

Moderating your portion sizes is essential. Use smaller cups, bowls, or plates to avoid giving yourself oversized portions.
Measure your food so you can keep an accurate record of how much you are eating:
• 	The size of a fist is equal to 1 cup.
• 	The palm is equal to 3 ounces.
• 	The tip of your thumb is equivalent to 1 teaspoon.
• 	A poker chip is equal to 1 tablespoon.

Substitution Tips:

• 	Use plain white flour instead of whole-wheat/whole-grain
• 	Use all-purpose flour instead of self-raising,
• 	Use Stevia instead of sugar,
• 	Use egg whites rather than whole eggs,
• 	Use soy milk or almond rice instead of cow's milk.

Other Advice:

Be careful when eating in restaurants -ask for dressings and condiments on the side and watch out for soups and cured meats.
• 	Watch out for convenience foods that are high in sodium.
• 	Prepare your meals and freeze them for future use.
• 	Drain liquids from canned vegetables and fruits to help control potassium levels.

Chapter 10. Breakfast

Breakfast Salad from Grains and Fruits

INGREDIENTS

- 1 8-oz low fat vanilla yogurt
- 1 orange
- 1 Red delicious apple
- 1 Granny Smith apple
- ¾ cup bulgur
- ¼ teaspoon salt
- 3 cups water

DIRECTION

- On high fire, place a large pot and bring water to a boil.
- Add bulgur and rice. Lower fire to a simmer and cooks for ten minutes while covered.
- Turn off fire, set aside for 2 minutes while covered.
- In baking sheet, transfer and evenly spread grains to cool.
- Meanwhile, peel oranges and cut into sections. Chop and core apples.
- Once grains are cool, transfer to a large serving bowl along with fruits.
- Add yogurt and mix well to coat.
- Serve and enjoy.

NUTRITIONAL

- Calories: 187;
- Carbs: g;
- Protein: g;
- Fats: g;
- Phosphorus: mg;
- Potassium: mg;
- Sodium: 117mg

Preparation Time: 5 minutes| Cooking Time: 15 minutes |Servings: 6

French toast with Applesauce

INGREDIENTS

- ¼ cup unsweetened apple-sauce
- ½ cup milk
- 1 teaspoon ground cinnamon
- 2 eggs
- 2 tablespoon white sugar

DIRECTION

- Mix well applesauce, sugar, cinnamon, milk and eggs in a mixing bowl.
- Soak the bread, one by one into applesauce mixture until wet.
- On medium fire, heat a nonstick skillet greased with cooking spray.
- Add soaked bread one at a time and cook for 2-3 minutes per side or until lightly browned.
- Serve and enjoy.

NUTRITIONAL

- Calories: 57;
- Carbs: 6g;
- Protein: 4g;
- Fats: 4g;
- Phosphorus: 69mg;
- Potassium: 88mg;
- Sodium: 43mg

Preparation Time: 5 minutes |Cooking Time: 15 minutes|Servings: 6

Bagels Made Healthy

INGREDIENTS

- 2 teaspoon yeast
- 1 ½ tablespoon olive oil
- 1 ¼ cups bread flour
- 2 cups whole wheat flour
- 1 tablespoon vinegar
- 2 tablespoon honey
- 1 ½ cups warm water

DIRECTION

- In a bread machine, mix all ingredients, and then process on dough cycle.
- Once done or end of cycle, create 8 pieces shaped like a flattened ball.
- In the centre of each ball, make a hole using your thumb then create a donut shape.
- In a greased baking sheet, place donut-shaped dough then covers and let it rise about ½ hour.
- Prepare about 2 inches of water to boil in a large pan.
- In a boiling water, drop one at a time the bagels and boil for 1 minute, then turn them once.
- Remove them and return them to baking sheet and bake at 350oF (175oC) for about 20 to 25 minutes until golden brown.

NUTRITIONAL

- Calories: 221;
- Carbs: 42g;
- Protein: 7g;
- Fats: g;
- Phosphorus: 130mg;
- Potassium: 166mg;
- Sodium: 47mg

Preparation Time: 5 minutes |Cooking Time: 25 minutes|Servings: 8

Cornbread with Southern Twist

INGREDIENTS

- 2 tablespoons shortening
- 1 ¼ cups skim milk
- ¼ cup egg substitute
- 4 tablespoons sodium free baking powder
- ½ cup flour
- 1 ½ cups cornmeal

DIRECTION

- Prepare 8 x 8-inch baking dish or a black iron skillet then add shortening.
- Put the baking dish or skillet inside the oven on 425oF, once the shortening has melted that means the pan is hot already.
- In a bowl, add milk and egg then mix well.
- Take out the skillet and add the melted shortening into the batter and stir well.
- Pour all mixed ingredients into skillet.
- For 15 to 20 minutes, cook in the oven until golden brown.

NUTRITIONAL

- Calories: 166;
- Carbs: 35g;
- Protein: 5g;
- Fats: 1g;
- Phosphorus: 79mg;
- Potassium: 122mg;
- Sodium: 34mg

Preparation Time: 15 minutes |Cooking Time: 60 minutes|Servings: 8

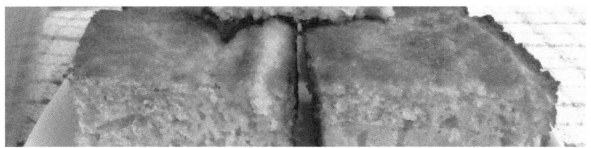

Grandma's Pancake Special

INGREDIENTS

- 1 tablespoon oil
- 1 cup milk
- 1 egg
- 2 teaspoons sodium free baking powder
- 2 tablespoons sugar
- 1 ¼ cups flour

DIRECTION

- Mix together all the dry ingredients such as the flour, sugar and baking powder.
- Combine oil, milk and egg in another bowl. Once done, add them all to the flour mixture.
- Make sure that as your stir the mixture, blend them together until slightly lumpy.
- In a hot greased griddle, pour-in at least ¼ cup of the batter to make each pancake.
- To cook, ensure that the bottom is a bit brown, then turn and cook the other side, as well.

NUTRITIONAL

- Calories: 167;
- Carbs: 50g;
- Protein: 11g;
- Fats: 11g;
- Phosphorus: 176mg;
- Potassium: 215mg;
- Sodium: 70mg

Preparation Time: 5 minutes | Cooking Time: 15 minutes|Servings: 3

Pasta with Indian Lentils

INGREDIENTS

- ¼-½ cup fresh cilantro (chopped)
- 3 cups water
- 2 small dry red peppers (whole)
- 1 teaspoon turmeric
- 1 teaspoon ground cumin
- 2-3 cloves garlic (minced)
- 1 can (15 ounces) cubed Red bell peppers (with juice)
- 1 large onion (chopped)
- ½ cup dry lentils (rinsed)
- ½ cup orzo or tiny pasta

DIRECTION

- In a skillet, combine all ingredients except for the cilantro then boil on medium-high heat.
- Ensure to cover and slightly reduce heat to medium-low and simmer until pasta is tender for about 35 minutes.
- Afterwards, take out the chili peppers then add cilantro and top it with low-fat sour cream.

NUTRITIONAL

- Calories: 175;
- Carbs: 40g;
- Protein: 3g;
- Fats: 2g;
- Phosphorus: 139mg;
- Potassium: 513mg;
- Sodium: 61mg

Preparation Time: 5 minutes |Cooking Time: 0 minutes|Servings: 6

Pineapple Bread

INGREDIENTS

- 1/3 cup Swerve
- 1/3 cup butter, unsalted
- 2 eggs
- 2 cups flour
- 3 teaspoons baking powder
- 1 cup pineapple, undrained
- 6 cherries, chopped

DIRECTION

- Whisk the Swerve with the butter in a mixer until fluffy.
- Stir in the eggs, then beat again.
- Add the baking powder and flour, then mix well until smooth.
- Fold in the cherries and pineapple.
- Spread this cherry-pineapple batter in a 9x5 inch baking pan.
- Bake the pineapple batter for 1 hour at 350 degrees F.
- Slice the bread and serve.

NUTRITIONAL

- Calories 197,
- Total Fat 7.2g,
- Sodium 85mg,
- Dietary Fiber 1.1g,
- Sugars 3 g,
- Protein 4g,
- Calcium 79mg,
- Phosphorous 316mg,
- Potassium 227mg

Preparation Time: 20 Minutes |Cooking Time: 1 Hour |Servings: 10

Parmesan Zucchini Frittata

INGREDIENTS

- 1 tablespoon olive oil
- 1 cup yellow onion, sliced
- 3 cups zucchini, chopped
- ½ cup Parmesan cheese, grated
- 8 large eggs
- 1/2 teaspoon black pepper
- 1/8 teaspoon paprika
- 3 tablespoons parsley, chopped

DIRECTION

- Toss the zucchinis with the onion, parsley, and all other ingredients in a large bowl.
- Pour this zucchini-garlic mixture in an 11x7 inches pan and spread it evenly.
- Bake the zucchini casserole for approximately 35 minutes at 350 degrees F.
- Cut in slices and serve.

NUTRITIONAL

- Calories 142,
- Total Fat 9.7g,
- Saturated Fat 2.8g,
- Cholesterol 250mg,
- Sodium 123mg,
- Carbohydrate 4.7g,
- Dietary Fiber 1.3g,
- Sugars 2.4g,
- Protein 10.2g,
- Calcium 73mg,
- Phosphorous 375mg,
- Potassium 286mg

Preparation Time: 10 minutes |Cooking Time: 35 minutes |Servings: 6

Garlic Mayo Bread

INGREDIENTS

- 3 tablespoons vegetable oil
- 4 cloves garlic, minced
- 2 teaspoons paprika
- Dash cayenne pepper
- 1 teaspoon lemon juice
- 2 tablespoons Parmesan cheese, grated
- 3/4 cup mayonnaise
- 1 loaf (1 lb.) French bread, sliced
- 1 teaspoon Italian herbs

DIRECTION

- Mix the garlic with the oil in a small bowl and leave it overnight.
- Discard the garlic from the bowl and keep the garlic-infused oil.
- Mix the garlic-oil with cayenne, paprika, lemon juice, mayonnaise, and Parmesan.
- Place the bread slices in a baking tray lined with parchment paper.
- Top these slices with the mayonnaise mixture and drizzle the Italian herbs on top.
- Broil these slices for 5 minutes until golden brown.
- Serve warm.

NUTRITIONAL

- Calories 217,
- Total Fat 7.9g,
- Sodium 423mg,
- Dietary Fiber 1.3g,
- Sugars 2g,
- Protein 7g,
- Calcium 56mg,
- Phosphorous 347mg,
- Potassium 72mg

Preparation Time: 10 minutes |Cooking Time: 5 minutes |Servings: 16

Strawberry Topped Waffles

INGREDIENTS

- 1 cup flour
- 1/4 cup Swerve
- 1 ¾ teaspoons baking powder
- 1 egg, separated
- ¾ cup milk
- ½ cup butter, melted
- ½ teaspoon vanilla extract
- Fresh strawberries, sliced

DIRECTION

- Prepare and preheat your waffle pan following the instructions of the machine.
- Begin by mixing the flour with Swerve and baking soda in a bowl.
- Separate the egg yolks from the egg whites, keeping them in two separate bowls.
- Add the milk and vanilla extract to the egg yolks.
- Stir the melted butter and mix well until smooth.
- Now beat the egg whites with an electric beater until foamy and fluffy.
- Fold this fluffy composition in the egg yolk mixture.
- Mix it gently until smooth, then add in the flour mixture.
- Stir again to make a smooth mixture.
- Pour a half cup of the waffle batter in a preheated pan and cook until the waffle is done.
- Cook more waffles with the remaining batter.
- Serve fresh with strawberries on top.

NUTRITIONAL

- Calories 342,
- Total Fat 20.5g,
- Sodium 156mg,
- Dietary Fiber 0.7g,
- Sugars 3.5g,
- Protein 4.8g,
- Calcium 107mg,
- Phosphorous 126mg,
- Potassium 233mg

Preparation Time: 15 minutes |Cooking Time: 20 minutes |Servings: 5

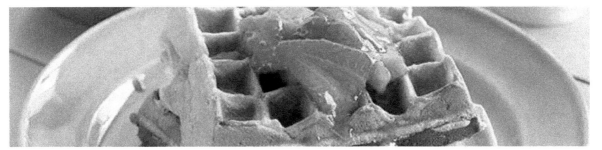

Cheese Spaghetti Frittata

INGREDIENTS

- 4 cups whole-wheat spaghetti, cooked
- 4 teaspoons olive oil
- 3 medium onions, chopped
- 4 large eggs
- 1/2 cup milk
- 1/3 cup Parmesan cheese, grated
- 2 tablespoons fresh parsley, chopped
- 2 tablespoons fresh basil, chopped
- 1/2 teaspoon black pepper
- 1 tomato, diced

DIRECTION

- Set a suitable non-stick skillet over moderate heat and add in the olive oil.
- Place the spaghetti in the skillet and cook by stirring for 2 minutes on moderate heat.
- Whisk the eggs with milk, parsley, and black pepper in a bowl.
- Pour this milky egg mixture over the spaghetti and top it all with basil, cheese, and tomato.
- Cover the spaghetti frittata again with a lid and cook for approximately 8 minutes on low heat.
- Slice and serve.

NUTRITIONAL

- Calories 230,
- Total Fat 7.8g,
- Sodium 77mg,
- Dietary Fiber 5.6g,
- Sugars 4.5g,
- Protein 11.1g,
- Calcium 88mg,
- Phosphorous 368 mg,
- Potassium 214mg,

Preparation Time: 10 minutes |Cooking Time: 10 minutes |Servings: 6

Shrimp Bruschetta

INGREDIENTS

- 13 oz. shrimps, peeled
- 1 tablespoon tomato sauce
- ½ teaspoon Splenda
- ¼ teaspoon garlic powder
- 1 teaspoon fresh parsley, chopped
- ½ teaspoon olive oil
- 1 teaspoon lemon juice
- 4 whole-grain bread slices
- 1 cup water, for cooking

DIRECTION

- In the saucepan, pour water and bring it to boil.
- Add shrimps and boil them over the high heat for 5 minutes.
- After this, drain shrimps and chill them to the room temperature.
- Mix up together shrimps with Splenda, garlic powder, tomato sauce, and fresh parsley.
- Add lemon juice and stir gently.
- Preheat the oven to 360f.
- Coat the slice of bread with olive oil and bake for 3 minutes.
- Then place the shrimp mixture on the bread. Bruschetta is cooked.

NUTRITIONAL

- Calories 199,
- Fat 3.7,
- Fiber 2.1,
- Carbs 15.3,
- Protein 24.1
- Calcium 79mg,
- Phosphorous 316mg,
- Potassium 227mg
- Sodium: 121 mg

Preparation Time: 15 minutes |Cooking Time: 10 minutes |Servings: 4

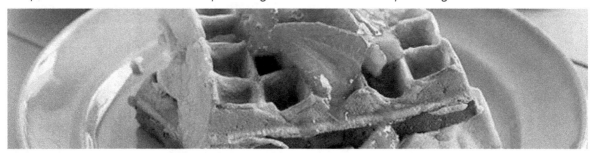

Strawberry Muesli

INGREDIENTS

- 2 cups Greek yogurt
- 1 ½ cup strawberries, sliced
- 1 ½ cup Muesli
- 4 teaspoon maple syrup
- ¾ teaspoon ground cinnamon

DIRECTION

- Put Greek yogurt in the food processor.
- Add 1 cup of strawberries, maple syrup, and ground cinnamon.
- Blend the ingredients until you get smooth mass.
- Transfer the yogurt mass in the serving bowls.
- Add Muesli and stir well.
- Leave the meal for 30 minutes in the fridge.
- After this, decorate it with remaining sliced strawberries.

NUTRITIONAL

- Calories 149,
- Fat 2.6,
- Fiber 3.6,
- Carbs 21.6,
- Protein 12
- Calcium 69mg,
- Phosphorous 216mg,
- Potassium 227mg
- Sodium: 151 mg

Preparation Time: 10 minutes |Cooking Time: 30 minutes |Servings: 4

Yogurt Bulgur

INGREDIENTS

- 1 cup bulgur
- 2 cups Greek yogurt
- 1 ½ cup water
- ½ teaspoon salt
- 1 teaspoon olive oil

DIRECTION

- Pour olive oil in the saucepan and add bulgur.
- Roast it over the medium heat for 2-3 minutes. Stir it from time to time.
- After this, add salt and water.
- Close the lid and cook bulgur for 15 minutes over the medium heat.
- Then chill the cooked bulgur well and combine it with Greek yogurt. Stir it carefully.
- Transfer the cooked meal into the serving plates. The yogurt bulgur tastes the best when it is cold.

NUTRITIONAL

- Calories 274,
- Fat 4.9,
- Fiber 8.5,
- Carbs 40.8,
- Protein 19.2
- Calcium 39mg,
- Phosphorous 216mg,
- Potassium 237mg
- Sodium: 131 mg

Preparation Time: 10 minutes |Cooking Time: 15 minutes |Servings: 3

Mozzarella Cheese Omelet

INGREDIENTS

- 4 eggs, beaten
- 1/4 cup mozzarella cheese, shredded
- 4 tomato slices
- 1/4 tsp. Italian seasoning
- 1/4 tsp. dried oregano
- Pepper
- Salt

DIRECTION

- In a small bowl, whisk eggs with salt.
- Spray pan with cooking spray and heat over medium heat.
- Pour egg mixture into the pan and cook over medium heat.
- Once eggs are set then sprinkle oregano and Italian seasoning on top.
- Arrange tomato slices on top of the omelet and sprinkle with shredded cheese.
- Cook omelet for 1 minute.
- Serve and enjoy.

NUTRITIONAL

- Calories 285
- Fat 19g
- Carbohydrates 4g
- Sugar 3g
- Protein 25g
- Cholesterol 655 mg

Preparation Time: 10 minutes |Cooking Time: 5 minutes |Servings: 1

Sun-Dried Tomato Frittata

INGREDIENTS

- 12 eggs
- 1/2 tsp. dried basil
- 1/4 cup parmesan cheese, grated
- 2 cups baby green lettuce, shredded
- 1/4 cup sun-dried Red bell peppers, sliced
- Pepper
- Salt

DIRECTION

- Preheat the oven to 425 F. In a large bowl, whisk eggs with pepper and salt.
- Add remaining ingredients and stir to combine. Spray oven-safe pan with cooking spray.
- Pour egg mixture into the pan and bake for 20 minutes.
- Slice and serve.

NUTRITIONAL

- Calories 115
- Fat 7g
- Carbohydrates 1g
- Sugar 1g
- Protein 10g
- Cholesterol 250 mg

Preparation Time: 10 minutes |Cooking Time: 20 minutes |Servings: 8

Italian Breakfast Frittata

INGREDIENTS

- 2 cups egg whites
- 1/2 cup mozzarella cheese, shredded
- 1 cup cottage cheese, crumbled
- 1/4 cup fresh basil, sliced
- 1/2 cup roasted red peppers, sliced
- Pepper
- Salt

DIRECTION

- Preheat the oven to 375 F.
- Add all ingredients into the large bowl and whisk well to combine.
- Pour frittata mixture into the baking dish and bake for 45 minutes.
- Slice and serve.

NUTRITIONAL

- Calories 131
- Fat 2g
- Carbohydrates 5g
- Sugar 2g
- Protein 22g
- Cholesterol 6mg

Preparation Time: 10 minutes   Cooking Time: 45 minutes Servings: 4

Sausage Cheese Bake Omelet

INGREDIENTS

- 16 eggs
- 2 cups cheddar cheese, shredded
- 1/2 cup salsa
- 1 lb. ground sausage
- 1 1/2 cups coconut milk
- Pepper
- Salt

DIRECTION

- Preheat the oven to 350 F.
- Add sausage in a pan and cook until browned. Drain excess fat.
- In a large bowl, whisk eggs and milk. Stir in cheese, cooked sausage, and salsa.
- Pour omelet mixture into the baking dish and bake for 45 minutes.
- Serve and enjoy.

NUTRITIONAL

- Calories 360
- Fat 24g
- Carbohydrates 4g
- Sugar 3g
- Protein 28g
- Cholesterol 400 mg

Preparation Time: 10 minutes |Cooking Time: 45 minutes |Servings: 8

Greek Egg Scrambled

INGREDIENTS

- 4 eggs
- 1/2 cup grape Red bell peppers, sliced
- 2 tbsp. green onions, sliced
- 1 bell pepper, diced
- 1 tbsp. olive oil
- 1/4 tsp. dried oregano
- 1/2 tbsp. capers
- Pepper
- Salt

DIRECTION

- Heat oil in a pan over medium heat
- Add green onions and bell pepper and cook until pepper is softened.
- Add eggs and stir until eggs are cooked. Season it with oregano, pepper, and salt.
- Serve and enjoy.

NUTRITIONAL

- Calories 230
- Fat 17g
- Carbohydrates 8g
- Sugar 5g
- Protein 12g
- Cholesterol 325 mg

Preparation Time: 10 minutes |Cooking Time: 10 minutes |Servings: 2

Feta Mint Omelet

INGREDIENTS

- 1/4 cup fresh mint, chopped
- 2 tbsp. coconut milk
- 1/2 tsp. olive oil
- 2 tbsp. feta cheese, crumbled
- Pepper
- Salt

DIRECTION

- In a bowl, whisk eggs with feta cheese, mint, milk, pepper, and salt.
- Heat olive oil in a pan over low heat. Pour egg mixture in the pan and cook until eggs are set.
- Flip omelet and cook for 2 minutes more.
- Serve and enjoy.

NUTRITIONAL

- Calories 275
- Fat 20g
- Carbohydrates 4g
- Sugar 2g
- Protein 20g
- Cholesterol 505 mg

Preparation Time: 10 minutes |Cooking Time: 5 minutes |Servings: 1

Sausage Breakfast Casserole

INGREDIENTS

- 12 eggs
- 1 lb. ground Italian sausage
- 2 1/2 Red bell peppers, sliced
- 3 tbsp. coconut flour
- 1/4 cup coconut milk
- 2 small zucchinis, shredded
- Pepper
- Salt

DIRECTION

- Preheat the oven to 350 F.
- Spray casserole dish with cooking spray and set aside.
- Cook sausage in a pan until brown.
- Transfer sausage to a mixing bowl.
- Add coconut flour, milk, eggs, zucchini, pepper, and salt. Stir well.
- Add eggs and whisk to combine.
- Transfer bowl mixture into the casserole dish and top with tomato slices.
- Bake for 50 minutes.
- Serve and enjoy.

NUTRITIONAL

- Calories 305
- Fat 21.8g
- Carbohydrates 6.3g
- Sugar 3.3g
- Protein 19.6g
- Cholesterol 286 mg

Preparation Time: 10 minutes |Cooking Time: 50 minutes |Servings: 8

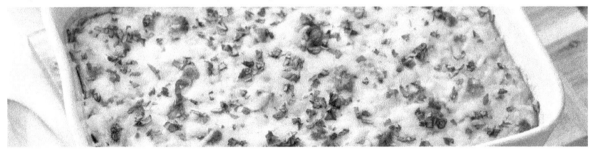

Easy Turnip Puree

INGREDIENTS

- 1 1/2 lbs. turnips, peeled and chopped
- 1 tsp. dill
- 3 bacon slices, cooked and chopped
- 2 tbsp. fresh chives, chopped

DIRECTION

- Add turnip into the boiling water and cook for 12 minutes. Drain well and place in a food processor.
- Add dill and process until smooth.
- Transfer turnip puree into the bowl and top with bacon and chives.
- Serve and enjoy.

NUTRITIONAL

- Calories 127
- Fat 6g
- Carbohydrates 11.6g
- Sugar 7g
- Protein 6.8g
- Cholesterol 16 mg

Preparation Time: 10 minutes |Cooking Time: 12 minutes |Servings: 4

Green lettuce Bacon Breakfast Bake

INGREDIENTS

- 10 eggs
- 3 cups baby green lettuce, chopped
- 1 tbsp. olive oil
- 8 bacon slices, cooked and chopped
- 2 Red bell peppers, sliced
- 2 tbsp. chives, chopped
- Pepper
- Salt

DIRECTION

- Preheat the oven to 350 F.
- Spray a baking dish with cooking spray and set aside.
- Heat oil in a pan
- Add green lettuce and cook until green lettuce wilted.
- In a mixing bowl, whisk eggs and salt. Add green lettuce and chives and stir well.
- Pour egg mixture into the baking dish.
- Top with Red bell peppers and bacon and bake for 45 minutes.
- Serve and enjoy.

NUTRITIONAL

- Calories 273
- Fat 20.4g
- Carbohydrates 3.1g
- Sugar 1.7g
- Protein 19.4g
- Cholesterol 301 mg

Preparation Time: 10 minutes |Cooking Time: 45 minutes |Servings: 6

Healthy Green lettuce Tomato Muffins

INGREDIENTS

- 12 eggs
- 1/2 tsp. Italian seasoning
- 1 cup Red bell peppers, chopped
- 4 tbsp. water
- 1 cup fresh green lettuce, chopped
- Pepper
- Salt

DIRECTION

- Preheat the oven to 350 F. Spray a muffin tray with cooking spray and set aside.
- In a mixing bowl, whisk eggs with water, Italian seasoning, pepper, and salt.
- Add green lettuce and Red bell peppers and stir well.
- Pour egg mixture into the prepared muffin tray and bake for 20 minutes.
- Serve and enjoy.

NUTRITIONAL

- Calories 67
- Fat 4.5g
- Carbohydrates 1g
- Sugar 0.8g
- Protein 5.7g
- Cholesterol 164 mg

Preparation Time: 10 minutes |Cooking Time: 20 minutes |Servings: 12

Chicken Egg Breakfast Muffins

INGREDIENTS

- 10 eggs
- 1 cup cooked chicken, chopped
- 3 tbsp. green onions, chopped
- 1/4 tsp. garlic powder
- Pepper
- Salt

DIRECTION

- Preheat the oven to 400 F.
- Spray a muffin tray with cooking spray and set aside.
- In a large bowl, whisk eggs with garlic powder, pepper, and salt.
- Add remaining ingredients and stir well.
- Pour egg mixture into the muffin tray and bake for 15 minutes.
- Serve and enjoy.

NUTRITIONAL

- Calories 71
- Fat 4 g
- Carbohydrates 0.4g
- Sugar 0.3g
- Protein 8g
- Cholesterol 145 mg

(Ready in about: 17 mins |Servings: 4 | Difficulty: Easy)

Breakfast Egg Salad

INGREDIENTS

- 6 eggs, hard-boiled, peeled and chopped
- 1 tbsp. fresh dill, chopped
- 4 tbsp. mayonnaise
- Pepper
- Salt

DIRECTION

- Add all ingredients into the large bowl and stir to mix. Serve and enjoy.

NUTRITIONAL

- Calories 140
- Fat 10g
- Carbohydrates 4g
- Sugar 1g
- Protein 8g
- Cholesterol 245 mg

Preparation Time: 10 minutes |Cooking Time: 5 minutes |Servings: 4

Vegetable Tofu Scramble

INGREDIENTS

- 1/2 block firm tofu, crumbled
- 1/4 tsp. ground cumin
- 1 tbsp. turmeric
- 1 cup green lettuce
- 1/4 cup zucchini, chopped
- 1 tbsp. olive oil
- 1 tomato, chopped
- 1 tbsp. chives, chopped
- 1 tbsp. coriander, chopped
- Pepper
- Salt

DIRECTION

- Heat oil in a pan over medium heat
- Add tomato, zucchini, and green lettuce and sauté for 2 minutes.
- Add tofu, cumin, turmeric, pepper, and salt and sauté for 5 minutes.
- Top with chives, and coriander.
- Serve and enjoy.

NUTRITIONAL

- Calories 101
- Fat 8.5 g
- Carbohydrates 5.1g
- Sugar 1.4g
- Protein 3.1g
- Cholesterol 0 mg

Preparation Time: 10 minutes |Cooking Time: 7 minutes |Servings: 2

Cheese Coconut Pancakes

INGREDIENTS

- 2 eggs
- 1 packet stevia
- 1/2 tsp. cinnamon
- 2 oz. cream cheese
- 1 tbsp. coconut flour
- 1/2 tsp. vanilla

DIRECTION

- Add all ingredients into the bowl and blend until smooth.
- Spray pan with cooking spray and heat over medium-high heat.
- Pour batter on the hot pan and make two pancakes.
- Cook pancake until lightly brown from both the sides.
- Serve and enjoy.

NUTRITIONAL

- Calories 386
- Fat 30g
- Carbohydrates 12g
- Sugar 1g
- Protein 16g
- Cholesterol 389 mg

Preparation Time: 10 minutes |Cooking Time: 5 minutes |Servings: 1

Cheesy Scrambled Eggs with Fresh Herbs

INGREDIENTS

- Eggs – 3
- Egg whites – 2
- Cream cheese – 1/2 cup
- Unsweetened rice milk – 1/4 cup
- Chopped scallion – 1 Tbsp. green part only
- Chopped fresh tarragon – 1 Tbsp.
- Unsalted butter – 2 Tbsps.
- Ground black pepper to taste

DIRECTION

- In a bowl, whisk the eggs, egg whites, cream cheese, rice milk, scallions, and tarragon until mixed and smooth.
- Melt the butter in a skillet.
- Pour in the egg mixture and cook, stirring, for 5 minutes or until the eggs are thick and curds creamy.
- Season with pepper and serve.

NUTRITIONAL

- Calories: 221
- Fat: 19g
- Carb: 3g
- Phosphorus: 119mg
- Potassium: 140mg
- Sodium: 193mg
- Protein: 8g

Preparation Time: 15 minutes |Cooking Time: 10 minutes |Servings: 4

Coconut Breakfast Smoothie

INGREDIENTS

- 1/4 cup whey protein powder
- 1/2 cup coconut milk
- 5 drops liquid stevia
- 1 tbsp. coconut oil
- 1 tsp. vanilla
- 2 tbsp. coconut butter
- 1/4 cup water
- 1/2 cup ice

DIRECTION

- Add all ingredients into the blender and blend until smooth.
- Serve and enjoy.

NUTRITIONAL

- Calories 560
- Fat 45g
- Carbohydrates 12g
- Sugar 4g
- Protein 25g
- Cholesterol 60 mg

Preparation Time: 5 minutes |Cooking Time: 5 minutes |Servings: 1

Turkey and Green lettuce Scramble on Melba Toast

INGREDIENTS

- Extra virgin olive oil – 1 tsp.
- Raw green lettuce – 1 cup
- Garlic – 1/2 clove, minced
- Nutmeg – 1 tsp. grated
- Cooked and diced turkey breast – 1 cup
- Melba toast – 4 slices
- Balsamic vinegar – 1 tsp.

DIRECTION

- Heat a skillet over medium heat and add oil.
- Add turkey and heat through for 6 to 8 minutes.
- Add green lettuce, garlic, and nutmeg and stir-fry for 6 minutes more.
- Plate up the Melba toast and top with green lettuce and turkey scramble.
- Drizzle with balsamic vinegar and serve.

NUTRITIONAL

- Calories: 301
- Fat: 19g
- Carb: 12g
- Phosphorus: 215mg
- Potassium: 269mg
- Sodium: 360mg
- Protein: 19g

Preparation Time: 2 minutes|Cooking Time: 15 minutes|Servings: 2

Vegetable Omelet

INGREDIENTS

- Egg whites – 4
- Egg – 1
- Chopped fresh parsley – 2 Tbsps.
- Water – 2 Tbsps.
- Olive oil spray
- Chopped and boiled red bell pepper – 1/2 cup
- Chopped scallion – 1/4 cup, both green and white parts
- Ground black pepper

DIRECTION

- Whisk together the egg, egg whites, parsley, and water until well blended. Set aside.
- Spray a skillet with olive oil spray and place over medium heat.
- Sauté the peppers and scallion for 3 minutes or until softened.
- Pour the egg mixture into the skillet over vegetables and cook, swirling the skillet, for 2 minutes or until the edges start to set. Cook until set.
- Season with black pepper and serve.

NUTRITIONAL

- Calories: 77
- Fat: 3g
- Carb: 2g
- Phosphorus: 67mg
- Potassium: 194mg
- Sodium: 229mg
- Protein: 12g

Preparation Time: 15 minutes|Cooking Time: 10 minutes|Servings: 3

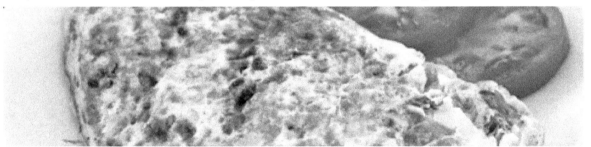

Mexican Style Burritos

INGREDIENTS

- Olive oil – 1 Tbsp.
- Corn tortillas – 2
- Red onion – 1/4 cup, chopped
- Red bell peppers – 1/4 cup, chopped
- Red chili – 1/2, deseeded and chopped
- Eggs – 2
- Juice of 1 lime
- Cilantro – 1 Tbsp. chopped

DIRECTION

- Turn the broiler to medium heat and place the tortillas underneath for 1 to 2 minutes on each side or until lightly toasted.
- Remove and keep the broiler on.
- Heat the oil in a skillet and sauté onion, chili and bell peppers for 5 to 6 minutes or until soft.
- Crack the eggs over the top of the onions and peppers and place skillet under the broiler for 5 to 6 minutes or until the eggs are cooked.
- Serve half the eggs and vegetables on top of each tortilla and sprinkle with cilantro and lime juice to serve.

NUTRITIONAL

- Calories: 202
- Fat: 13g
- Carb: 19g
- Phosphorus: 184mg
- Potassium: 233mg
- Sodium: 77mg
- Protein: 9g

Preparation Time: 5 minutes|Cooking Time: 15 minutes|Servings: 2

Bulgur, Couscous and Buckwheat Cereal

INGREDIENTS

- Water – 2 1/4 cups
- Vanilla rice milk – 1 1/4 cups
- Uncooked bulgur – 6 Tbsps.
- Uncooked whole buckwheat – 2 Tbsps.
- Sliced apple – 1 cup
- Plain uncooked couscous – 6 Tbsps.
- Ground cinnamon – 1/2 tsp.

DIRECTION

- In a saucepan, heat the water and milk over medium heat.
- Bring to a boil, and add the bulgur, buckwheat, and apple.
- Reduce the heat to low and simmer, occasionally stirring until the bulgur is tender, about 20 to 25 minutes.
- Remove the saucepan from the heat and stir in the couscous and cinnamon.
- Let the saucepan stand, covered, for 10 minutes.
- Fluff the cereal with a fork before serving.

NUTRITIONAL

- Calories: 159
- Fat: 1g
- Carb: 34g
- Phosphorus: 130mg
- Potassium: 116mg
- Sodium: 33mg
- Protein: 4g

Preparation Time: 10 minutes|Cooking Time: 25 minutes|Servings: 4

Sweet Pancakes

INGREDIENTS

- All-purpose flour – 1 cup
- Granulated sugar – 1 Tbsp.
- Baking powder – 2 tsps.
- Egg whites – 2
- Almond milk – 1 cup
- Olive oil – 2 Tbsps.
- Maple extract – 1 Tbsp.

DIRECTION

- Mix the flour, sugar and baking powder in a bowl.
- Make a well in the center and place to one side.
- In another bowl, mix the egg whites, milk, oil, and maple extract.
- Add the egg mixture to the well and gently mix until a batter is formed.
- Heat skillet over medium heat.
- Add 1/5 of the batter to the pan and cook 2 minutes on each side or until the pancake is golden.
- Repeat with the remaining batter and serve.

NUTRITIONAL

- Calories: 178
- Fat: 6g
- Carb: 25g
- Phosphorus: 116mg
- Potassium: 126mg
- Sodium: 297mg
- Protein: 6g

Preparation Time: 10 minutes|Cooking Time: 5 minutes|Servings: 5

Breakfast Smoothie

INGREDIENTS

- Frozen blueberries – 1 cup
- Pineapple chunks – 1/2 cup
- English cucumber – 1/2 cup
- Apple – 1/2
- Water – 1/2 cup

DIRECTION

- Put the pineapple, blueberries, cucumber, apple, and water in a blender and blend until thick and smooth.
- Pour into 2 glasses and serve.

NUTRITIONAL

- Calories: 87
- Fat: g
- Carb: 22g
- Phosphorus: 28mg
- Potassium: 192mg
- Sodium: 3mg
- Protein: 0.7g

Preparation Time: 15 minutes|Cooking Time: 0 minutes|Servings: 2

Buckwheat and Grapefruit Porridge

INGREDIENTS

- Buckwheat – 1/2 cup
- Grapefruit – 1/4, chopped
- Honey – 1 Tbsp.
- Almond milk – 1 1/2 cups
- Water – 2 cups

DIRECTION

- Bring the water to a boil on the stove.
- Add the buckwheat and place the lid on the pan.
- Lower heat slightly and simmer for 7 to 10 minutes, checking to ensure water does not dry out.
- When most of the water is absorbed, remove and set aside for 5 minutes.
- Drain any excess water from the pan and stir in almond milk, heating through for 5 minutes.
- Add the honey and grapefruit.
- Serve.

NUTRITIONAL

- Calories: 231
- Fat: 4g
- Carb: 43g
- Phosphorus: 165mg
- Potassium: 370mg
- Sodium: 135mg

Preparation Time: 5 minutes|Cooking Time: 20 minutes|Servings: 2

Egg and Veggie Muffins

INGREDIENTS

- Cooking spray
- Eggs – 4
- Unsweetened rice milk – 2 Tbsp.
- Sweet onion – 1/2, chopped
- Red bell pepper – 1/2, chopped
- Pinch red pepper flakes
- Pinch ground black pepper

DIRECTION

- Preheat the oven to 350F.
- Spray 4 muffin pans with cooking spray. Set aside.
- In a bowl, whisk together the milk, eggs, onion, red pepper, parsley, red pepper flakes, and black pepper until mixed.
- Pour the egg mixture into prepared muffin pans.
- Bake until the muffins are puffed and golden, about 18 to 20 minutes.
- serve

NUTRITIONAL

- Calories: 84
- Fat: 5g
- Carb: 3g
- Phosphorus: 110mg
- Potassium: 117mg
- Sodium: 75mg
- Protein: 7g

Preparation Time: 15 minutes|Cooking Time: 20 minutes|Servings: 4

Salad with Vinaigrette

INGREDIENTS

- For the vinaigrette:
- Olive oil – 1/2 cup
- Balsamic vinegar - 4 Tbsps.
- Chopped fresh oregano – 2 Tbsps.
- Pinch red pepper flakes
- Ground black pepper
- For the salad
- Shredded green leaf lettuce – 4 cups
- Carrot – 1, shredded
- Fresh green beans – ¾ cup, cut into 1-inch pieces
- Large radishes – 3, sliced thin

DIRECTION

- To make the vinaigrette: put the vinaigrette Ingredients in a bowl and whisk.
- To make the salad, in a bowl, toss together the carrot, lettuce, green beans, and radishes.
- Add the vinaigrette to the vegetables and toss to coat.
- Arrange the salad on plates and serve.

NUTRITIONAL

- Calories: 273
- Fat: 27g
- Carb: 7g
- Phosphorus: 30mg
- Potassium: 197mg
- Sodium: 27mg
- Protein: 1g

Preparation Time: 25 minutes|Cooking Time: 0 minutes|Servings: 4

Salad with Lemon Dressing

INGREDIENTS

- Heavy cream – 1/4 cup
- Freshly squeezed lemon juice – 1/4 cup
- Granulated sugar – 2 Tbsps.
- Chopped fresh dill – 2 Tbsps.
- Finely chopped scallion – 2 Tbsps. green part only
- Ground black pepper – 1/4 tsp.
- English cucumber – 1, sliced thin
- Shredded green cabbage – 2 cups

DIRECTION

- In a small bowl, stir together the lemon juice, cream, sugar, dill, scallion, and pepper until well blended.
- In a large bowl, toss together the cucumber and cabbage.
- Place the salad in the refrigerator and chill for 1 hour.
- Stir before serving.

NUTRITIONAL

- Calories: 99
- Fat: 6g
- Carb: 13g
- Phosphorus: 38mg
- Potassium: 200mg
- Sodium: 14mg
- Protein: 2g

Preparation Time: 10 minutes|Cooking Time: 0 minutes|Servings: 4

Shrimp with Salsa

INGREDIENTS

- Olive oil – 2 Tbsp.
- Large shrimp – 6 ounces, peeled and deveined, tails left on
- Minced garlic – 1 tsp.
- Chopped English cucumber – 1/2 cup
- Chopped mango – 1/2 cup
- Zest of 1 lime
- Juice of 1 lime
- Ground black pepper
- Lime wedges for garnish

DIRECTION

- Soak 4 wooden skewers in water for 30 minutes.
- Preheat the barbecue to medium heat.
- In a bowl, toss together the olive oil, shrimp, and garlic.
- Thread the shrimp onto the skewers, about 4 shrimp per skewer.
- In a bowl, stir together the mango, cucumber, lime zest, and lime juice, and season the salsa lightly with pepper. Set aside.
- Grill the shrimp for 10 minutes, turning once or until the shrimp is opaque and cooked through.
- Season the shrimp lightly with pepper.
- Serve the shrimp on the cucumber salsa with lime wedges on the side.

NUTRITIONAL

- Calories: 120
- Fat: 8g
- Carb: 4g
- Phosphorus: 91mg
- Potassium: 129mg
- Sodium: 60mg
- Protein: 9g
- Calories: 120
- Fat: 8g
- Carb: 4g
- Phosphorus: 91mg
- Potassium: 129mg
- Sodium: 60mg
- Protein: 9g

Preparation Time: 15 minutes|Cooking Time: 10 minutes|Servings: 4

Pesto Pork Chops

INGREDIENTS

- Pork top-loin chops – 4 (3-ounce) boneless, fat trimmed
- Herb pesto – 8 tsps.
- Breadcrumbs – 1/2 cup
- Olive oil – 1 Tbsp.

DIRECTION

- Preheat the oven to 450F.
- Line a baking sheet with foil. Set aside.
- Rub 1 tsp. of pesto evenly over both sides of each pork chop.
- Lightly dredge each pork chop in the breadcrumbs.
- Heat the oil in a skillet.
- Brown the pork chops on each side for 5 minutes.
- Place the pork chops on the baking sheet.
- Bake for 10 minutes or until pork reaches 145F in the center.

NUTRITIONAL

- Calories: 210
- Fat: 7g
- Carb: 10g
- Phosphorus: 179mg
- Potassium: 220mg
- Sodium: 148mg
- Protein: 24g

Preparation Time: 20 minutes|Cooking Time: 20 minutes|Servings: 4

Turkey Burgers

INGREDIENTS

- 1 ripe pear, peeled, cored and chopped roughly
- 1-pound lean ground turkey
- 1 teaspoon fresh ginger, grated finely
- 2 minced garlic cloves
- 1 teaspoon fresh rosemary, minced
- 1 teaspoon fresh sage, minced
- Salt, to taste
- Freshly ground black pepper, to taste
- 1-2 tablespoons coconut oil

DIRECTION

- In a blender, add pear and pulse till smooth.
- Transfer the pear mixture in a large bowl with remaining ingredients except for oil and mix till well combined.
- Make small equal sized 10 patties from the mixture.
- In a heavy-bottomed frying pan, heat oil on medium heat.
- Add the patties and cook for around 4-5 minutes.
- Flip the inside and cook for approximately 2-3 minutes.

NUTRITIONAL

- Calories: 477
- Fat: 15g
- Carbohydrates: 26g
- Fiber: 11g
- Protein: 35g

Preparation Time: 15 minutes |Cooking Time: 8 minutes |Servings: 5

Chapter 11.
Lunch

Dolmas Wrap

INGREDIENTS

- 2 whole wheat wraps
- 6 dolmas (stuffed grape leaves)
- 1 tomato, chopped
- 1 cucumber, chopped
- 2 oz. Greek yogurt
- ½ teaspoon minced garlic
- ¼ cup lettuce, chopped
- 2 oz. Feta, crumbled

DIRECTION

- In the mixing bowl combine together chopped tomato, cucumber, Greek yogurt, minced garlic, lettuce, and Feta.
- When the mixture is homogenous transfer it in the center of every wheat wrap.
- Arrange dolma over the vegetable mixture.
- Carefully wrap the wheat wraps.

NUTRITIONAL

- fat 12.9,
- fiber 9.2,
- carbs 52.4,
- protein 13.2
- Phosphorus: 110mg
- Potassium: 117mg
- Sodium: 75mg

Preparation Time: 10 minutes |Cooking Time: 5 minutes|Servings: 2

Salad al Tonno

INGREDIENTS

- 1 ½ cup lettuce leaves, teared
- ½ cup cherry Red bell peppers, halved
- ½ teaspoon garlic powder
- ½ teaspoon salt
- ½ teaspoon ground black pepper
- 1 tablespoon lemon juice
- 6 oz. tuna, canned, drained

DIRECTION

- Chop the tuna roughly and put it in the salad bowl.
- Add cherry Red bell peppers, lettuce leaves, salt, garlic powder, ground black pepper. Lemon juice, and olive oil.
- Give a good shake to the salad.
- Salad can be stored in the fridge for up to 3 hours.

NUTRITIONAL

- calories 235,
- fat 12, fiber 1, carbs 6.5,
- protein 23.4
- Phosphorus: 120mg
- Potassium: 217mg
- Sodium: 75mg

Preparation Time: 15 minutes |Cooking Time: 0 minutes|Servings: 2

Arlecchino Rice Salad

INGREDIENTS

- ½ cup white rice, dried
- 1 cup chicken stock
- 1 zucchini, shredded
- 2 tablespoons capers
- 1 carrot, shredded
- 1 tomato, chopped
- 1 tablespoon apple cider vinegar
- ½ teaspoon salt
- 2 tablespoons fresh parsley, chopped
- 1 tablespoon canola oil

DIRECTION

- Put rice in the pan.
- Add chicken stock and boil it with the closed lid for 15-20 minutes or until rice absorbs all water.
- Meanwhile, in the mixing bowl combine together shredded zucchini, capers, carrot, and tomato.
- Add fresh parsley.
- Make the dressing: mix up together canola oil, salt, and apple cider vinegar.
- Chill the cooked rice little and add it in the salad bowl to the vegetables.
- Add dressing and mix up salad well.

NUTRITIONAL

- calories 183,
- fat 5.3, fiber 2.1,
- carbs 30.4,
- protein 3.8
- Phosphorus: 110mg
- Potassium: 117mg
- Sodium: 75mg

Preparation Time: 10 minutes |Cooking Time: 15 minutes |Servings: 3

Sauteed Chickpea and Lentil Mix

INGREDIENTS

- 1 cup chickpeas, half-cooked
- 1 cup lentils
- 5 cups chicken stock
- ½ cup fresh cilantro, chopped
- 1 teaspoon salt
- ½ teaspoon chili flakes
- ¼ cup onion, diced
- 1 tablespoon tomato paste

DIRECTION

- Place chickpeas in the pan.
- Add water, salt, and chili flakes.
- Boil the chickpeas for 30 minutes over the medium heat.
- Then add diced onion, lentils, and tomato paste. Stir well.
- Close the lid and cook the mix for 15 minutes.
- After this, add chopped cilantro, stir the meal well and cook it for 5 minutes more.
- Let the cooked lunch chill little before serving.

NUTRITIONAL

- calories 370,
- fat 4.3,
- fiber 23.7,
- carbs 61.6,
- protein 23.2
- Phosphorus: 110mg
- Potassium: 117mg
- Sodium: 75mg

Preparation Time: 10 minutes |Cooking Time: 50 minutes |Servings: 4

Crazy Japanese Potato and Beef Croquettes

INGREDIENTS

- 3 medium russet potatoes, peeled and chopped
- 1 tablespoon almond butter
- 1 tablespoon vegetable oil
- 3 onions, diced
- ¾ pound ground beef
- 4 teaspoons light coconut aminos
- All-purpose flour for coating
- 2 eggs, beaten
- Panko bread crumbs for coating
- ½ cup oil, frying

DIRECTION

- Take a saucepan and place it over medium-high heat; add potatoes and sunflower seeds water, boil for 16 minutes.
- Remove water and put potatoes in another bowl, add almond butter and mash the potatoes.
- Take a frying pan and place it over medium heat, add 1 tablespoon oil and let it heat up.
- Add onions and stir fry until tender.
- Add coconut aminos to beef to onions.
- Keep frying until beef is browned.
- Mix the beef with the potatoes evenly.
- Take another frying pan and place it over medium heat; add half a cup of oil.
- Form croquettes using the mashed potato mixture and coat them with flour, then eggs and finally breadcrumbs.
- Fry patties until golden on all sides.
- Enjoy!

NUTRITIONAL

- Calories: 239 Fat: 4g
- Carbohydrates: 20g
- Protein: 10g
- Phosphorus: 120mg
- Potassium: 107mg
- Sodium: 75mg

Preparation Time: 10 minutes |Cooking Time: 20 minutes |Servings: 10

Traditional Black Bean Chili

INGREDIENTS

- 1 ½ cups red bell pepper, chopped
- 1 cup yellow onion, chopped
- 1 ½ cups mushrooms, sliced
- 1 tablespoon olive oil
- 1 tablespoon chili powder
- 2 garlic cloves, minced
- 1 teaspoon chipotle chili pepper, chopped
- ½ teaspoon cumin, ground
- 16 ounces canned black beans, drained and rinsed
- 2 tablespoons cilantro, chopped
- 1 cup Red bell peppers, chopped

DIRECTION

- Add red bell peppers, onion, dill, mushrooms, chili powder, garlic, chili pepper, cumin, black beans, and Red bell peppers to your Slow Cooker.
- Stir well.
- Place lid and cook on HIGH for 4 hours.
- Sprinkle cilantro on top.
- Serve and enjoy!

NUTRITIONAL

- Calories: 211
- Fat: 3g
- Carbohydrates: 22g
- Protein: 5g
- Phosphorus: 90mg
- Potassium: 107mg
- Sodium: 75mg

Preparation Time: 10 minutes |Cooking Time: 4 hours|Servings: 4

Green Palak Paneer

INGREDIENTS

- 1-pound green lettuce
- 2 cups cubed paneer (vegan)
- 2 tablespoons coconut oil
- 1 teaspoon cumin
- 1 chopped up onion
- 1-2 teaspoons hot green chili minced up
- 1 teaspoon minced garlic
- 15 cashews
- 4 tablespoons almond milk
- 1 teaspoon Garam masala
- Flavored vinegar as needed

DIRECTION

- Add cashews and milk to a blender and blend well.
- Set your pot to Sauté mode and add coconut oil; allow the oil to heat up.
- Add cumin seeds, garlic, green chilies, ginger and sauté for 1 minute.
- Add onion and sauté for 2 minutes.
- Add chopped green lettuce, flavored vinegar and a cup of water.
- Lock up the lid and cook on HIGH pressure for 10 minutes.
- Quick-release the pressure.
- Add ½ cup of water and blend to a paste.
- Add cashew paste, paneer and Garam Masala and stir thoroughly.
- Serve over hot rice!

NUTRITIONAL

- Calories: 367
- Fat: 26g
- Carbohydrates: 21g
- Protein: 16g
- Phosphorus: 110mg
- Potassium: 117mg
- Sodium: 75mg

Preparation Time: 5 minutes |Cooking Time: 10 minutes |Servings: 4

Cucumber Sandwich

INGREDIENTS

- 6 tsp. of cream cheese
- 1 pinch of dried dill weed
- 3 tsp. of mayonnaise
- .25 tsp. dry Italian dressing mix
- 4 slices of white bread
- .5 of a cucumber

DIRECTION

- Prepare the cucumber and cut it into slices.
- Mix cream cheese, mayonnaise, and Italian dressing. Chill for one hour.
- Distribute the mixture onto the white bread slices.
- Place cucumber slices on top and sprinkle with the dill weed.
- Cut in halves and serve.

NUTRITIONAL

- Calories: 143
- Fat: 6g
- Carbs: 16.7g
- Protein: 4g
- Sodium: 255mg
- Potassium: 127mg
- Phosphorus: 64mg

Preparation Time: 1 hour Cooking Time: 5 minutes Servings: 2

Pizza Pitas

INGREDIENTS

- .33 cup of mozzarella cheese
- 2 pieces of pita bread, 6 inches in size
- 6 tsp. of chunky tomato sauce
- 2 cloves of garlic (minced)
- .25 cups of onion, chopped small
- .25 tsp. of red pepper flakes
- .25 cup of bell pepper, chopped small
- 2 ounces of ground pork, lean
- No-stick oil spray
- .5 tsp. of fennel seeds

DIRECTION

- Preheat oven to 400.
- Put the garlic, ground meat, pepper flakes, onion, and bell pepper in a pan. Sauté until cooked.
- Grease a flat baking pan and put pitas on it. Use the mixture to spread on the pita bread.
- Spread one tablespoon of the tomato sauce and top with cheese.
- Bake for five to eight minutes, until the cheese is bubbling.

NUTRITIONAL

- Calories: 284
- Fat: 10g
- Carbs: 34g
- Protein: 16g
- Sodium: 795mg
- Potassium: 706mg
- Phosphorus: 416mg

Preparation Time: 10 minutes Cooking Time: 10 minutes Servings: 1

Lettuce Wraps with Chicken

INGREDIENTS

- 8 lettuce leaves
- .25 cups of fresh cilantro
- .25 cups of mushroom
- 1 tsp. of five spices seasoning
- .25 cups of onion
- 6 tsp. of rice vinegar
- 2 tsp. of hoisin
- 6 tsp. of oil (canola)
- 3 tsp. of oil (sesame)
- 2 tsp. of garlic
- 2 scallions
- 8 ounces of cooked chicken breast

DIRECTION

- Mince together the cooked chicken and the garlic. Chop up the onions, cilantro, mushrooms, and scallions.
- Use a skillet overheat, combine chicken to all remaining ingredients, minus the lettuce leaves. Cook for fifteen minutes, stirring occasionally.
- Place .25 cups of the mixture into each leaf of lettuce.
- Wrap the lettuce around like a burrito and eat.

NUTRITIONAL

- Calories: 84
- Fat: 4g
- Carbs: 9g
- Protein: 5.9g
- Sodium: 618mg
- Potassium: 258mg
- Phosphorus: 64mg

Preparation Time: 10 minutes|Cooking Time: 15 minutes|Servings: 4

Turkey Pinwheels

INGREDIENTS

- 6 toothpicks
- 8 oz. of spring mix salad greens
- 1 ten-inch tortilla
- 2 ounces of thinly sliced deli turkey
- 9 tsp. of whipped cream cheese
- 1 roasted red bell pepper

DIRECTION

- Cut the red bell pepper into ten strips about a quarter-inch thick.
- Spread the whipped cream cheese on the tortilla evenly.
- Add the salad greens to create a base layer and then lay the turkey on top of it.
- Space out the red bell pepper strips on top of the turkey.
- Tuck the end and begin rolling the tortilla inward.
- Use the toothpicks to hold the roll into place and cut it into six pieces.
- Serve with the swirl facing upward.

NUTRITIONAL

- Calories: 206
- Fat: 9g
- Carbs: 21g
- Protein: 9g
- Sodium: 533mg
- Potassium: 145mg
- Phosphorus: 47mg

Preparation Time: 10 minutes|Cooking Time: 15 minutes|Servings: 6

Chicken Tacos

INGREDIENTS

- 8 corn tortillas
- 1.5 tsp. of Sodium-free taco seasoning
- 1 juiced lime
- .5 cups of cilantro
- 2 green onions, chopped
- 8 oz. of iceberg or romaine lettuce, shredded or chopped
- .25 cup of sour cream
- 1 pound of boneless and skinless chicken breast

DIRECTION

- Cook chicken, by boiling, for twenty minutes. Shred or chop cooked chicken into fine bite-sized pieces.
- Mix the seasoning and lime juice with the chicken.
- Put chicken mixture and lettuce in tortillas.
- Top with the green onions, cilantro, and sour cream.

NUTRITIONAL

- Calories: 260
- Fat: 3g
- Carbs: 36g
- Protein: 23g
- Sodium: 922mg
- Potassium: 445mg
- Phosphorus: 357mg

Preparation Time: 5 minutes|Cooking Time: 20 minutes|Servings: 4

Tuna Twist

INGREDIENTS

- 1 can of unsalted or water packaged tuna, drained
- 6 tsp. of vinegar
- .5 cup of cooked peas
- .5 cup celery (chopped)
- 3 tsp. of dried dill weed
- 12 oz. cooked macaroni
- .75 cup of mayonnaise

DIRECTION

- Stir together the macaroni, vinegar, and mayonnaise together until blended and smooth.
- Stir in remaining ingredients.
- Chill before serving.

NUTRITIONAL

- Calories: 290
- Fat: 10g
- Carbs: 32g
- Protein: 16g
- Sodium: 307mg
- Potassium: 175mg
- Phosphorus: 111mg

Preparation Time: 10 minutes|Cooking Time: 30 minutes|Servings: 4

Ciabatta Rolls with Chicken Pesto

INGREDIENTS

- 6 tsp. of Greek yogurt
- 6 tsp. of pesto
- 2 small ciabatta rolls
- 8 oz. of a shredded iceberg or romaine lettuce
- 8 oz. of cooked boneless and skinless chicken breast, shredded
- .125 tsp. of pepper

DIRECTION

- Combine the shredded chicken, pesto, pepper, and Greek yogurt in a medium-sized bowl.
- Slice and toast the ciabatta rolls.
- Divide the shredded chicken and pesto mixture in half and make sandwiches with the ciabatta rolls.
- Top with shredded lettuce if desired.

NUTRITIONAL

- Calories: 374
- Fat: 10g
- Carbs: 40g
- Protein: 30g
- Sodium: 522mg
- Potassium: 360mg
- Phosphorus: 84mg

Preparation Time: 10 minutes|Cooking Time: 20 minutes|Servings: 2

Marinated Shrimp Pasta Salad

INGREDIENTS

- 1/4 cup of honey
- 1/4 cup of balsamic vinegar
- 1/2 of an English cucumber, cubed
- 1/2 pound of fully cooked shrimp
- 15 baby carrots
- 1.5 cups of dime-sized cut cauliflower
- 4 stalks of celery, diced
- 1/2 large yellow bell pepper (diced)
- 1/2 red onion (diced)
- 1/2 large red bell pepper (diced)
- 12 ounces of uncooked tri-color pasta (cooked)
- 3/4 cup of olive oil
- 3 tsp. of mustard (Dijon)
- 1/2 tsp. of garlic (powder)
- 1/2 tsp. pepper

DIRECTION

- Cut vegetables and put them in a bowl with the shrimp.
- Whisk together the honey, balsamic vinegar, garlic powder, pepper, and Dijon mustard in a small bowl. While still whisking, slowly add the oil and whisk it all together.
- Add the cooked pasta to the bowl with the shrimp and vegetables and mix it.
- Toss the sauce to coat the pasta, shrimp, and vegetables evenly.
- Cover and chill for a minimum of five hours before serving. Stir and serve while chilled.

NUTRITIONAL

- Calories: 205
- Fat: 13g
- Carbs: 10g
- Protein: 12g
- Sodium: 363mg
- Potassium: 156mg
- Phosphorus: 109mg

Preparation Time: 15 minutes|Cooking Time: 5 hours|Servings: 1

Peanut Butter and Jelly Grilled Sandwich

INGREDIENTS

- 2 tsp. butter (unsalted)
- 6 tsp. butter (peanut)
- 3 tsp. of flavored jelly
- 2 pieces of bread

DIRECTION

- Put the peanut butter evenly on one bread. Add the layer of jelly.
- Butter the outside of the pieces of bread.
- Add the sandwich to a frying pan and toast both sides.

NUTRITIONAL

- Calories: 300
- Fat: 7g
- Carbs: 49g
- Protein: 8g
- Sodium: 460mg
- Potassium: 222mg
- Phosphorus: 80mg

Preparation Time: 5 minutes|Cooking Time: 5 minutes|Servings: 1

Grilled Onion and Pepper Jack Grilled Cheese Sandwich

INGREDIENTS

- 1 tsp. of oil (olive)
- 6 tsp. of whipped cream cheese
- 1/2 of a medium onion
- 2 ounces of pepper jack cheese
- 4 slices of rye bread
- 2 tsp. of unsalted butter

DIRECTION

- Set out the butter so that it becomes soft. Slice up the onion into thin slices.
- Sauté onion slices. Continue to stir until cooked. Remove and put it to the side.
- Spread one tablespoon of the whipped cream cheese on two of the slices of bread.
- Then add grilled onions and cheese to each slice. Then top using the other two bread slices.
- Spread the softened butter on the outside of the slices of bread.
- Use the skillet to toast the sandwiches until lightly brown and the cheese is melted.

NUTRITIONAL

- Calories: 350
- Fat: 18g
- Carbs: 34g
- Protein: 13g
- Sodium: 589mg
- Potassium: 184mg
- Phosphorus: 226mg

Preparation Time: 5 minutes|Cooking Time: 5 minutes|Servings: 2

Crispy Lemon Chicken

INGREDIENTS

- 1 lb. boneless and skinless chicken breast
- ½ cup of all-purpose flour
- 1 large egg
- ½ cup of lemon juice
- 2 tbsp. of water
- ¼ tsp salt
- ¼ tsp lemon pepper
- 1 tsp of mixed herb seasoning
- 2 tbsp. of olive oil
- A few lemon slices for garnishing
- 1 tbsp. of chopped parsley (for garnishing)
- 2 cups of cooked plain white rice

DIRECTION

- Slice the chicken breast into thin and season with the herb, salt, and pepper.
- In a small bowl, whisk together the egg with the water.
- Keep the flour in a separate bowl.
- Dip the chicken slices in the egg bath and then into the flour.
- Heat your oil in a medium frying pan.
- Shallow fry the chicken in the pan until golden brown.
- Add the lemon juice and cook for another couple of minutes.
- Taken the chicken out of the pan and transfer on a wide dish with absorbing paper to absorb any excess oil.
- Garnish with some chopped parsley and lemon wedges on top.
- Serve with rice.

NUTRITIONAL

- Calories: 232
- Carbohydrate: 24g
- Protein: 18g
- Fat: 8g
- Sodium: 100g
- Potassium: 234mg
- Phosphorus: 217mg

Preparation Time: 10 minutes|Cooking Time: 10 minutes|Servings: 6

Mexican Steak Tacos

INGREDIENTS

- 1 pound of flank or skirt steak
- ¼ cup of fresh cilantro, chopped
- ¼ cup white onion, chopped
- 3 limes, juiced
- 3 cloves of garlic, minced
- 2 tsp of garlic powder
- 2 tbsp. of olive oil
- ½ cup of Mexican or mozzarella cheese, grated
- 1 tsp of Mexican seasoning
- 8 medium-sized (6") corn flour tortillas

DIRECTION

- Combine the juice from two limes, Mexican seasoning, and garlic powder in a dish or bowl and marinate the steak with it for at least half an hour in the fridge.
- In a separate bowl, combine the chopped cilantro, garlic, onion, and juice from one lime to make your salsa. Cover and keep in the fridge.
- Slice steak into thin strips and cook for approximately 3 minutes on each side.
- Preheat your oven to 350F/180C.
- Distribute evenly the steak strips in each tortilla. Top with a tablespoon of the grated cheese on top.
- Wrap each taco in aluminum foil and bake in the oven for 7-8 minutes or until cheese is melted.
- Serve warm with your cilantro salsa.

NUTRITIONAL

- Calories: 230
- Carbohydrate: 19.5 g
- Protein: 15 g
- Fat: 11 g
- Sodium: 486.75 g
- Potassium: 240 mg
- Phosphorus: 268 mg

Preparation Time: 10 minutes|Cooking Time: 15 minutes|Servings: 8

Beer Pork Ribs

INGREDIENTS

- 2 pounds of pork ribs, cut into two units/racks
- 18 oz. of root beer
- 2 cloves of garlic, minced
- 2 tbsp. of onion powder
- 2 tbsp. of vegetable oil (optional)

DIRECTION

- Wrap the pork ribs with vegetable oil and place one unit on the bottom of your slow cooker with half of the minced garlic and the onion powder.
- Place the other rack on top with the rest of the garlic and onion powder.
- Pour over the root beer and cover the lid.
- Let simmer for 8 hours on low heat.
- Take off and finish optionally in a grilling pan for a nice sear.

NUTRITIONAL

- Calories: 301
- Carbohydrate: 36 g
- Protein: 21 g
- Fat: 18 g
- Sodium: 729 mg
- Potassium: 200 mg
- Phosphorus: 209 mg

Preparation Time: 10 minutes|Cooking Time: 8 hours|Servings: 1

Mexican Chorizo Sausage

INGREDIENTS

- 2 pounds of boneless pork but coarsely ground
- 3 tbsp. of red wine vinegar
- 2 tbsp. of smoked paprika
- ½ tsp of cinnamon
- ½ tsp of ground cloves
- ¼ tsp of coriander seeds
- ¼ tsp ground ginger
- 1 tsp of ground cumin
- 3 tbsp. of brandy

DIRECTION

- In a large mixing bowl, combine the ground pork with the seasonings, brandy, and vinegar and mix with your hands well.
- Place the mixture into a large Ziploc bag and leave in the fridge overnight.
- Form into 15-16 patties of equal size.
- Heat the oil in a large pan and fry the patties for 5-7 minutes on each side, or until the meat inside is no longer pink and there is a light brown crust on top.
- Serve hot.

NUTRITIONAL

- Calories: 134
- Carbohydrate: 0 g
- Protein: 10 g
- Fat: 7 g
- Sodium: 40 mg
- Potassium: 138 mg
- Phosphorus: 128 mg

Preparation Time: 10 minutes|Cooking Time: 15 minutes|Servings: 1

Eggplant Casserole

INGREDIENTS

- 3 cups of eggplant, peeled and cut into large chunks
- 2 egg whites
- 1 large egg, whole
- ½ cup of unsweetened vegetable
- ¼ tsp of sage
- ½ cup of breadcrumbs
- 1 tbsp. of margarine, melted
- 1/4 tsp garlic salt

DIRECTION

- Preheat the oven at 350F/180C.
- Place the eggplants chunks in a medium pan, cover with a bit of water and cook with the lid covered until tender. Drain from the water and mash with a tool or fork.
- Beat the eggs with the non-dairy vegetable cream, sage, salt, and pepper. Whisk in the eggplant mush.
- Combine the melted margarine with the breadcrumbs.
- Bake in the oven for 20-25 minutes or until the casserole has a golden-brown crust.

NUTRITIONAL

- Calories: 186
- Carbohydrate: 19 g
- Protein: 7 g
- Fat: 9 g
- Sodium: 503 mg
- Potassium: 230 mg
- Phosphorus: 62 mg

Preparation Time: 10 minutes|Cooking Time: 25 – 30 minutes|Servings: 4

Pizza with Chicken and Pesto

INGREDIENTS

- 1 ready-made frozen pizza dough
- 2/3 cup cooked chicken, chopped
- 1/2 cup of orange bell pepper, diced
- 1/2 cup of green bell pepper, diced
- 1/4 cup of purple onion, chopped
- 2 tbsp. of green basil pesto
- 1 tbsp. of chives, chopped
- 1/3 cup of parmesan or Romano cheese, grated
- 1/4 cup of mozzarella cheese
- 1 tbsp. of olive oil

DIRECTION

- Thaw the pizza dough according to instructions on the package.
- Heat the olive oil in a pan and sauté the peppers and onions for a couple of minutes. Set aside
- Once the pizza dough has thawed, spread the Bali pesto over its surface.
- Top with half of the cheese, the peppers, the onions, and the chicken. Finish with the rest of the cheese.
- Bake at 350F/180C for approx. 20 minutes (or until crust and cheese are baked).
- Slice in triangles with a pizza cutter or sharp knife and serve.

NUTRITIONAL

- Calories: 225
- Carbohydrate: 13.9 g
- Protein: 11.1 g
- Fat: 12 g
- Sodium: 321 mg
- Potassium: 174 mg
- Phosphorus: 172 mg

Preparation Time: 10 minutes|Cooking Time: 25 minutes|Servings: 4

Shrimp Quesadilla

INGREDIENTS

- 5 oz. of shrimp, shelled and deveined
- 4 tbsp. of Mexican salsa
- 2 tbsp. of fresh cilantro, chopped
- 1 tbsp. of lemon juice
- 1 tsp of ground cumin
- 1 tsp of cayenne pepper
- 2 tbsp. of unsweetened soy yogurt or creamy tofu
- 2 medium corn flour tortillas
- 2 tbsp. of low-fat cheddar cheese

DIRECTION

- Mix the cilantro, cumin, lemon juice, and cayenne in a Ziploc bag to make your marinade.
- Put the shrimps and marinate for 10 minutes.
- Heat a pan over medium heat with some olive oil and toss in the shrimp with the marinade. Let cook for a couple of minutes or as soon as shrimps have turned pink and opaque.
- Add the soy cream or soft tofu to the pan and mix well. Remove from the heat and keep the marinade aside.
- Heat tortillas in the grill or microwave for a few seconds.
- Place 2 tbsp. of salsa on each tortilla. Top one tortilla with the shrimp mixture and add the cheese on top.
- Stack one tortilla against each other (with the spread salsa layer facing the shrimp mixture).
- Transfer this on a baking tray and cook for 7-8 minutes at 350F/180C to melt the cheese and crisp up the tortillas.
- Serve warm.

NUTRITIONAL

- Calories: 255
- Carbohydrate: 21 g
- Fat: 9 g
- Protein: 24 g
- Sodium: 562 g
- Potassium: 235 mg
- Phosphorus: 189 mg

Preparation Time: 10 minutes|Cooking Time: 10 minutes|Servings: 2

Grilled Corn on the Cob

INGREDIENTS

- 4 frozen corn on the cob, cut in half
- ½ tsp of thyme
- 1 tbsp. of grated parmesan cheese
- ¼ tsp of black pepper

DIRECTION

- Combine the oil, cheese, thyme, and black pepper in a bowl.
- Place the corn in the cheese/oil mix and roll to coat evenly.
- Fold all 4 pieces in aluminum foil, leaving a small open surface on top.
- Place the wrapped corns over the grill and let cook for 20 minutes.
- Serve hot.

NUTRITIONAL

- Calories: 125
- Carbohydrate: 29.5 g
- Protein: 2 g
- Fat: 1.3 g
- Sodium: 26 g
- Potassium: 145 mg
- Phosphorus: 91.5 mg

Preparation Time: 5 minutes|Cooking Time: 20 minutes|Servings: 4

Couscous with Veggies

INGREDIENTS

- ½ cup of uncooked couscous
- ¼ cup of white mushrooms, sliced
- ½ cup of red onion, chopped
- 1 garlic clove, minced
- ½ cup of frozen peas
- 2 tbsp. of dry white wine
- ½ tsp of basil
- 2 tbsp. of fresh parsley, chopped
- 1 cup water or vegetable stock
- 1 tbsp. of margarine or vegetable oil

DIRECTION

- Thaw the peas by setting them aside at room temperature for 15-20 minutes.
- In a medium pan, heat the margarine or vegetable oil.
- Add the onions, peas, mushroom, and garlic and sauté for around 5 minutes. Add the wine and let it evaporate.
- Add all the herbs and spices and toss well. Take off the heat and keep aside.
- In a small pot, cook the couscous with 1 cup of hot water or vegetable stock. Bring to a boil, take off the heat, and sit for a few minutes with a lid covered.
- Add the sauté veggies to the couscous and toss well.
- Serve in a serving bowl warm or cold.

NUTRITIONAL

- Calories: 110.4
- Carbohydrate: 18 g
- Protein: 3 g
- Fat: 2 g
- Sodium: 112.2 mg
- Potassium: 69.6 mg
- Phosphorus: 46.8 mg

Preparation Time: 10 minutes|Cooking Time: 10 minutes|Servings: 5

Easy Egg Salad

INGREDIENTS

- 4 large eggs
- ½ cup of sweet onion, chopped
- ¼ cup of celery, chopped
- 1 tbsp. of yellow mustard
- 1 tsp of smoked paprika
- 3 tbsp. of mayo

DIRECTION

- Hard boil the eggs in a small pot filled with water for approx. 7-8 minutes. Leave the eggs in the water for an extra couple of minutes before peeling.
- Peel the eggs and chop finely with a knife or tool.
- Combine all the chopped veggies with the mayo and mustard. Add in the eggs and mix well.
- Sprinkle with some smoked paprika on top.
- Serve cold with pitta, white bread slices, or lettuce wraps.

NUTRITIONAL

- Calories: 127
- Carbohydrate: 6 g
- Protein: 7 g
- Fat: 13 g
- Sodium: 170.7 mg
- Potassium: 87.5 mg
- Phosphorus: 101 mg

Preparation Time: 5 minutes|Cooking Time: 8 minutes|Servings: 4

Cauliflower Rice and Coconut

INGREDIENTS

- 3 cups cauliflower, riced
- 2/3 cups full-fat coconut milk
- 1-2 teaspoons sriracha paste
- ¼- ½ teaspoon onion powder
- Salt as needed
- Fresh basil for garnish

DIRECTION

- Take a pan and place it over medium-low heat
- Add all of the ingredients and stir them until fully combined
- Cook for about 5-10 minutes, making sure that the lid is on
- Remove the lid and keep cooking until there's no excess liquid
- Once the rice is soft and creamy, enjoy it!

NUTRITIONAL

- Calories: 95
- Fat: 7g
- Carbohydrates: 4g
- Protein: 1g

Preparation Time: 20 minutes |Cooking Time: 20 minutes|Serving: 4

Kale and Garlic Platter

INGREDIENTS

- 1 bunch kale
- 2 tablespoons olive oil
- 4 garlic cloves, minced

DIRECTION

- Carefully tear the kale into bite-sized portions, making sure to remove the stem
- Discard the stems
- Place on a pot over medium heat.
- Add olive oil, let heat.
- Add garlic and stir for 2 minutes
- Add kale and cook for 5-10 minutes
- Serve!

NUTRITIONAL

- Calories: 121
- Fat: 8g
- Carbohydrates: 5g
- Protein: 4g

Preparation Time: 5 minutes|Cooking Time: 10 minutes|Serving: 4

Blistered Beans and Almond

INGREDIENTS

- 1-pound fresh green beans, ends trimmed
- 1 ½ tablespoon olive oil
- ¼ teaspoon salt
- 1 ½ tablespoons fresh dill, minced
- Juice of 1 lemon
- ¼ cup crushed almonds
- Salt as needed

DIRECTION

- Preheat your oven to 400 °F
- Add in the green beans with your olive oil and also the salt
- Then spread them in one single layer on a large-sized sheet pan
- Roast for 10 minutes and stir nicely, then roast for another 8-10 minutes
- Remove it from the oven and keep stirring in the lemon juice alongside the dill
- Top it with crushed almonds, some flaky sea salt and serve

NUTRITIONAL

- Calories: 347
- Fat: 16g
- Carbohydrates: 6g
- Protein: 45g

Preparation Time: 10 minutes |Cooking Time: 20 minutes|Serving: 4

Cucumber Soup

INGREDIENTS

- 2 tablespoons garlic, minced
- 4 cups English cucumbers, peeled and diced
- ½ cup onions, diced
- 1 tablespoon lemon juice
- 1 ½ cups vegetable broth
- ½ teaspoon salt
- ¼ teaspoon red pepper flakes
- ¼ cup parsley, diced
- ½ cup Greek yogurt, plain

DIRECTION

- Emulsify all the ingredients by blending them (except ½ cup of chopped cucumbers)
- Blend until smooth
- Divide the soup amongst 4 servings and top with extra cucumbers
- Enjoy chilled!

NUTRITIONAL

- Calories: 371
- Fat: 36g
- Carbohydrates: 8g
- Protein: 4g

Preparation Time: 14 minutes|Cooking Time: 0 minutes|Serving: 4

Eggplant Salad

INGREDIENTS

- 2 eggplants, peeled and sliced
- 2 garlic cloves
- 2 green bell paper, sliced, seeds removed
- ½ cup fresh parsley
- ½ cup egg-free mayonnaise
- Salt and black pepper

DIRECTION

- Preheat your oven to 480 °F
- Take a baking pan and add the eggplants and black pepper
- Bake for about 30 minutes
- Flip the vegetables after 20 minutes
- Then, take a bowl and add baked vegetables and all the remaining ingredients
- Mix well
- Serve and enjoy!

NUTRITIONAL

- Calories: 196
- Fat: 108.g
- Carbohydrates: 13.4g
- Protein: 14.6g

Preparation Time: 10 minutes|Cooking Time: 30 minutes |Serving: 3

Cajun Crab

INGREDIENTS

- 1 lemon, fresh and quartered
- 3 tablespoons Cajun seasoning
- 2 bay leaves
- 4 snow crab legs, precooked and defrosted
- Golden ghee

DIRECTION

- Fill half large pot with salted water about.
- Bring the water to a boil
- Squeeze lemon juice into a pot and toss in remaining lemon quarters
- Add bay leaves and Cajun seasoning
- Then season for 1 minute
- Add crab legs and boil for 8 minutes (make sure to keep them submerged the whole time)
- Melt ghee in the microwave and use as a dipping sauce, enjoy!

NUTRITIONAL

- Calories: 643
- Fat: 51g
- Carbohydrates: 3g
- Protein: 41g

Preparation Time: 10 minutes|Cooking Time: 10 minutes |Serving: 2

Mushroom Pork Chops

INGREDIENTS

- 8 ounces mushrooms, sliced
- 1 teaspoon garlic
- 1 onion, peeled and chopped
- 1 cup egg-free mayonnaise
- 3 pork chops, boneless
- 1 teaspoon ground nutmeg
- 1 tablespoon balsamic vinegar
- ½ cup of coconut oil

DIRECTION

- Take a pan and place it over medium heat
- Add oil and let it heat up
- Add mushrooms, onions, and stir
- Cook for 4 minutes
- Add pork chops, season with nutmeg, garlic powder, and brown both sides
- Transfer the pan in the oven and bake for 30 minutes at 350 °F
- Transfer pork chops to plates and keep it warm
- Take a pan and place it over medium heat
- Add vinegar, mayonnaise over mushroom mix and stir for a few minutes
- Drizzle sauce over pork chops
- Enjoy!

NUTRITIONAL

- Calories: 600
- Fat: 10g
- Carbohydrates: 8g
- Protein: 30g

Preparation Time: 10 minutes|Cooking Time: 40 minutes|Serving: 3

Caramelized Pork Chops

INGREDIENTS

- 4 pounds chuck roast
- 4 ounces green chili, chopped
- 2 tablespoons chili powder
- ½ teaspoon dried oregano
- ½ teaspoon ground cumin
- 2 garlic cloves, minced
- Salt as needed

DIRECTION

- Rub your chop with 1 teaspoon of pepper and 2 teaspoons of seasoning salt
- Take a skillet and heat some oil over medium heat
- Brown your pork chops on each side
- Add water and onions to the pan
- Simmer it for about 20 minutes
- Turn your chops over and add the rest of the pepper and salt
- Put the lid and cook until there is no water and the onions turn a medium brown texture
- Remove the chops from your pan and serve with some onions on top!

NUTRITIONAL

- Calories: 271
- Fat: 19g
- Carbohydrates: 4g
- Protein: 27g

Preparation Time: 5 minutes|Cooking Time: 30 minutes|Serving: 4

Mediterranean Pork

INGREDIENTS

- 4 pork chops, bone-in
- Salt and pepper to taste
- 1 teaspoon dried rosemary
- 3 garlic cloves, peeled and minced

DIRECTION

- Season pork chops with salt and pepper
- Place in roasting pan
- Add rosemary, garlic in a pan
- Preheat your oven to 425 ° F
- Bake for 10 minutes
- Lower heat to 350 ° F
- Roast for 25 minutes more
- Slice pork and divide on plates
- Drizzle pan juice all over
- Serve and enjoy!

NUTRITIONAL

- Calories: 165
- Fat: 2g
- Carbohydrates: 2g
- Protein: 26g

Preparation Time: 10 minutes|Cooking Time: 35 minutes |Serving: 4

Ground Beef and Bell Peppers

INGREDIENTS

- 1 onion, chopped
- 2 tablespoons coconut oil
- 1-pound ground beef
- 1 red bell pepper, diced
- 2 cups green lettuce, chopped
- Salt and pepper to taste

DIRECTION

- Place over medium heat on a skillet
- Add onion and cook until slightly browned
- Add green lettuce and ground beef
- Stir fry until done
- Take the mixture and fill up the bell peppers
- Serve and enjoy!

NUTRITIONAL

- Calories: 350
- Fat: 23g
- Carbohydrates: 4g
- Protein: 28g

Preparation Time: 10 minutes|Cooking Time: 10 minutes|Serving: 3

Spiced Up Pork Chops

INGREDIENTS

- ¼ cup lime juice
- 4 pork rib chops
- 1 tablespoon coconut oil, melted
- 2 garlic cloves, peeled and minced
- 1 tablespoon chili powder
- 1 teaspoon ground cinnamon
- 2 teaspoons cumin
- Salt and pepper to taste
- ½ teaspoon hot pepper sauce
- Mango, sliced

DIRECTION

- Take a bowl and mix in lime juice, oil, garlic, cumin, cinnamon, chili powder, salt, pepper, hot pepper sauce
- Whisk well
- Add pork chops and toss
- Keep it on the side and refrigerate for 4 hours
- Pre-heat your grill to medium and transfer pork chops to a pre-heated grill
- Grill for 7 minutes both sides
- Divide between serving platters and serve with mango slices
- Enjoy!

NUTRITIONAL

- Calories: 200
- Fat: 8g
- Carbohydrates: 3g
- Protein: 26g

Preparation Time: 4 hours 10 minutes|Cooking Time: 15 minutes|Serving: 4

Juicy Salmon Dish

INGREDIENTS

- ¾ cup of water
- Few sprigs of parsley, basil, tarragon, basil
- 1 pound of salmon, skin on
- 3 teaspoons of ghee
- ¼ teaspoon of salt
- ½ teaspoon of pepper
- ½ of lemon, thinly sliced
- 1 whole carrot, julienned

DIRECTION

- Set your pot to Sauté mode and add water and herbs
- Place a steamer rack inside your pot and place salmon
- Drizzle ghee on top of the salmon and season with salt and pepper
- Cover with lemon slices
- Cook on HIGH pressure with locked lid for 3 minutes
- Release the pressure naturally over 10 minutes
- Transfer the salmon to a serving platter
- Set your pot to Sauté mode and add vegetables
- Cook for 1-2 minutes
- Serve with vegetables and salmon
- Enjoy!

NUTRITIONAL

- Calories: 464
- Fat: 34g
- Carbohydrates: 3g
- Protein: 34g

Preparation Time: 5 minutes|Cooking Time: 6 minutes |Serving: 3

Platter-O-Brussels

INGREDIENTS

- 2 tablespoons olive oil
- 1 yellow onion, chopped
- 2 pounds Brussels sprouts, trimmed and halved
- 4 cups chicken stock
- ¼ cup coconut cream

DIRECTION

- Take a pot and place over medium heat
- Add oil and let it heat up
- Add onion and stir cook for 3 minutes
- Add Brussels sprouts and stir, cook for 2 minutes
- Add stock and black pepper, stir and bring to a simmer
- Cook for 20 minutes more
- Blend until creamy.
- Add coconut cream and stir well
- Ladle into soup bowls and serve
- Enjoy!

NUTRITIONAL

- Calories: 200
- Fat: 11g
- Carbohydrates: 6g
- Protein: 11g

Preparation Time: 10 minutes|Cooking Time: 20 minutes |Serving: 4

Almond Chicken

INGREDIENTS

- 2 large chicken breasts, boneless and skinless
- 1/3 cup lemon juice
- 1 ½ cups seasoned almond meal
- 2 tablespoons coconut oil
- Lemon pepper, to taste
- Parsley for decoration

DIRECTION

- Slice chicken breast in half
- Pound out each half until ¼ inch thick
- Take a pan and place over medium heat, add oil and heat it up
- Dip each chicken breast slice into lemon juice and let it sit for 2 minutes
- Turnover and let the other side sit for 2 minutes as well
- Transfer to almond meal and coat both sides
- Add coated chicken and fry for 4 minutes per side, making sure to sprinkle lemon pepper liberally
- Transfer to a paper-lined sheet and repeat until all chicken is fried
- Garnish with parsley and enjoy!

NUTRITIONAL

- Calories: 325
- Fat: 24g
- Carbohydrates: 3g
- Protein: 16g

Preparation Time: 15 minutes|Cooking Time: 15 minutes|Serving: 3

BlackBerry Chicken Wings

INGREDIENTS

- 3 pounds chicken wings, about 20 pieces
- ½ cup blackberry chipotle jam
- Salt and pepper to taste
- ½ cup of water

DIRECTION

- Add water and jam to a bowl and mix well
- Place chicken wings in a zip bag and add two-thirds of the marinade
- Season with salt and pepper
- Let it marinate for 30 minutes
- Preheat your oven to 400°F
- Prepare a baking sheet and wire rack, place chicken wings in a wire rack and bake for 15 minutes
- Brush remaining marinade and bake for 30 minutes more
- Enjoy!

NUTRITIONAL

- Calories: 502
- Fat: 39g
- Carbohydrates: 01.8g
- Protein: 34g

Preparation Time: 35 minutes|Cooking Time: 50 minutes|Serving: 4

Aromatic Carrot Cream

INGREDIENTS

- 1 tablespoon olive oil
- ½ sweet onion, chopped
- 2 teaspoons fresh ginger, peeled and grated
- 1 teaspoon fresh garlic, minced
- 4 cups water
- 3 carrots, chopped
- 1 teaspoon ground turmeric
- ½ cup coconut milk

DIRECTION

- Heat the olive oil into a big pan over medium-high heat.
- Add the onion, garlic and ginger. Softly cook for about 3 minutes until softened.
- Include the water, turmeric and the carrots. Softly cook for about 20 minutes (until the carrots are softened).
- Blend the soup adding coconut milk until creamy.
- Serve and enjoy!

NUTRITIONAL

- Calories 112
- Fat 10 g
- Cholesterol 0 mg
- Carbohydrates 8 g
- Sugar 5 g
- Fiber 2 g
- Protein 2 g
- Sodium 35 mg
- Calcium 32 mg
- Phosphorus 59 mg
- Potassium 241 mg

Preparation Time:15 minutes |Cooking Time:25 minutes|Servings: 4

Mushrooms Velvet Soup

INGREDIENTS

- 1 teaspoon olive oil
- ½ teaspoon fresh ground black pepper
- 3 medium (85g) shallots, diced
- 2 stalks (80g) celery, chopped
- 1 clove garlic, diced
- 12-ounces cremini mushrooms, sliced
- 5 tablespoons flour
- 4 cups low sodium vegetable stock, divided
- 3 sprigs fresh thyme
- 2 bay leaves
- ½ cup regular yogurt

DIRECTION

- Heat oil in a large pan.
- Add ground pepper, shallots and celery. Cook over medium-high heat.
- Sauté for 2 minutes until golden.
- Add garlic and stir.
- Include the sliced mushrooms. Stir and cook until the mushrooms give out their liquid.
- Sprawl the flour on the mushrooms and toast for about 2 min.
- Add one cup of hot stock, thyme sprigs and bay leaves. Stir and add the second cup of stock
- Stir until well combined.
- Add the remaining cups of stock.
- Slowly cook for 15 minutes.
- Take out bay leaves and thyme sprigs.
- Blend until mixture is smooth.
- Include the yogurt and stir well.
- Slowly cook for 4 minutes.
- Serve and enjoy!

NUTRITIONAL

- Calories 126
- Fat 8 g
- Cholesterol 0 mg
- Carbohydrate 14 g
- Sugar 4 g
- Fiber 2 g
- Protein 3 g
- Sodium 108 mg
- Calcium 55 mg
- Phosphorus 70 mg
- Potassium 298 mg

Preparation Time:40 minutes |Cooking Time:40 minutes |Servings: 6

Easy Lettuce Wraps

INGREDIENTS

- 8 ounces cooked chicken, shredded
- 1 scallion, chopped
- ½ cup seedless red grapes, halved
- 1 celery stalk, chopped
- ¼ cup mayonnaise
- A pinch ground black pepper
- 4 large lettuce leaves

DIRECTION

- In a mixing bowl add the scallion, chicken, celery, grapes and mayonnaise.
- Stir well until incorporated.
- Season with pepper.
- Place the lettuce leaves onto serving plates.
- Place the chicken salad onto the leaves.
- Serve and enjoy!

NUTRITIONAL

- Calories 146
- Fat 5 g
- Cholesterol 35 mg
- Carbohydrates 8 g
- Sugar 4 g
- Fiber 0 g
- Protein 16 g
- Sodium 58 mg
- Calcium 18 mg
- Phosphorus 125 mg
- Potassium 212 mg

Preparation Time:15 minutes|Cooking Time:0 minutes|Servings: 4

Spaghetti with Pesto

INGREDIENTS

- 8 ounces spaghetti (package pasta)
- 2 cups packed basil leaves
- 2 cups packed arugula leaves
- 1/3 cup walnut pieces
- 3 cloves of garlic
- ¼ cup extra-virgin olive oil
- Black pepper

DIRECTION

- Cook pasta with boiling water. Drain.
- Add the basil, garlic, olive oil, walnuts, pepper and arugula in a blender and mix until creamy.
- Mix pesto mixture into pasta in a large bowl.
- Serve and enjoy!

NUTRITIONAL

- Calories 400
- Fat 21 g
- Cholesterol 0 mg
- Carbohydrates 46 g
- Sugar 2 g
- Fiber 3 g
- Protein 11 g
- Sodium 6 mg
- Calcium 64 mg
- Phosphorus 113 mg
- Potassium 202 mg

Preparation Time:10 minutes|Cooking Time: 10 minutes|Servings: 4

Vegetable Casserole

INGREDIENTS

- 1 teaspoon olive oil
- 1 sweet onion, chopped
- 1 teaspoon garlic, minced
- 2 zucchinis, chopped
- 1 red bell pepper, diced
- 2 carrots, chopped
- 2 cups low-sodium vegetable stock
- 2 large Red bell peppers, chopped
- 2 cups broccoli florets
- 1 teaspoon ground coriander
- ½ teaspoon ground comminutes
- Black pepper

DIRECTION

- Heat the olive oil into a big pan over medium-high heat.
- Add onion and garlic. Softly cook for about 3 minutes until softened.
- Include the zucchini, carrots, bell pepper and softly cook for 5-6 minutes.
- Pour the vegetable stock, Red bell peppers, broccoli, coriander, cumin, pepper and stir well.
- Softly cook for about 5 minutes over medium-high heat until the vegetables are tender.
- Serve hot and enjoy!

NUTRITIONAL

- Calories 47
- Fat 1 g
- Cholesterol 0 g
- Carbohydrates 8 g
- Sugar 6 g
- Fiber 2 g
- Protein 2 g
- Sodium 104 mg
- Calcium 36 mg
- Phosphorus 52 mg
- Potassium 298 mg

Preparation Time:15 minutes|Cooking Time:15 minutes|Servings: 8

Appetizing Rice Salad

INGREDIENTS

- 1 cup wild rice
- 2 cups water
- 1 tablespoon olive oil
- 2/3 cup walnuts, chopped
- 1 (4 inches) celery rib, sliced
- 4 scallions, thinly sliced
- 1 medium red apple, cored and diced
- ½ cup pomegranate seeds
- ½ tablespoon lemon zest
- 3 tablespoons lemon juice
- Black pepper
- 1/3 cup olive oil

DIRECTION

- In a big pot place the wild strained rice together with water and olive oil.
- Bring to a boil and simmer for about 50 minutes until rice is tender.
- In a mixing bowl add celery, walnuts, apple, scallions, pomegranate seeds and lemon zest.
- Mix well with a blender the lemon juice, pepper, and olive oil.
- Spread half of this dressing on the apple mixture and mix well.
- When the rice is cooked, let it cool and incorporate with the fruit mixture
- Season with the remaining dressing.
- Serve at room temperature and enjoy!

NUTRITIONAL

- Calories 300
- Fat 19 g
- Cholesterol 0 mg
- Carbohydrates 34 g
- Sugar 11 g
- Fiber 5 g
- Protein 6 g
- Sodium 6 mg
- Calcium 30 mg
- Phosphorus 144 mg
- Potassium 296 mg

Preparation Time:20 minutes|Cooking Time:1 hour|Servings: 8

Spiced Wraps

INGREDIENTS

- 6 ounces cooked chicken breast, minced
- 1 scallion, chopped
- ½ red apple, cored and chopped
- ½ cup bean sprouts
- ¼ cucumber, chopped
- Juice of 1 lime
- Zest of 1 lime
- 2 tablespoons fresh cilantro, chopped
- ½ teaspoon Chinese five-spice powder
- 8 lettuce leaves

DIRECTION

- Combine the chicken, apple, bean sprouts, cucumber, lime juice, lime zest, cilantro, five-spice powder and scallions.
- Place the lettuce leaves onto 8 serving plates.
- Spoon the chicken mixture onto lettuce leaves.
- Wrap the lettuce around the chicken mixture.
- Serve and enjoy!

NUTRITIONAL

- Calories 53
- Fat 3 g
- Cholesterol 19 mg
- Carbohydrates 3 g
- Sugar 3 g
- Fiber 2 g
- Protein 7 g
- Sodium 19 mg
- Calcium 16 mg
- Phosphorus 58 mg
- Potassium 134

Preparation Time:30 minutes|Cooking Time:0 minutes|Servings: 8

Rump Roast

INGREDIENTS

- 1-pound rump roast
- ½ teaspoon black pepper
- 1 tablespoon olive oil
- ½ small onion, chopped
- 2 teaspoons garlic, minced
- 1 teaspoon dried thyme
- 1 cup + 3 tablespoons water
- 2 tablespoons cornstarch

DIRECTION

- Heat the olive oil into a big saucepan over medium heat.
- Add the peppered meat and brown the roast all over. Set aside the meat.
- Softly cook the garlic and onion in the same saucepan for about 3 minutes until they are tendered.
- Incorporate the roast to the saucepan, add 1 cup of water and the thyme.
- Cover, simmer until the meat is tender or for 4 and half hours.
- In a mixing bowl, stir the cornstarch with 3 tablespoons water to form a slurry.
- Beat the slurry into the liquid in the pan and cook for about 15 minutes to thicken the sauce.
- Serve and enjoy!

NUTRITIONAL

- Calories 156
- Fat 12 g
- Cholesterol 42 mg
- Carbohydrates 4 g
- Sugar 2 g
- Fiber 0 g
- Protein 14 g
- Sodium 48 mg
- Calcium 18 mg
- Phosphorus 114 mg
- Potassium 220 mg

Preparation Time:10 minutes|Cooking Time:5 hours |Servings: 8

Couscous and Sherry Vinaigrette

INGREDIENTS

- *For Sherry Vinaigrette: (makes 2/3 cup)*
- *2 tablespoons sherry vinegar*
- *¼ cup lemon juice*
- *1 clove garlic, pressed*
- *1/3 cup olive oil*
- *For Roasted Carrots, Cranberries and Couscous:*
- *1 medium onion, sliced*
- *2 large carrots, sliced*
- *2 tablespoons extra-virgin olive oil*
- *2 cups pearl couscous*
- *2 ½ to 3 cups no sodium vegetable broth*
- *½ cup dried cranberries*
- *¼ cup Sherry vinaigrette*

DIRECTION

- For Sherry Vinaigrette:
- Beat the vinegar with garlic and lemon juice.
- Slowly whisk in olive oil.
- Store refrigerated in a glass jar.
- For Carrots, Cranberries and Couscous:
- Preheat oven to 400°F.
- Spray a baking dish with cooking spray (olive oil) and place the carrots and onions on it.
- Roast the vegetables in oven for about 20 minutes until starting to brown. Stir halfway cooking.
- Heat the couscous in a pan over medium-high heat.
- Toast the couscous until light brown (about 10 minutes). Stir well.
- Check the package instructions for the amount of liquid needed for couscous.
- Bring to a boil the added vegetable stock. Cover and reduce for about 10 minutes. The vegetable stock has to be absorbed.
- In a mixing bowl, incorporate the couscous with the onions, carrots, cranberries, and sherry vinaigrette.
- Serve and enjoy!

NUTRITIONAL

- *Calories 365*
- *Fat 11 g*
- *Cholesterol 0 mg*
- *Carbohydrate 58 g*
- *Sugar 11 g*
- *Fiber 4 g*
- *Protein 9 g*
- *Sodium 95 mg*
- *Calcium 41 mg*
- *Phosphorus 119 mg*
- *Potassium 264 mg*

Preparation Time:10 minutes|Cooking Time:30 minutes|Servings: 6

Persian Chicken

INGREDIENTS

- *½ small sweet onion,*
- *¼ cup freshly squeezed lemon juice*
- *1 tablespoon dried oregano*
- *1/2 tablespoon of sweet paprika,*
- *½ tablespoon of ground cumin*
- *½ cup olive oil*
- *6 boneless, skinless chicken thighs*

DIRECTION

- Put the vegetables in a blender. Mix it well.
- Put the olive while the motor is running.
- In a sealable bag for the freezer, place the chicken thighs and put the mixture in the sealable bag.
- Refrigerate it for 2 hours, while turning it two times.
- Remove the marinade thighs and discard the additional marinade. Preheat to medium the barbecue. Grill the chicken, turning once or until the internal

NUTRITIONAL

- *Fat: 21 g;*
- *Carbohydrates: 3 g;*
- *Potassium: 220 mg;*
- *Sodium: 86 mg;*
- *Protein: 22 g*

Preparation Time: 10 minutes, |Cooking Time: 20 minutes |Servings: 6

Ratatouille

INGREDIENTS

- 1 cup Water
- 3 tbsp. oil
- 2 Zucchinis, sliced in rings
- 2 Eggplants, sliced in rings
- 1 medium Red Onion, sliced in thin rings
- 3 cloves Garlic, minced
- 2 sprigs Fresh Thyme
- Salt to taste
- Black Pepper to taste
- 4 tsp Plain Vinegar

DIRECTION

- Place all veggies in a bowl, sprinkle with salt and pepper; toss. Line foil in a spring form tin and arrange 1 slice each of the vegetables in, one after the other in a tight circular arrangement.
- Fill the entire tin. Sprinkle the garlic over, some more black pepper and salt, and arrange the thyme sprigs on top. Drizzle olive oil and vinegar over the veggies.
- Place a trivet to fit in the Instant Pot, pour the water in and place the veggies on the trivet. Seal the lid, secure the pressure valve and select Manual mode on High Pressure for 6 minutes. Once ready, quickly release the pressure. Carefully remove the tin and serve ratatouille.

NUTRITIONAL

- Calories 152,
- Protein 2g,
- Net Carbs 4g,
- Fat 12g

Preparation Time: 5 minutes |Cooking Time: 15 minutes|Servings: 4

Chapter 12.
Dinner

Baked Pork Chops

INGREDIENTS

- 1/2 cup flour
- 1 large egg
- 1/4 cup water
- 3/4 cup breadcrumbs
- 6 (3 1/2 oz.) pork chops
- 2 tablespoons butter, unsalted
- 1 teaspoon paprika

DIRECTION

- Begin by switching the oven to 350 degrees F to preheat.
- Mix and spread the flour in a shallow plate.
- Whisk the egg with water in another shallow bowl.
- Spread the breadcrumbs on a separate plate.
- Firstly, coat the pork with flour, then dip in the egg mix and then in the crumbs.
- Grease a baking sheet and place the chops in it.
- Drizzle the pepper on top and bake for 40 minutes.
- Serve.

NUTRITIONAL

- Calories: 221 kcal
- Total Fat: 7.8 g
- Saturated Fat: 1.9 g
- Cholesterol: 93 mg
- Sodium: 135 mg
- Total Carbs: 11.9 g

Preparation Time: 15 minutes |Cooking Time: 40 minutes |Servings: 6

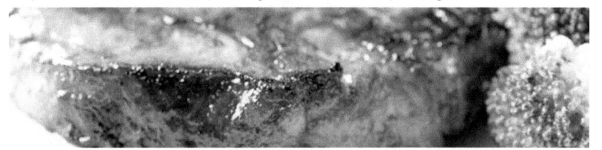

Beef Kabobs with Pepper

INGREDIENTS

- 1 Pound of beef sirloin
- 1/2 Cup of vinegar
- 2 tbsp. of salad oil
- 1 Medium, chopped onion
- 2 tbsp. of chopped fresh parsley
- 1/4 tsp. of black pepper
- 2 Cut into strips green peppers

DIRECTION

- Trim the fat from the meat; then cut it into cubes of 1 and 1/2 inches each
- Mix the vinegar, the oil, the onion, the parsley and the pepper in a bowl
- Place the meat in the marinade and set it aside for about 2 hours; make sure to stir from time to time.
- Remove the meat from the marinade and alternate it on skewers instead with green pepper
- Brush the pepper with the marinade and broil for about 10 minutes 4 inches from the heat
- Serve and enjoy your kabobs

NUTRITIONAL

- Calories: 357 kcal
- Total Fat: 24 g
- Saturated Fat: 0 g
- Cholesterol: 9 mg
- Sodium: 60 mg
- Total Carbs: 0 g

Preparation Time: 5 Minutes |Cooking Time: 10 Minutes |Servings: 8

One-Pot Beef Roast

INGREDIENTS

- 3 1/2 pounds beef roast
- 4 ounces mushrooms, sliced
- 12 ounces beef stock
- 1-ounce onion soup mix
- 1/2 cup Italian dressing

DIRECTION

- Take a bowl and add the stock, onion soup mix, and Italian dressing
- Stir
- Put beef roast in pan
- Add the mushrooms and stock mix to the pan and cover with foil
- Preheat your oven to 300 °F
- Bake for 1 hour and 15 minutes
- Let the roast cool
- Slice and serve
- Enjoy the gravy on top!

NUTRITIONAL

- Calories: 700 kcal
- Total Fat: 56 g
- Saturated Fat: 0 g
- Cholesterol: 0 mg
- Sodium: 0 mg
- Total Carbs: 10 g

Preparation Time: 10 minutes |Cooking Time: 75 minutes |Servings: 4

Cabbage and Beef Fry

INGREDIENTS

- 1 pound beef, ground
- 1/2 pound bacon
- 1 onion
- 1 garlic cloves, minced
- 1/2 head cabbage
- Salt and pepper to taste

DIRECTION

- Take a skillet and place it over medium heat
- Add chopped bacon, beef and onion until slightly browned
- Transfer to a bowl and keep it covered
- Add minced garlic and cabbage to the skillet and cook until slightly browned
- Return the ground beef mixture to the skillet and simmer for 3-5 minutes over low heat
- Serve and enjoy!

NUTRITIONAL

- Calories: 360 kcal
- Total Fat: 22 g
- Saturated Fat: 0 g
- Cholesterol: 0 mg
- Sodium: 0 mg
- Total Carbs: 5 g

Preparation Time: 5 minutes |Cooking Time: 15 minutes |Servings: 4

Mushroom and Olive Sirloin Steak

INGREDIENTS

- 1 pound boneless beef sirloin steak, ¾ inch thick, cut into 4 pieces
- 1 large red onion, chopped
- 1 cup mushrooms
- 4 garlic cloves, thinly sliced
- 4 tablespoons olive oil
- 1 cup parsley leaves, finely cut

DIRECTION

- Take a large-sized skillet and place it over medium-high heat
- Add oil and let it heat p
- Add beef and cook until both sides are browned, remove beef and drain fat
- Add the rest of the oil to skillet and heat it up
- Add onions, garlic and cook for 2-3 minutes
- Stir well
- Return beef to skillet and lower heat to medium
- Cook for 3-4 minutes (covered)
- Stir in parsley
- Serve and enjoy!

NUTRITIONAL

- Calories: 386 kcal
- Total Fat: 30 g
- Saturated Fat: 0 g
- Cholesterol: 0 mg
- Sodium: 0 mg
- Total Carbs: 11 g

Preparation Time: 10 minutes |Cooking Time: 14 minutes |Servings: 4

California Pork Chops

INGREDIENTS

- 1 tbsp. fresh cilantro, chopped
- 1/2 cup chives, chopped
- 2 large green bell peppers, chopped
- 1 lb. 1" thick boneless pork chops
- 1 tbsp. fresh lime juice
- 2 cups cooked rice
- 1/8 tsp. dried oregano leaves
- 1/4 tsp. ground black pepper
- 1/4 tsp. ground cumin
- 1 tbsp. butter
- 1 lime

DIRECTION

- Start by seasoning the pork chops with lime juice and cilantro.
- Place them in a shallow dish.
- Toss the chives with pepper, cumin, butter, oregano and rice in a bowl.
- Stuff the bell peppers with this mixture and place them around the pork chops.
- Cover the chop and bell peppers with a foil sheet and bake them for 10 minutes in the oven at 375 degrees f.
- Serve warm.

NUTRITIONAL

- Calories: 265 kcal
- Total Fat: 15 g
- Saturated Fat: 0 g
- Cholesterol: 86 mg
- Sodium: 70 mg
- Total Carbs: 24 g
- Fiber: 1 g
- Sugar: 0 g
- Protein: 34 g

Preparation Time: 10 minutes |Cooking Time: 10 minutes |Servings: 2

Caribbean Turkey Curry

INGREDIENTS

- 3 1/2 lbs. turkey breast, with skin
- 1/4 cup butter, melted
- 1/4 cup honey
- 1 tbsp. mustard
- 2 tsp. curry powder
- 1 tsp. garlic powder

DIRECTION

- Place the turkey breast in a shallow roasting pan.
- Insert a meat thermometer to monitor the temperature.
- Bake the turkey for 1.5 hours at 350 degrees f until its internal temperature reaches 170 degrees f.
- Meanwhile, thoroughly mix honey, butter, curry powder, garlic powder, and mustard in a bowl.
- Glaze the cooked turkey with this mixture liberally.
- Let it sit for 15 minutes for absorption.
- Slice and serve.

NUTRITIONAL

- Calories: 275 kcal
- Total Fat: 13 g
- Saturated Fat: 0 g
- Cholesterol: 82 mg
- Sodium: 122 mg
- Total Carbs: 90 g

Preparation Time: 10 minutes |Cooking Time: 1 hour an 30 minutes |Servings: 6

Chicken Fajitas

INGREDIENTS

- 8 flour tortillas, 6" size
- 1/4 cup green pepper, cut in strips
- 1/4 cup red pepper, cut in strips
- 1/2 cup onion, sliced
- 1/2 cup cilantro
- 2 tbsp. canola oil
- 12 oz. boneless chicken breasts
- 1/4 tsp. black pepper
- 2 tsp. chili powder
- 1/2 tsp. cumin
- 2 tbsp. lemon juice

DIRECTION

- Start by wrapping the tortillas in a foil.
- Warm them up for 10 minutes in a preheated oven at 300 degrees f.
- Add oil to a nonstick pan.
- Add lemon juice chicken and seasoning
- Stir fry for 5 minutes then add onion and peppers.
- Continue cooking for 5 minutes or until chicken is tender.
- Stir in cilantro, mix well and serve in tortillas.

NUTRITIONAL

- Calories: 343 kcal
- Total Fat: 13 g
- Saturated Fat: 0 g
- Cholesterol: 53 mg
- Sodium: 281 mg
- Total Carbs: 33 g

Preparation Time: 10 minutes |Cooking Time: 10 minutes |Servings: 8

Chicken Veronique

INGREDIENTS

- 2 boneless skinless chicken breasts
- 1/2 shallot, chopped
- 2 tablespoons butter
- 2 tablespoons dry white wine
- 2 tablespoons chicken broth
- 1/2 cup green grapes, halved
- 1 teaspoon dried tarragon
- 1/4 cup cream

DIRECTION

- Place an 8-inch skillet over medium heat and add butter to melt.
- Sear the chicken in the melted butter until golden-brown on both sides.
- Place the boneless chicken on a plate and set it aside.
- Add shallot to the same skillet and stir until soft.
- Whisk cornstarch with broth and wine in a small bowl.
- Pour this slurry into the skillet and mix well.
- Place the chicken in the skillet and cook it on a simmer for 6 minutes.
- Transfer the chicken to the serving plate.
- Add cream, tarragon, and grapes.
- Cook for 1 minute, and then pour this sauce over the chicken.
- Serve.

NUTRITIONAL

- Calories: 306 kcal
- Total Fat: 18 g
- Saturated Fat: 0 g
- Cholesterol: 124 mg
- Sodium: 167 mg
- Total Carbs: 9 g

Preparation Time: 10 minutes |Cooking Time: 10 minutes |Servings: 4

Chicken and Apple Curry

INGREDIENTS

- 8 boneless skinless chicken breasts
- 1/4 teaspoon black pepper
- 2 medium apples, peeled, cored, and chopped
- 2 small onions, chopped
- 1 garlic clove, minced
- 3 tablespoons butter
- 1 tablespoon curry powder
- 1/2 tablespoon dried basil
- 3 tablespoons flour
- 1 cup chicken broth
- 1 cup of rice milk

DIRECTION

- Preheat oven to 350°F.
- Set the chicken breasts in a baking pan and sprinkle black pepper over it.
- Place a suitably-sized saucepan over medium heat and add butter to melt.
- Add onion, garlic, and apple, then sauté until soft.
- Stir in basil and curry powder, and then cook for 1 minute.
- Add flour and continue mixing for 1 minute.
- Stir in rice milk and chicken broth, then stir cook for 5 minutes.
- Pour this sauce over the chicken breasts in the baking pan.
- Bake the chicken for 60 minutes then serve.

NUTRITIONAL

- Calories: 232 kcal
- Total Fat: 8 g
- Saturated Fat: 0 g
- Cholesterol: 85 mg
- Sodium: 118 mg
- Total Carbs: 11 g

Preparation Time: 10 minutes |Cooking Time: 1 hour and 11 minutes |Servings: 8

London Broil

INGREDIENTS

- *2 pounds flank steak*
- *1/4 teaspoon meat tenderizer*
- *1 tablespoon sugar*
- *2 tablespoons lemon juice*
- *2 tablespoons soy sauce*
- *1 tablespoon honey*
- *1 teaspoon herb seasoning blend*

DIRECTION

- Pound the meat with a mallet then place it in a shallow dish.
- Sprinkle meat tenderizer over the meat.
- Whisk rest of the ingredients and spread this marinade over the meat.
- Marinate the meat for 4 hours in the refrigerator.
- Bake the meat for 5 minutes per side at 350°F.
- Slice and serve.

NUTRITIONAL

- *Calories: 184 kcal*
- *Total Fat: 8 g*
- *Saturated Fat: 0 g*
- *Cholesterol: 43 mg*
- *Sodium: 208 mg*
- *Total Carbs: 3 g*

Preparation Time: 10 minutes |Cooking Time: 5 minutes |Servings: 4

Sirloin with Squash and Pineapple

INGREDIENTS

- *8 ounces canned pineapple slices*
- *2 garlic cloves, minced*
- *2 teaspoons ginger root, minced*
- *3 teaspoons olive oil*
- *1 pound sirloin tips*
- *1 medium zucchini, diced*
- *1 medium yellow squash, diced*
- *1/2 medium red onion, diced*

DIRECTION

- Mix pineapple juice with 1 teaspoon olive oil, ginger, and garlic in a Ziplock bag.
- Add sirloin tips to the pineapple juice marinade and seal the bag.
- Place the bag in the refrigerator overnight.
- Preheat oven to 450°F.
- Layer 2 sheet pans with foil and grease it with 1 teaspoon olive oil.
- Spread the squash, onion, and pineapple rings in the prepared pans.
- Bake them for 5 minutes then transfer to the serving plate.
- Place the marinated sirloin tips on a baking sheet and bake for 4 minutes in the oven.
- Transfer the sirloin tips to the roasted vegetables.
- Serve.

NUTRITIONAL

- *Calories: 264 kcal*
- *Total Fat: 12 g*
- *Saturated Fat: 0 g*
- *Cholesterol: 74 mg*
- *Sodium: 150 mg*
- *Total Carbs: 14 g*

Preparation Time: 10 minutes |Cooking Time: 9 minutes |Servings: 2

Slow-Cooked BBQ Beef

INGREDIENTS

- 4-pound pot roast
- 2 cups of water
- ¾ cup ketchup
- 1/4 cup brown sugar
- 1/3 cup vinegar
- 1/2 teaspoon allspice
- 1/4 cup onion

DIRECTION

- Add 2 cups water and roast to a Crockpot and cover it.
- Cook for 10 hours on LOW setting, then drain it while keeping 1 cup of its liquid.
- Transfer the cooked meat to a 9x13 pan and set it aside.
- Whisk 1 cup liquid, ketchup, vinegar, brown sugar, minced onion, and allspice in a bowl.
- Add beef to the marinade and mix well to coat, then marinate overnight in the refrigerator.
- Spread it on a baking pan then bake for 30 minutes at 350°F.
- Serve.

NUTRITIONAL

- Calories: 303 kcal
- Total Fat: 17 g
- Saturated Fat: 0 g
- Cholesterol: 71 mg
- Sodium: 207 mg
- Total Carbs: 7 g

Preparation Time: 10 minutes |Cooking Time: 30 minutes |Servings: 4

Lemon Sprouts

INGREDIENTS

- 1 pound Brussels sprouts, trimmed and shredded
- 8 tablespoons olive oil
- 1 lemon, juiced and zested
- Salt and pepper to taste
- ¾ cup spicy almond and seed mix

DIRECTION

- Take a bowl and mix in lemon juice, salt, pepper and olive oil
- Mix well
- Stir in shredded Brussels sprouts and toss
- Let it sit for 10 minutes
- Add nuts and toss
- Serve and enjoy!

NUTRITIONAL

- Calories: 382
- Fat: 36g
- Carbohydrates: 9g
- Protein: 7g

Preparation Time: 10 minutes |Cooking Time: 0 |Servings: 4

Lemon and Broccoli Platter

INGREDIENTS

- 2 heads broccoli, separated into florets
- 2 teaspoons extra virgin olive oil
- 1 teaspoon salt
- 1/2 teaspoon black pepper
- 1 garlic clove, minced
- 1/2 teaspoon lemon juice

DIRECTION

- Preheat your oven to 400 °F
- Take a large-sized bowl and add broccoli florets
- Drizzle olive oil and season with pepper, salt, and garlic
- Spread the broccoli out in a single even layer on a baking sheet
- Bake for 15-20 minutes until fork tender
- Squeeze lemon juice on top
- Serve and enjoy!

NUTRITIONAL

- Calories: 49
- Fat: 1.9g
- Carbohydrates: 7g
- Protein: 3g

Preparation Time: 10 minutes |Cooking Time: 15 minutes |Servings: 6

Chicken Liver Stew

INGREDIENTS

- 10 ounces chicken livers
- 1-ounce onion, chopped
- 2 ounces sour cream
- 1 tablespoon olive oil
- Salt to taste

DIRECTION

- Take a pan and place it over medium heat
- Add oil and let it heat up
- Add onions and fry until just browned
- Add livers and season with salt
- Cook until livers are half cooked
- Transfer the mix to a stew pot
- Add sour cream and cook for 20 minutes
- Serve and enjoy!

NUTRITIONAL

- Calories: 146
- Fat: 9g
- Carbohydrates: 2g
- Protein: 15g

Preparation Time: 10 minutes |Cooking Time: 20 minutes|Servings: 2

Simple Lamb Chops

INGREDIENTS

- 1/4 cup olive oil
- 1/4 cup mint, fresh and chopped
- 8 lamb rib chops
- 1 tablespoon garlic, minced
- 1 tablespoon rosemary, fresh and chopped

DIRECTION

- Add rosemary, garlic, mint, olive oil into a bowl and mix well
- Keep a tablespoon of the mixture on the side for later use
- Toss lamb chops into the marinade, letting them marinate for 30 minutes
- Take a cast-iron skillet and place it over medium-high heat
- Add lamb and cook for 2 minutes per side for medium-rare
- Let the lamb rest for a few minutes and drizzle the remaining marinade
- Serve and enjoy!

NUTRITIONAL

- Calories: 566
- Fat: 40g
- Carbohydrates: 2g
- Protein: 47g

Preparation Time: 35 minutes |Cooking Time: 5 minutes |Servings: 3

Chicken and Mushroom Stew

INGREDIENTS

- 4 chicken breast halves, cut into bite-sized pieces
- 1 pound mushrooms, sliced (5-6 cups)
- 1 bunch spring onion, chopped
- 4 tablespoons olive oil
- 1 teaspoon thyme
- Salt and pepper as needed

DIRECTION

- Take a large deep frying pan and place it over medium-high heat
- Add oil and let it heat up
- Add chicken and cook for 4-5 minutes per side until slightly browned
- Add spring onions and mushrooms, season with salt and pepper according to your taste
- Stir
- Cover with lid and bring the mix to a boil
- Lower heat and simmer for 25 minutes
- Serve!

NUTRITIONAL

- Calories: 247
- Fat: 12g
- Carbohydrates: 10g
- Protein: 23g

Preparation Time: 10 minutes |Cooking Time: 35 minutes |Servings: 4

Roasted Carrot Soup

INGREDIENTS

- 8 large carrots, washed and peeled
- 6 tablespoons olive oil
- 1-quart broth
- Cayenne pepper to taste
- Salt and pepper to taste

DIRECTION

- Preheat your oven to 425 °F
- Take a baking sheet and add carrots, drizzle olive oil and roast for 30-45 minutes
- Put roasted carrots into a blender and add the broth, puree
- Pour into saucepan and heat soup
- Season with salt, pepper, and cayenne
- Drizzle olive oil
- Serve and enjoy!

NUTRITIONAL

- Calories: 222
- Fat: 18g
- Net Carbohydrates: 7g
- Protein: 5g

Preparation Time: 10 minutes |Cooking Time: 50 minutes |Servings: 4

Garlic and Butter-Flavored Cod

INGREDIENTS

- 3 Cod fillets, 8 ounces each
- ¾ pound baby bok choy halved
- 1/3 cup almond butter, thinly sliced
- 1 1/2 tablespoons garlic, minced
- Salt and pepper to taste

DIRECTION

- Preheat your oven to 400 °F
- Cut 3 sheets of aluminum foil (large enough to fit fillet)
- Place cod fillet on each sheet and add butter and garlic on top
- Add bok choy, season with pepper and salt
- Fold packet and enclose them in pouches
- Arrange on baking sheet
- Bake for 20 minutes
- Transfer to a cooling rack and let them cool
- Enjoy!

NUTRITIONAL

- Calories: 355
- Fat: 21g
- Carbohydrates: 3g
- Protein: 37g

Preparation Time: 5 minutes |Cooking Time: 20 minutes |Servings: 3

Tilapia Broccoli Platter

INGREDIENTS

- 6 ounces of tilapia, frozen
- 1 tablespoon of almond butter
- 1 tablespoon of garlic, minced
- 1 teaspoon of lemon pepper seasoning
- 1 cup of broccoli florets, fresh

DIRECTION

- Preheat your oven to 350 °F
- Add fish in aluminum foil packets
- Arrange the broccoli around fish
- Sprinkle lemon pepper on top
- Close the packets and seal
- Bake for 14 minutes
- Take a bowl and add garlic and butter, mix well and keep the mixture on the side
- Remove the packet from the oven and transfer to a platter
- Place butter on top of the fish and broccoli, serve and enjoy!

NUTRITIONAL

- Calories: 362
- Fat: 25g
- Carbohydrates: 2g
- Protein: 29g

Preparation Time: 4 minutes |Cooking Time: 14 minutes |Servings: 2

Parsley Scallops

INGREDIENTS

- 8 tablespoons almond butter
- 2 garlic cloves, minced
- 16 large sea scallops
- Salt and pepper to taste
- 1 1/2 tablespoons olive oil

DIRECTION

- Seasons scallops with salt and pepper
- Take a skillet and place it over medium heat, add oil and let it heat up
- Sauté scallops for 2 minutes per side, repeat until all scallops are cooked
- Add butter to the skillet and let it melt
- Stir in garlic and cook for 15 minutes
- Return scallops to skillet and stir to coat
- Serve and enjoy!

NUTRITIONAL

- Calories: 417
- Fat: 31g
- Net Carbohydrates: 5g
- Protein: 29g

Preparation Time: 5 minutes |Cooking Time: 25 minutes |Servings: 4

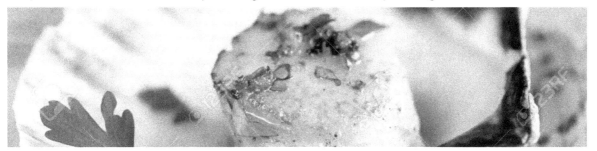

Blackened Chicken

INGREDIENTS

- 1/2 teaspoon paprika
- 1/8 teaspoon salt
- 1/4 teaspoon cayenne pepper
- 1/4 teaspoon ground cumin
- 1/4 teaspoon dried thyme
- 1/8 teaspoon ground white pepper
- 1/8 teaspoon onion powder
- 2 chicken breasts, boneless and skinless

DIRECTION

- Preheat your oven to 350 °F
- Grease baking sheet
- Take a cast-iron skillet and place it over high heat
- Add oil and heat it up for 5 minutes until smoking hot
- Take a small bowl and mix salt, paprika, cumin, white pepper, cayenne, thyme, onion powder
- Oil the chicken breast on both sides and coat the breast with the spice mix
- Transfer to your hot pan and cook for 1 minute per side
- Transfer to your prepared baking sheet and bake for 5 minutes
- Serve and enjoy!

NUTRITIONAL

- Calories: 136
- Fat: 3g
- Carbohydrates: 1g
- Protein: 24g

Preparation Time: 10 minutes |Cooking Time: 10 minutes |Servings: 4

Spicy Paprika Lamb Chops

INGREDIENTS

- 2 lamb racks, cut into chops
- Salt and pepper to taste
- 3 tablespoons paprika
- ¾ cup cumin powder
- 1 teaspoon chili powder

DIRECTION

- Take a bowl and add the paprika, cumin, chili, salt, pepper, and stir
- Add lamb chops and rub the mixture
- Heat grill over medium-temperature and add lamb chops, cook for 5 minutes
- Flip and cook for 5 minutes more, flip again
- Cook for 2 minutes, flip and cook for 2 minutes more
- Serve and enjoy!

NUTRITIONAL

- Calories: 200
- Fat: 5g
- Carbohydrates: 4g
- Protein: 8g

Preparation Time: 10 minutes |Cooking Time: 15 minutes |Servings: 4

Mushroom and Olive Sirloin Steak

INGREDIENTS

- 1 pound boneless beef sirloin steak, ¾ inch thick, cut into 4 pieces
- 1 large red onion, chopped
- 1 cup mushrooms
- 4 garlic cloves, thinly sliced
- 4 tablespoons olive oil
- 1 cup parsley leaves, finely cut

DIRECTION

- Take a large-sized skillet and place it over medium-high heat
- Add oil and let it heat up
- Add beef and cook until both sides are browned, remove beef and drain fat
- Add the rest of the oil to skillet and heat it up
- Add onions, garlic and cook for 2-3 minutes
- Stir well
- Return beef to skillet and lower heat to medium
- Cook for 3-4 minutes (covered)
- Stir in parsley
- Serve and enjoy!

NUTRITIONAL

- Calories: 386
- Fat: 30g
- Carbohydrates: 11g
- Protein: 21g

Preparation Time: 10 minutes |Cooking Time: 14 minutes |Servings: 4

Parsley and Chicken Breast

INGREDIENTS

- 1 tablespoon dry parsley
- 1 tablespoon dry basil
- 4 chicken breast halves, boneless and skinless
- 1/2 teaspoon salt
- 1/2 teaspoon red pepper flakes, crushed

DIRECTION

- Preheat your oven to 350 °F
- Take a 9x13 inch baking dish and grease it with cooking spray
- Sprinkle 1 tablespoon of parsley, 1 teaspoon of basil and spread the mixture over your baking dish
- Arrange the chicken breast halves over the dish and sprinkle garlic slices on top
- Take a small bowl and add 1 teaspoon parsley, 1 teaspoon of basil, salt, basil, red pepper and mix well. Pour the mixture over the chicken breast
- Bake for 25 minutes
- Remove the cover and bake for 15 minutes more
- Serve and enjoy!

NUTRITIONAL

- Calories: 150
- Fat: 4g
- Carbohydrates: 4g
- Protein: 25g

Preparation Time: 10 minutes |Cooking Time: 40 minutes |Servings: 4

Simple Mustard Chicken

INGREDIENTS

- 4 chicken breasts
- 1/2 cup chicken broth
- 3-4 tablespoons mustard
- 3 tablespoons olive oil
- 1 teaspoon paprika
- 1 teaspoon chili powder
- 1 teaspoon garlic powder

DIRECTION

- Take a small bowl and mix mustard, olive oil, paprika, chicken broth, garlic powder, chicken broth, and chili
- Add chicken breast and marinate for 30 minutes
- Take a lined baking sheet and arrange the chicken
- Bake for 35 minutes at 375 °F
- Serve and enjoy!

NUTRITIONAL

- Calories: 531
- Fat: 23g
- Carbohydrates: 10g
- Protein: 64g

Preparation Time: 10 minutes |Cooking Time: 40 minutes |Servings: 4

Golden Eggplant Fries

INGREDIENTS

- 2 eggs
- 2 cups almond flour
- 2 tablespoons coconut oil, spray
- 2 eggplant, peeled and cut thinly
- Sunflower seeds and pepper

DIRECTION

- Preheat your oven to 400 degrees F.
- Take a bowl and mix with sunflower seeds and black pepper.
- Take another bowl and beat eggs until frothy.
- Dip the eggplant pieces into the eggs.
- Then coat them with the flour mixture.
- Add another layer of flour and egg.
- Then, take a baking sheet and grease with coconut oil on top.
- Bake for about 15 minutes.
- Serve and enjoy!

NUTRITIONAL

- Calories: 212
- Fat: 15.8g
- Carbohydrates: 12.1g
- Protein: 8.6g
- Phosphorus: 150mg
- Potassium: 147mg
- Sodium: 105mg

Preparation Time: 10 minutes |Cooking Time: 15 minutes |Servings: 8

Very Wild Mushroom Pilaf

INGREDIENTS

- 1 cup wild rice
- 2 garlic cloves, minced
- 6 green onions, chopped
- 2 tablespoons olive oil
- ½ pound baby Bella mushrooms
- 2 cups water

DIRECTION

- Add rice, garlic, onion, oil, mushrooms and water to your Slow Cooker.
- Stir well until mixed.
- Place lid and cook on LOW for 3 hours.
- Stir pilaf and divide between serving platters.
- Enjoy!

NUTRITIONAL

- Calories: 210
- Fat: 7g
- Carbohydrates: 16g
- Protein: 4g
- Phosphorus: 110mg
- Potassium: 117mg
- Sodium: 75mg

Preparation Time: 10 minutes |Cooking Time: 3 hours |Servings: 4

Sporty Baby Carrots

INGREDIENTS

- 1-pound baby carrots
- 1 cup water
- 1 tablespoon clarified ghee
- 1 tablespoon chopped up fresh mint leaves
- Sea flavored vinegar as needed

DIRECTION

- Place a steamer rack on top of your pot and add the carrots.
- Add water.
- Lock the lid and cook at HIGH pressure for 2 minutes.
- Do a quick release.
- Pass the carrots through a strainer and drain them.
- Wipe the insert clean.
- Return the insert to the pot and set the pot to Sauté mode.
- Add clarified butter and allow it to melt.
- Add mint and sauté for 30 seconds.
- Add carrots to the insert and sauté well.
- Remove them and sprinkle with bit of flavored vinegar on top.
- Enjoy!

NUTRITIONAL

- Calories: 131
- Fat: 10g
- Carbohydrates: 11g
- Protein: 1g
- Phosphorus: 130mg
- Potassium: 147mg
- Sodium: 85mg

Preparation Time: 5 minutes |Cooking Time: 5 minutes |Servings: 4

Saucy Garlic Greens

INGREDIENTS

- 1 bunch of leafy greens
- Sauce
- ½ cup cashews soaked in water for 10 minutes
- ¼ cup water
- 1 tablespoon lemon juice
- 1 teaspoon coconut aminos
- 1 clove peeled whole clove
- 1/8 teaspoon of flavored vinegar

DIRECTION

- Make the sauce by draining and discarding the soaking water from your cashews and add the cashews to a blender.
- Add fresh water, lemon juice, flavored vinegar, coconut aminos, and garlic.
- Blitz until you have a smooth cream and transfer to bowl.
- Add ½ cup of water to the pot.
- Place the steamer basket to the pot and add the greens in the basket.
- Lock the lid and steam for 1 minute.
- Quick-release the pressure.
- Transfer the steamed greens to strainer and extract excess water.
- Place the greens into a mixing bowl.
- Add lemon garlic sauce and toss.
- Enjoy!

NUTRITIONAL

- Calories: 77
- Fat: 5g
- Carbohydrates: 0g
- Protein: 2g
- Phosphorus: 120mg
- Potassium: 137mg
- Sodium: 85mg

Preparation Time: 5 minutes |Cooking Time: 20 minutes |Servings: 4

Garden Salad

INGREDIENTS

- 1-pound raw peanuts in shell
- 1 bay leaf
- 2 medium-sized chopped up Red bell peppers
- ½ cup diced up green pepper
- ½ cup diced up sweet onion
- ¼ cup finely diced hot pepper
- ¼ cup diced up celery
- 2 tablespoons olive oil
- ¾ teaspoon flavored vinegar
- ¼ teaspoon freshly ground black pepper

DIRECTION

- Boil your peanuts for 1 minute and rinse them.
- The skin will be soft, so discard the skin.
- Add 2 cups of water to the Instant Pot.
- Add bay leaf and peanuts.
- Lock the lid and cook on HIGH pressure for 20 minutes.
- Drain the water.
- Take a large bowl and add the peanuts, diced up vegetables.
- Whisk in olive oil, lemon juice, pepper in another bowl.
- Pour the mixture over the salad and mix.
- Enjoy!

NUTRITIONAL

- Calories: 140
- Fat: 4g
- Carbohydrates: 24g
- Protein: 5g
- Phosphorus: 110mg
- Potassium: 117mg
- Sodium: 75mg

Preparation Time: 5 minutes |Cooking Time: 20 minutes |Servings: 6

Spicy Cabbage Dish

INGREDIENTS

- 2 yellow onions, chopped
- 10 cups red cabbage, shredded
- 1 cup plums, pitted and chopped
- 1 teaspoon cinnamon powder
- 1 garlic clove, minced
- 1 teaspoon cumin seeds
- ¼ teaspoon cloves, ground
- 2 tablespoons red wine vinegar
- 1 teaspoon coriander seeds
- ½ cup water

DIRECTION

- Add cabbage, onion, plums, garlic, cumin, cinnamon, cloves, vinegar, coriander and water to your Slow Cooker.
- Stir well.
- Place lid and cook on LOW for 4 hours.
- Divide between serving platters.
- Enjoy!

NUTRITIONAL

- Calories: 197
- Fat: 1g
- Carbohydrates: 14g
- Protein: 3g
- Phosphorus: 115mg
- Potassium: 119mg
- Sodium: 75mg

Preparation Time: 10 minutes |Cooking Time: 4 hours |Servings: 4

Extreme Balsamic Chicken

INGREDIENTS

- 3 boneless chicken breasts, skinless
- Sunflower seeds to taste
- ¼ cup almond flour
- 2/3 cups low-fat chicken broth
- 1 ½ teaspoons arrowroot
- ½ cup low sugar raspberry preserve
- 1 ½ tablespoons balsamic vinegar

DIRECTION

- Cut chicken breast into bite-sized pieces and season them with seeds.
- Dredge the chicken pieces in flour and shake off any excess.
- Take a non-stick skillet and place it over medium heat.
- Add chicken to the skillet and cook for 15 minutes, making sure to turn them half-way through.
- Remove chicken and transfer to platter.
- Add arrowroot, broth, raspberry preserve to the skillet and stir.
- Stir in balsamic vinegar and reduce heat to low, stir-cook for a few minutes.
- Transfer the chicken back to the sauce and cook for 15 minutes more.
- Serve and enjoy!

NUTRITIONAL

- Calories: 546
- Fat: 35g
- Carbohydrates: 11g
- Protein: 44g
- Phosphorus: 120mg
- Potassium: 117mg
- Sodium: 85mg

Preparation Time: 10 minutes Cooking Time: 35 minutes Servings: 4

Enjoyable Green lettuce and Bean Medley

INGREDIENTS

- 5 carrots, sliced
- 1 ½ cups great northern beans, dried
- 2 garlic cloves, minced
- 1 yellow onion, chopped
- Pepper to taste
- ½ teaspoon oregano, dried
- 5 ounces baby green lettuce
- 4 ½ cups low sodium veggie stock
- 2 teaspoons lemon peel, grated
- 3 tablespoon lemon juice

DIRECTION

- Add beans, onion, carrots, garlic, oregano and stock to your Slow Cooker.
- Stir well.
- Place lid and cook on HIGH for 4 hours.
- Add green lettuce, lemon juice and lemon peel.
- Stir and let it sit for 5 minutes.
- Divide between serving platters and enjoy!

NUTRITIONAL

- Calories: 219
- Fat: 8g
- Carbohydrates: 14g
- Protein: 8g
- Phosphorus: 210mg
- Potassium: 217mg
- Sodium: 85mg

Servings: 4 |Preparation Time: 10 minutes |Cooking Time: 4 hours

Tantalizing Cauliflower and Dill Mash

INGREDIENTS

- 1 cauliflower head, florets separated
- 1/3 cup dill, chopped
- 6 garlic cloves
- 2 tablespoons olive oil
- Pinch of black pepper

DIRECTION

- Add cauliflower to Slow Cooker.
- Add dill, garlic and water to cover them.
- Place lid and cook on HIGH for 5 hours.
- Drain the flowers.
- Season with pepper and add oil, mash using potato masher.
- Whisk and serve.
- Enjoy!

NUTRITIONAL

- Calories: 207
- Fat: 4g
- Carbohydrates: 14g
- Protein: 3g
- Phosphorus: 130mg
- Potassium: 107mg
- Sodium: 105mg

Preparation Time: 10 minutes |Cooking Time: 6 hours |Servings: 6

Peas Soup

INGREDIENTS

- 1 white onion, chopped
- 1 quart veggie stock
- 2 eggs
- 3 tablespoons lemon juice
- 2 cups peas
- 2 tablespoons parmesan, grated
- Salt and black pepper to the taste

DIRECTION

- Heat up a pot with the oil over medium-high heat, add the onion and sauté for 4 minutes.
- Add the rest of the ingredients except the eggs, bring to a simmer and cook for 4 minutes.
- Add whisked eggs, stir the soup, cook for 2 minutes more, divide into bowls and serve.

NUTRITIONAL

- Calories 293,
- fat 11.2 fiber 3.4,
- carbs 27,
- protein 4.45

Preparation Time: 10 minutes |Cooking Time: 10 minutes |Servings: 4

Minty Lamb Stew

INGREDIENTS

- ½ cup mint, chopped
- Salt and black pepper to the taste
- 2 pounds lamb shoulder, boneless and cubed
- 3 tablespoons oil
- 1 carrot, chopped
- 1 yellow onion, chopped
- 1 celery rib, chopped
- 1 tablespoon ginger, grated
- 1 tablespoon garlic, minced
- ½ cup mint, chopped
- 15 ounces canned chickpeas, drained
- 6 tablespoons Greek yogurt

DIRECTION

- Heat up a pot with 2 tablespoons oil over medium-high heat, add the meat and brown for 5 minutes.
- Add the carrot, onion, celery, garlic and the ginger, stir and sauté for 5 minutes more.
- Add the rest of the ingredients except the yogurt, bring to a simmer and cook over medium heat for 1 hour and 30 minutes.
- Divide the stew into bowls, top each serving with the yogurt and serve.

NUTRITIONAL

- Calories 355,
- fat 14.3,
- fiber 6.7,
- carbs 22.6,
- protein 15.4

Preparation Time: 10 minutes |Cooking Time: 1 hour and 45 minutes |Servings: 4

Chapter 13.
Drinks, Smoothies and Juices

Almonds & Blueberries Smoothie

INGREDIENTS

- 1/4 cup ground almonds, unsalted
- 1 cup fresh blueberries
- Fresh juice of a 1 lemon
- 1 cup fresh kale leaf
- 1/2 cup coconut water
- 1 cup water
- 2 tablespoon plain yogurt (optional)

DIRECTION

- Dump all ingredients in your high-speed blender, and blend until your smoothie is smooth.
- Pour the mixture in a chilled glass.
- Serve and enjoy!

NUTRITIONAL

- Calories: 110,
- Carbohydrates: 8g,
- Proteins: 2g,
- Fat: 7g,
- Fiber: 2g,
- Calcium 19mg,
- Phosphorous 16mg,
- Potassium 27mg
- Sodium: 101 mg

Preparation Time: 5 minutes | Cooking Time: 3 minutes | Servings: 2

Almonds and Zucchini Smoothie

INGREDIENTS

- 1 cup zucchini, cooked and mashed - unsalted
- 1 1/2 cups almond milk
- 1 tablespoon almond butter (plain, unsalted)
- 1 teaspoon pure almond extract
- 2 tablespoon ground almonds or macadamia almonds
- 1/2 cup water
- 1 cup ice cubes crushed (optional, for serving)

DIRECTION

- Dump all ingredients from the list above in your fast-speed blender; blend for 45 - 60 seconds or to taste.
- Serve with crushed ice.

NUTRITIONAL

- Calories: 322,
- Carbohydrates: 6g,
- Proteins: 6g,
- Fat: 30g,
- Fiber: 3.5g,
- Calcium 9mg,
- Phosphorous 26mg,
- Potassium 27mg
- Sodium: 121 mg

Preparation Time: 5 minutes | Cooking Time: 3 minutes | Servings: 2

Blueberries and Coconut Smoothie

INGREDIENTS

- 1 cup of frozen blueberries, unsweetened
- 1 cup stevia or erythritol sweetener
- 2 cups coconut milk (canned)
- 1 cup of fresh green lettuce leaves
- 2 tablespoon shredded coconut (unsweetened)
- 3/4 cup water

DIRECTION

- Place all ingredients from the list in food-processor or in your strong blender.
- Blend for 45 - 60 seconds or to taste.
- Ready for drink! Serve!

NUTRITIONAL

- Calories: 190,
- Carbohydrates: 8g,
- Proteins: 3g,
- Fat: 18g,
- Fiber: 2g,
- Calcium 79mg,
- Phosphorous 216mg,
- Potassium 207mg
- Sodium: 121 mg

Preparation Time: 5 minutes |Cooking Time: 3 minutes |Servings: 5

Creamy Dandelion Greens and Celery Smoothie

INGREDIENTS

- 1 handful of raw dandelion greens
- 2 celery sticks
- 2 tablespoon chia seeds
- 1 small piece of ginger, minced
- 1/2 cup almond milk
- 1/2 cup of water
- 1/2 cup plain yogurt

DIRECTION

- Rinse and clean dandelion leaves from any dirt; add in a high-speed blender.
- Clean the ginger; keep only inner part and cut in small slices; add in a blender.
- Blend all remaining ingredients until smooth.
- Serve and enjoy!

NUTRITIONAL

- Calories: 58,
- Carbohydrates: 5g,
- Proteins: 3g,
- Fat: 6g,
- Fiber: 3g
- Calcium 29mg,
- Phosphorous 76mg,
- Potassium 27mg
- Sodium: 121 mg

Preparation Time: 10 minutes |Cooking Time: 3 minutes |Servings: 2

Dark Turnip Greens Smoothie

INGREDIENTS

- 1 cup of raw turnip greens
- 1 1/2 cup of almond milk
- 1 tablespoon of almond butter
- 1/2 cup of water
- 1/2 teaspoon of cocoa powder, unsweetened
- 1/4 teaspoon of cinnamon
- A pinch of salt
- 1/2 cup of crushed ice

DIRECTION

- Rinse and clean turnip greens from any dirt.
- Place the turnip greens in your blender along with all other ingredients.
- Blend it for 45 - 60 seconds or until done; smooth and creamy.
- Serve with or without crushed ice.

NUTRITIONAL

- Calories: 131,
- Carbohydrates: 6g,
- Proteins: 4g,
- Fat: 10g,
- Fiber: 2.5g

Preparation Time: 10 minutes |Cooking Time: 3 minutes |Servings: 2

Butter Pecan and Coconut Smoothie

INGREDIENTS

- 1 cup coconut milk, canned
- 1 scoop butter pecan powdered creamer
- 2 cups fresh green lettuce leaves, chopped
- 1/2 banana frozen or fresh
- 2 tablespoon stevia granulated sweetener to taste
- 1/2 cup water
- 1 cup ice cubes crushed

DIRECTION

- Place ingredients from the list above in your high-speed blender.
- Blend for 35 - 50 seconds or until all ingredients combined well.
- Add less or more crushed ice.
- Drink and enjoy!

NUTRITIONAL

- Calories: 268,
- Carbohydrates: 7g,
- Proteins: 6g,
- Fat: 26g,
- Fiber: 1.5g

Preparation Time: 5 minutes |Cooking Time: 2 minutes |Servings: 2

Fresh Cucumber, Kale and Raspberry

INGREDIENTS
- 1 1/2 cups of cucumber, peeled
- 1/2 cup raw kale leaves
- 1 1/2 cups fresh raspberries
- 1 cup of almond milk
- 1 cup of water
- Ice cubes crushed (optional)
- 2 tablespoon natural sweetener (stevia, erythritol...etc.)

DIRECTION
- Place all Ingredients listed in a High-Speed Blender; Blend For 35 - 40 Seconds.
- Serve Into Chilled Glasses.
- Add More Natural Sweeter if you like. Enjoy!

NUTRITIONAL
- Calories: 70,
- Carbohydrates: 8g,
- Proteins: 3g,
- Fat: 6g,
- Fiber: 5g

Preparation Time: 10 minutes |Cooking Time: 3 minutes |Servings: 3

Fresh Lettuce and Cucumber-Lemon Smoothie

INGREDIENTS
- 2 cups fresh lettuce leaves, chopped (any kind)
- 1 cup of cucumber
- 1 lemon washed and sliced.
- 2 tablespoon chia seeds
- 1 1/2 cup water or coconut water
- 1/4 cup stevia granulate sweetener (or to taste)

DIRECTION
- Add all ingredients from the list above in the high-speed blender; blend until completely smooth.
- Pour your smoothie into chilled glasses and enjoy!

NUTRITIONAL
- Calories: 51,
- Carbohydrates: 4g,
- Proteins: 2g,
- Fat: 4g,
- Fiber: 3.5g

Preparation Time: 10 minutes |Cooking Time: 3 minutes |Servings: 2

Green Coconut Smoothie

INGREDIENTS

- 1 1/4 cup coconut milk (canned)
- 2 tablespoon chia seeds
- 1 cup of fresh kale leaves
- 1 cup of green lettuce leaves
- 1 scoop vanilla protein powder
- 1 cup ice cubes
- Granulated stevia sweetener (to taste; optional)
- 1/2 cup water

DIRECTION

- Rinse and clean kale and the green lettuce leaves from any dirt.
- Add all ingredients in your blender.
- Blend until you get a nice smoothie.
- Serve into chilled glass.

NUTRITIONAL

- Calories: 179,
- Carbohydrates: 5g,
- Proteins: 4g,
- Fat: 18g,
- Fiber: 2.5g
- Calcium 22mg,
- Phosphorous 46mg,
- Potassium 34mg
- Sodium: 131 mg

Preparation Time: 10 minutes | Cooking Time: 3 minutes | Servings: 2

Fruity Smoothie

INGREDIENTS

- 8 oz. canned fruits, with juice
- 2 scoops vanilla-flavored whey protein powder
- 1 cup cold water
- 1 cup crushed ice

DIRECTION

- First, start by putting all the ingredients in a blender jug.
- Give it a pulse for 30 seconds until blended well.
- Serve chilled and fresh.

NUTRITIONAL

- Calories 186
- Protein 23 g
- Fat 2g
- Cholesterol 41 mg
- Potassium 282 mg
- Calcium 160 mg
- Fiber 1.1 g

Preparation Time:10minutes |Cooking Time:0 minutes |Servings:2

Mixed Berry Protein Smoothie

INGREDIENTS

- 4 oz. cold water
- 1 cup frozen mixed berries
- 2 ice cubes
- 1 tsp blueberry essence
- 1/2 cup whipped cream topping
- 2 scoops whey protein powder

DIRECTION

- First, start by putting all the ingredients in a blender jug.
- Give it a pulse for 30 seconds until blended well.
- Serve chilled and fresh.

NUTRITIONAL

- Calories 104
- Protein 6 g
- Fat 4 g
- Cholesterol 11 mg
- Potassium 141 mg
- Calcium 69 mg
- Fiber 2.4 g

Preparation Time:10minutes |Cooking Time:0 minutes |Servings:2

Peach High-Protein Smoothie

INGREDIENTS

- 1/2 cup ice
- 2 tbsp. powdered egg whites
- 3/4 cup fresh peaches
- 1 tbsp. sugar

DIRECTION

- First, start by putting all the ingredients in a blender jug.
- Give it a pulse for 30 seconds until blended well.
- Serve chilled and fresh.

NUTRITIONAL

- Calories 132
- Protein 10 g
- Fat 0 g
- Cholesterol 0 mg
- Potassium 353 mg
- Calcium 9 mg
- Fiber 1.9 g

Preparation Time:10minutes |Cooking Time:0 minutes |Servings:1

Strawberry Fruit Smoothie

INGREDIENTS

- 3/4 cup fresh strawberries
- 1/2 cup liquid pasteurized egg whites
- 1/2 cup ice
- 1 tbsp. sugar

DIRECTION

- First, start by putting all the ingredients in a blender jug.
- Give it a pulse for 30 seconds until blended well.
- Serve chilled and fresh.

NUTRITIONAL

- Calories 156
- Protein 14 g
- Fat 0 g
- Cholesterol 0 mg
- Potassium 400 mg
- Phosphorus 49 mg
- Calcium 29 mg
- Fiber 2.5 g

Preparation Time:10minutes |Cooking Time:0 minutes |Servings:1

Watermelon Bliss

INGREDIENTS

- 2 cups watermelon
- 1 medium-sized cucumber, peeled and sliced
- 2 mint sprigs, leaves only
- 1 celery stalk
- Squeeze of lime juice

DIRECTION

- First, start by putting all the ingredients in a blender jug.
- Give it a pulse for 30 seconds until blended well.
- Serve chilled and fresh.

NUTRITIONAL

- Calories 156
- Protein 14 g
- Fat 0 g
- Cholesterol 0 mg
- Potassium 400 mg
- Calcium 29 mg
- Fiber 2.5g

Preparation Time:10minutes |Cooking Time:0 minutes |Servings:2

Cranberry Smoothie

INGREDIENTS

- 1 cup frozen cranberries
- 1 medium cucumber, peeled and sliced
- 1 stalk of celery
- Handful of parsley
- Squeeze of lime juice

DIRECTION

- First, start by putting all the ingredients in a blender jug. Give it a pulse for 30 seconds until blended well.
- Serve chilled and fresh.

NUTRITIONAL

- Calories 126
- Protein 12 g
- Fat 0.03 g
- Cholesterol 0 mg
- Potassium 220 mg
- Calcium 19 mg
- Fiber 1.4g

Preparation Time:10minutes |Cooking Time:0 minutes |Servings:1

Berry Cucumber Smoothie

INGREDIENTS

- 1 medium cucumber, peeled and sliced
- ½ cup fresh blueberries
- ½ cup fresh or frozen strawberries
- ½ cup unsweetened rice milk
- Stevia, to taste

DIRECTION

- First, start by putting all the ingredients in a blender jug.
- Give it a pulse for 30 seconds until blended well.
- Serve chilled and fresh.

NUTRITIONAL

- Calories 141
- Protein 10 g
- Carbohydrates 15 g
- Fat 0 g
- Sodium 113 mg
- Potassium 230 mg
- Phosphorus 129 mg

Preparation Time:10minutes |Cooking Time:0 minutes |Servings: 1

Raspberry Peach Smoothie

INGREDIENTS

- 1 cup frozen raspberries
- 1 medium peach, pit removed, sliced
- ½ cup silken tofu
- 1 tbsp. honey
- 1 cup unsweetened vanilla almond milk

DIRECTION

- First, start by putting all the ingredients in a blender jug.
- Give it a pulse for 30 seconds until blended well.
- Serve chilled and fresh.

NUTRITIONAL

- Calories 132
- Protein 9 g.
- Carbohydrates 14 g
- Sodium 112 mg
- Potassium 310 mg
- Phosphorus 39 mg
- Calcium 32 mg

Preparation Time:10minutes |Cooking Time:0 minutes |Servings:2

Power-Boosting Smoothie

INGREDIENTS

- ½ cup water
- ½ cup non-dairy whipped topping
- 2 scoops whey protein powder
- 1½ cups frozen blueberries

DIRECTION

- In a high-speed blender, add all ingredients and pulse till smooth.
- Transfer into 2 serving glass and serve immediately.

NUTRITIONAL

- Calories 242
- Fat 7g
- Carbs 23.8g
- Protein 23.2g
- Potassium (K) 263mg
- Sodium (Na) 63mg
- Phosphorous 30 mg

Preparation Time: 5 minutes|Cooking Time:0 minutes|Servings:2

Distinctive Pineapple Smoothie

INGREDIENTS

- ¼ cup crushed ice cubes
- 2 scoops vanilla whey protein powder
- 1 cup water
- 1½ cups pineapple

DIRECTION

- In a high-speed blender, add all ingredients and pulse till smooth.
- Transfer into 2 serving glass and serve immediately.

NUTRITIONAL

- Calories 117
- Fat 2.1g
- Carbs 18.2g
- Protein 22.7g
- Potassium (K) 296mg
- Sodium (Na) 81mg
- Phosphorous 28 mg

Preparation Time: 5 minutes|Cooking Time:0 minutes|Servings: 2

Strengthening Smoothie Bowl

INGREDIENTS

- ¼ cup fresh blueberries
- ¼ cup fat-free plain Greek yogurt
- 1/3 cup unsweetened almond milk
- 2 tbsp. of whey protein powder
- 2 cups frozen blueberries

DIRECTION

- In a blender, add blueberries and pulse for about 1 minute.
- Add almond milk, yogurt and protein powder and pulse till desired consistency.
- Transfer the mixture into 2 bowls evenly.
- Serve with the topping of fresh blueberries.

NUTRITIONAL

- Calories 176
- Fat 2.1g
- Carbs 27g
- Protein 15.1g
- Potassium (K) 242mg
- Sodium (Na) 72mg
- Phosphorous 555.3 mg

Preparation Time: 5 minutes|Cooking Time: 4 minutes|Servings: 2

Pineapple Juice

INGREDIENTS

- ½ cup canned pineapple
- 1 cup water

DIRECTION

Blend all ingredients and serve over ice.

NUTRITIONAL

- Calories 135
- Protein 0 g
- Carbs 0 g
- Fat 0 g
- Sodium (Na) 0 mg
- Potassium (K) 180 mg
- Phosphorus 8 mg

Preparation Time:5 minutes|Cooking Time: 0 minutes|Servings: 2

Grapefruit Sorbet

INGREDIENTS

- ½ cup sugar
- ¼ cup water
- 1 fresh thyme sprig
- For the sorbet
- Juice of 6 pink grapefruit
- ¼ cup thyme simple syrup

DIRECTION

- In a blender, combine the grapefruit juice and ¼ cup of simple syrup, and process.
- Transfer to an airtight container and freeze for 3 to 4 hours, until firm. Serve.
- Substitution tip: Try this with other citrus fruits, such as oranges, lemons, or limes, for an equally delicious treat.

NUTRITIONAL

- Calories 117
- Fat 2.1g
- Carbs 18.2g
- Protein 22.7g
- Potassium (K) 296mg
- Sodium (Na) 81mg
- Phosphorous 28 mg

Preparation Time: 10 minutes|Cooking Time: 5 minutes|Servings: 6

Apple and Blueberry Crisp

INGREDIENTS

- Crisp
- 1/4 cup of brown sugar
- 1 1/4 cups quick cooking rolled oats
- 6 tbsp. non-hydrogenated melted margarine
- 1/4 cup all-purpose flour (unbleached)
- Filling:
- 2 tbsp. cornstarch
- 1/2 cup of brown sugar
- 2 cups chopped or grated apples
- cups frozen or fresh blueberries (not thawed)
- 1 tbsp. fresh lemon juice
- 1 tbsp. melted margarine

DIRECTION

- Preheat the oven to 350°F with the rack in the middle position.
- Pour all the dry ingredients into a bowl, then the butter and stir until it is moistened. Set the mixture aside.
- In an 8-inch (20-cm) square baking dish, mix the cornstarch and brown sugar. Add lemon juice and the rest of the fruits. Toss to blend the mixture. Add the crisp mixture, then bake until the crisp turns golden brown (or for 55 minutes to 1 hour). You can either serve cold or warm.

NUTRITIONAL

- Calories 127
- Fat 2.1g
- Carbs 18.2g
- Protein 22.7g
- Potassium (K) 256mg
- Sodium (Na) 61mg
- Phosphorous 28 mg

Preparation Time: 1 hour 10 minutes |Cooking Time: 1 hour |Serving: 8

Mini Pineapple Upside Down Cakes

INGREDIENTS

- 1 tbsp. melted unsalted butter
- 12 canned unsweetened pineapple slices
- 1/3 cup packed brown sugar
- 2/3 cup sugar
- fresh cherries cut into halves and pitted
- 1 tbsp. canola oil
- 2/3 cup milk (fat-free)
- ½ tbsp. lemon juice
- 1 large egg
- 1-1/3 cups cake flour
- 1/4 tbsp. vanilla extract
- 1/4 tsp salt
- 1-1/4 tsp baking powder

DIRECTION

- Coat 12 serving muffin pan with butter or you could use a square baking pan.
- Sprinkle little brown sugar into each of the sections.
- Crush 1 pineapple slice into each section to take the shape of the cup. Place 1 half cherry in the center of the pineapple with the cut side facing up.
- Get a large bowl and beat the egg, milk, and the extracts until it is evenly blended.
- Beat the flour, salt, and baking powder into sugar mixture until it is well blended to attain homogeneity and pour it into the batter prepared in the muffin pan.
- Bake at 350°s until a toothpick sinks in and comes out clean (or for 35-40 minutes). Invert the muffin pan immediately and allow the cooked cakes to drop onto a serving plate. (If necessary, you can use a small spatula or butter knife to release them from the pan gently.)
- Serve warm.

NUTRITIONAL

- Calories 119
- Fat 2.1g
- Carbs 16.2g
- Protein 22.7g
- Potassium (K) 296mg
- Sodium (Na) 81mg
- Phosphorous 28 mg

Preparation Time: 50 minutes|Cooking Time: 50 minutes |Serving: 12

Chapter 14.
Snack Recipes

Veggie Snack

INGREDIENTS	DIRECTION	NUTRITIONAL
• 1 large yellow pepper • 5 carrots • 5 stalks celery	• Clean the carrots and rinse under running water. • Rinse celery and yellow pepper. Remove seeds of pepper and chop the veggies into small sticks. • Put in a bowl and serve.	• Calories: 189 • Fat: 0.5 g • Carbs: 44.3 g • Protein: 5 g • Sodium: 282 mg • Potassium: 0mg • Phosphorus: 0mg

Preparation Time: 5 minutes|Cooking Time: 10 minutes|Servings: 1

Healthy Spiced Nuts

INGREDIENTS

- 1 tbsp. extra virgin olive oil
- ¼ cup walnuts
- ¼ cup pecans
- ¼ cup almonds
- ½ tsp. sea salt
- ½ tsp. cumin
- ½ tsp. pepper
- 1 tsp. chili powder

DIRECTION

- Put the skillet on medium heat and toast the nuts until lightly browned.
- Prepare the spice mixture and add black pepper, cumin, chili, and salt.
- Put extra virgin olive oil and sprinkle with spice mixture to the toasted nuts before serving.

NUTRITIONAL

- Calories: 88
- Fat: 8g
- Carbs: 4g
- Protein: 2.5g
- Sodium: 51mg
- Potassium: 88mg
- Phosphorus: 6.3mg

Preparation Time: 10 minutes|Cooking Time: 10 minutes|Servings: 4

Roasted Asparagus

INGREDIENTS

- 1 tbsp. extra virgin olive oil
- 1-pound fresh asparagus
- 1 medium lemon, zested
- 1/2 tsp. freshly grated nutmeg
- 1/2 tsp. kosher salt
- ½ tsp. black pepper

DIRECTION

- Preheat your oven to 500 degrees F.
- Put asparagus on an aluminum foil and add extra virgin olive oil.
- Prepare asparagus in a single layer and fold the edges of the foil.
- Cook in the oven for 5 minutes. Continue roasting until browned.
- Add the roasted asparagus with nutmeg, salt, zest, and pepper before serving.

NUTRITIONAL

- Calories: 55
- Fat: 3.8 g
- Carbs: 4.7 g
- Protein: 2.5 g
- Sodium: 98mg
- Potassium: 172mg
- Phosphorus: 35mg

Preparation Time: 5 minutes|Cooking Time: 10 minutes|Servings: 4

Low-Fat Mango Salsa

INGREDIENTS

- 1 cup cucumber, chopped
- 2 cups mango, diced
- ½ cup cilantro, minced
- 2 tablespoons fresh lime juice
- 1 tablespoon scallions, minced
- ¼ teaspoon chipotle powder
- ¼ teaspoon sea salt

DIRECTION

- Mix the ingredients in a bowl and serve or refrigerate.

NUTRITIONAL

- Calories: 155
- Fat: 0.6 g
- Carbs: 38.2 g
- Protein: 1.4 g
- Sodium: 3.2 mg
- Potassium: 221mg
- Phosphorus: 27mg

Preparation Time: 10 minutes|Cooking Time: 10 minutes|Servings: 4

Vinegar & Salt Kale

INGREDIENTS

- • 1 head kale, chopped
- • 1 teaspoon extra virgin olive oil
- • 1 tablespoon apple cider vinegar
- • ½ teaspoon of sea salt

DIRECTION

- Prepare kale in a bowl and put vinegar and extra virgin olive oil.
- Sprinkle with salt and massage the ingredients with hands.
- Spread the kale out onto two paper-lined baking sheets and bake at 375°F for about 12 minutes or until crispy.
- Let cool for about 10 minutes before serving.

NUTRITIONAL

- Calories: 152
- Fat: 8.2 g
- Carbs: 15.2 g
- Protein: 4 g
- Sodium: 170mg
- Potassium: 304mg
- Phosphorus: 37mg

Preparation Time: 10 minutes|Cooking Time: 12 minutes|Servings: 2

Carrot and Parsnips French Fries

INGREDIENTS

- 6 large carrots
- 6 large parsnips
- 2 tablespoons extra virgin olive oil
- ½ teaspoon of sea salt

DIRECTION

- Chop the carrots and parsnips into 2-inch slices and then cut each into thin sticks.
- Toss together the carrots and parsnip sticks with extra virgin olive oil and salt in a bowl and spread into a baking sheet lined with parchment paper.
- Bake the sticks at 425° for about 20 minutes or until browned.

NUTRITIONAL

- Calories: 179
- Fat: 4g
- Carbs: 14g
- Protein: 11g
- Sodium: 27.3mg
- Potassium: 625mg
- Phosphorus: 116mg

Preparation Time: 15 minutes|Cooking Time: 20 minutes|Servings: 2

Apple & Strawberry Snack

INGREDIENTS

- ½ apple, cored and sliced
- 2-3 strawberries
- dash of ground cinnamon
- 2-3 drops stevia 2-3 drops

DIRECTION

- In a bowl, mix strawberries and apples and sprinkle with stevia and cinnamon.
- Microwave for about 1-2 minutes. Serve warm.

NUTRITIONAL

- Calories: 145
- Fat: 0.8 g
- Carbs: 34.2 g
- Protein: 1.6 g
- Sodium: 20 mg
- Potassium: 0mg
- Phosphorus: 0mg

Preparation Time: 5 minutes|Cooking Time: 2 minutes|Servings: 1

Candied Macadamia Nuts

INGREDIENTS

- 2 cups macadamia nuts
- 1 tablespoon extra-virgin olive oil
- 2 tablespoons honey

DIRECTION

- Toss ingredients in bowl and spread into a baking dish.
- Bake for 15 minutes at 350°F.
- Let cool before serving.

NUTRITIONAL

- Calories: 200
- Fat: 18 g
- Carbs: 10g
- Protein: 1g
- Sodium: 5 mg
- Potassium: 55mg
- Phosphorus: 10mg

Preparation Time: 5 minutes|Cooking Time: 15 minutes|Servings: 2

Cinnamon Apple Fries

INGREDIENTS

- 1 apple, sliced thinly
- Dash of cinnamon
- Stevia

DIRECTION

- Coat apple slices with cinnamon and stevia.
- Bake for 15 minutes or until tender and crispy at 325 degrees F.

NUTRITIONAL

- Calories: 146
- Fat: 0.7 g
- Carbs: 36.4 g
- Protein: 1.6 g
- Sodium: 10 mg
- Potassium: 100mg
- Phosphorus: 0mg

Preparation Time: 5 minutes|Cooking Time: 15 minutes|Servings: 1

Lemon Pops

INGREDIENTS

- 4 tablespoons fresh lemon juice
- Powdered stevia

DIRECTION

- Mix orange or lemon juice and stevia and pour into molds.
- Freeze until firm.

NUTRITIONAL

- Calories: 46
- Fat: 0.2g
- Carbs: 16g
- Protein: 0.9g
- Sodium: 3.7mg
- Potassium: 104mg
- Phosphorus: 11mg

Preparation Time: 5 minutes|Cooking Time: 5 minutes|Servings: 1

Easy No-Bake Coconut Cookies

INGREDIENTS

- 3 cups finely shredded coconut flakes
- 1 cup melted coconut oil
- 1 teaspoon liquid stevia

DIRECTION

- Prepare all ingredients in a large bowl; stir until well blended.
- Form the mixture into small balls and arrange them on a paper-lined baking tray.
- Press each cookie down with a fork and refrigerate until firm. Enjoy!

NUTRITIONAL

- Calories: 99
- Fat: 10 g
- Carbs: 2 g
- Protein: 3 g
- Sodium: 7 mg
- Potassium: 105mg
- Phosphorus: 11mg

Preparation Time: 5 minutes|Cooking Time: 10 minutes|Servings: 20

Roasted Chili-Vinegar Peanuts

INGREDIENTS

- 1 tablespoon coconut oil
- 2 cups raw peanuts, unsalted
- 2 teaspoon sea salt
- 2 tablespoon apple cider vinegar
- 1 teaspoon chili powder
- 1 teaspoon fresh lime zest

DIRECTION

- Preheat oven to 350°F.
- In a large bowl, toss together coconut oil, peanuts, and salt until well coated.
- Transfer to a rimmed baking sheet and roast in the oven for about 15 minutes or until fragrant.
- Transfer the roasted peanuts to a bowl and add vinegar, chili powder, and lime zest.
- Toss to coat well and serve.

NUTRITIONAL

- Calories: 447
- Fat: 39.5g
- Carbs: 12.3 g
- Protein: 18.9 g
- Sodium: 160 mg
- Potassium: 200mg
- Phosphorus: 0mg

Preparation Time: 5 minutes|Cooking Time: 10 minutes|Servings: 4

Popcorn with Sugar and Spice

INGREDIENTS

- 8 cups hot popcorn
- 2 tablespoons unsalted butter
- 2 tablespoons sugar
- 1/2 teaspoon cinnamon
- 1/4 teaspoon nutmeg

DIRECTION

- Popping the corn; put aside.
- Heat the butter, sugar, cinnamon, and nutmeg in the microwave or saucepan over a range fire until the butter is melted, and the sugar dissolved.
- Sprinkle the corn with the spicy butter, mix well.
- Serve immediately for optimal flavor.

NUTRITIONAL

- 185.2 calories;
- protein 2.1g 4% DV;
- carbohydrates 21.5g 7% DV;
- fat 10.4g 16% DV;
- cholesterol mg;
- Sodium 73.6mg 3% DV.

Preparation Time: 10 minutes|Cooking Time: 10 minutes|Servings: 2

Eggplant and Chickpea Bites

INGREDIENTS

- 3 large aubergine cut in half (make a few cuts in the flesh with a knife)
- 2 large cloves garlic, peeled and deglazed
- 2 tbsp. coriander powder
- 2 tbsp. cumin seeds
- 400 g canned chickpeas, rinsed and drained
- 2 Tbsp. chickpea flour
- Zest and juice of 1/2 lemon
- 1/2 lemon quartered for serving
- 3 tbsp. tablespoon of polenta

DIRECTION

- Heat the oven to 200°C. Spray the eggplant halves generously with oil and place them on the meat side up on a baking sheet.
- Sprinkle with coriander and cumin seeds, and then place the cloves of garlic on the plate.
- Season and roast for 40 minutes until the flesh of eggplant is completely tender. Reserve and let cool a little.
- Scrape the flesh of the eggplant in a bowl with a spatula and throw the skins in the compost. Thoroughly scrape and make sure to incorporate spices and crushed roasted garlic.
- Add chickpeas, chickpea flour, zest, and lemon juice. Crush roughly and mix well.
- Check to season. Do not worry if the mixture seems a bit soft - it will firm up in the fridge.
- Form about twenty pellets and place them on a baking sheet covered with parchment paper. Refrigerate for at least 30 minutes.
- Preheat oven to 180°C. Remove the meatballs from the fridge and coat them by rolling them in the polenta.
- Place them back on the baking sheet and spray a little oil on each. Roast for 20 minutes until golden and crisp.
- Serve with lemon wedges. You can also serve these dumplings with a spicy yogurt dip.

NUTRITIONAL

- Calories: 72
- Fat: 1g
- Carbs: 18g
- Protein: 3g
- Sodium: 63mg
- Potassium: 162mg
- Phosphorus: 36mg

Preparation Time: 15 minutes|Cooking Time: 50 minutes|Servings: 6

Baba Ghanouj

INGREDIENTS

- 1 large aubergine, cut in half lengthwise
- 1 head of garlic, unpeeled
- 30 ml (2 tablespoons) of olive oil
- Lemon juice to taste

DIRECTION

- Preheat the oven to 350 degrees F.
- Place the eggplant on the plate, skin side up. Roast until the meat is very tender and detaches easily from the skin, about 1 hour depending on the eggplant's size. Let cool. Meanwhile, cut the tip of the garlic cloves. Put garlic cloves in a square aluminum foil. Fold the edges of the sheet and fold together to form a tightly wrapped foil.
- Roast with the eggplant until tender, about 20 minutes. Let cool. Purée the pods with a garlic press.
- With a spoon, scoop out the eggplant's flesh and place it in the bowl of a food processor. Add the garlic puree, the oil, and the lemon juice. Stir until purée is smooth and pepper.
- Serve with mini pita bread.

NUTRITIONAL

- Calories: 110
- Fat: 12g
- Carbs: 5g
- Protein: 1g
- Sodium: 180mg
- Potassium: 207mg
- Phosphorus: 81mg

Preparation Time: 10 minutes|Cooking Time: 1 hour and 20 minutes|Servings: 1

Baked Pita Fries

INGREDIENTS

- 3 pita loaves (6 inches)
- 3 tablespoons olive oil
- Chili powder

DIRECTION

- Separate each bread in half with scissors to obtain 6 round pieces.
- Cut each piece into eight points. Brush each with olive oil and sprinkle with chili powder.
- Bake at 350 degrees F for about 15 minutes until crisp.

NUTRITIONAL

- Calories: 120
- Fat: 2.5g
- Carbs: 22g
- Protein: 3g
- Sodium: 70mg
- Potassium: 0mg
- Phosphorus: 0mg

Preparation Time: 5 minutes|Cooking Time: 15 minutes|Servings: 6

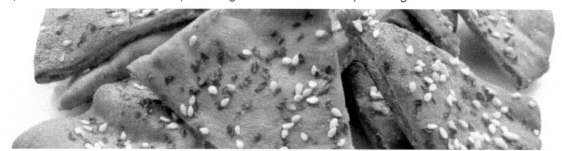

Herbal Cream Cheese Tartines

INGREDIENTS

- 1 clove garlic, halved
- 1 cup cream cheese spread
- ¼ cup chopped herbs such as chives, dill, parsley, tarragon, or thyme
- 2 tbsp. minced French shallot or onion
- ½ tsp. black pepper
- 2 tbsp. tablespoons water

DIRECTION

- In a medium-sized bowl, combine the cream cheese, herbs, shallot, pepper, and water with a hand blender.
- Serve the cream cheese with the rusks

NUTRITIONAL

- Calories: 476
- Fat: 9g
- Carbs: 75g
- Protein: 23g
- Sodium: 885mg
- Potassium: 312mg
- Phosphorus: 165mg

Preparation Time: 15 minutes|Cooking Time: 15 minutes|Servings: 2

Mixes of Snacks

INGREDIENTS

- 6 c. margarine
- 2 tbsp. Worcestershire sauce
- 1 ½ tbsp. spice salt
- ¾ c. garlic powder
- ½ tsp. onion powder
- 3 cups Cheerios
- 3 cups corn flakes
- 1 cup pretzel
- 1 cup broken bagel chip into 1-inch pieces

DIRECTION

- Preheat the oven to 250F (120C)
- Melt the margarine in a large roasting pan. Stir in the seasoning. Gradually add the ingredients remaining by mixing so that the coating is uniform.
- Cook 1 hour, stirring every 15 minutes.
- Spread on paper towels to let cool. Store in a tightly closed container.

NUTRITIONAL

- Calories: 150
- Fat: 6g
- Carbs: 20g
- Protein: 3g
- Sodium: 300mg
- Potassium: 93mg
- Phosphorus: 70mg

Preparation Time: 15 minutes|Cooking Time: 1 hour|Servings: 1

Spicy Crab Dip

INGREDIENTS

- 1 can of 8 oz. softened cream cheese
- 1 tbsp. finely chopped onions
- 1 tbsp. lemon juice
- 2 tbsp. Worcestershire sauce
- 1/8 tsp. black pepper Cayenne pepper to taste
- 2 tbsp. to s. of milk or non-fortified rice drink
- 1 can of 6 oz. of crabmeat

DIRECTION

- Preheat the oven to 375 degrees F.
- Pour the cheese cream into a bowl. Add the onions, lemon juice, Worcestershire sauce, black pepper, and cayenne pepper. Mix well. Stir in the milk/rice drink.
- Add the crabmeat and mix until you obtain a homogeneous mixture.
- Pour the mixture into a baking dish. Cook without covering for 15 minutes or until bubbles appear. Serve hot with triangle cut pita bread.
- Microwave until bubbles appear, about 4 minutes, stirring every 1 to 2 minutes.

NUTRITIONAL

- Calories: 42
- Fat: 0.5g
- Carbs: 2g
- Protein: 7g
- Sodium: 167mg
- Potassium: 130mg
- Phosphorus: 139mg

Preparation Time: 10 minutes|Cooking Time: 20 minutes|Servings: 1

Chapter 15.
Soup and stew

Creamy Tuna Salad

INGREDIENTS

- 3.5 oz. can tuna, drained and flaked
- 1 1/2 tsp garlic powder
- 1 tbsp. dill, chopped
- 1 tsp curry powder
- 2 tbsp. fresh lemon juice
- 1/2 cup onion, chopped
- 1/2 cup celery, chopped
- 1/4 cup parmesan cheese, grated
- 3/4 cup mayonnaise

DIRECTION

- Add all ingredients into the large bowl and mix until well combined.
- Serve and enjoy.

NUTRITIONAL

- Calories 224 Fat 15.5 g
- Carbohydrates 14.1 g
- Sugar 4.2 g
- Protein 8 g
- Cholesterol 20 mg
- Phosphorus: 110mg
- Potassium: 117mg
- Sodium: 75mg

Preparation Time: 10 minutes |Cooking Time: 5 minutes |Servings: 4

Creamy Mushroom Soup

INGREDIENTS

- 1 lb. mushrooms, sliced
- 1/2 cup heavy cream
- 4 cups chicken broth
- 1 tbsp. sage, chopped
- 1/4 cup butter
- Pepper
- Salt

DIRECTION

- Melt butter in a large pot over medium heat.
- Add sage and saute for 1 minute.
- Add mushrooms and cook for 3-5 minutes or until lightly browned.
- Add broth and stir well and simmer for 5 minutes.
- Puree the soup using an immersion blender until smooth.
- Add heavy cream and stir well. Season soup with pepper and salt.
- Serve hot and enjoy.

NUTRITIONAL

- Calories 145
- Fat 12.5 g
- Carbohydrates 3.6 g
- Sugar 1.8 g Protein 5.9 g
- Cholesterol 34 mg
- Phosphorus: 140mg
- Potassium: 127mg
- Sodium: 75mg

Preparation Time: 10 minutes |Cooking Time: 15 minutes |Servings: 6

Pork Soup

INGREDIENTS

- 2 lbs. country pork ribs, boneless and cut into 1-inch pieces
- 2 cups cauliflower rice
- 1 1/2 tbsp. fresh oregano, chopped
- 1 cup of water
- 2 cups Red bell peppers, chopped
- 1 cup chicken stock
- 1/2 cup dry white wine
- 1 onion, chopped
- 3 garlic cloves, chopped
- 1 tbsp. olive oil
- Pepper
- Salt

DIRECTION

- Heat oil in a saucepan over medium heat.
- Season pork with pepper and salt.
- Add pork into the saucepan and cook until lightly brown from all the sides.
- Add onion and garlic and saute for 2 minutes.
- Add Red bell peppers, water, stock, and white wine and stir well. Bring to boil.
- Pour saucepan mixture into the slow cooker.
- Cover and cook on high for 4 hours.
- Add cauliflower rice and oregano in the last 20 minutes of cooking.
- Stir well and serve.

NUTRITIONAL

- Calories 263
- Fat 15.1 g
- Carbohydrates 5.8 g Sugar 2.6 g
- Protein 23.4 g
- Cholesterol 85 mg
- Phosphorus: 130mg
- Potassium: 117mg
- Sodium: 105mg

Preparation Time: 10 minutes |Cooking Time: 4 hours 15 minutes |Servings: 8

Thai Chicken Soup

INGREDIENTS

- 4 chicken breasts, slice into 1/4-inch strips
- 1 tbsp. fresh basil, chopped
- 1 tsp ground ginger
- 1 oz. fresh lime juice
- 1 tbsp. coconut aminos
- 2 tbsp. chili garlic paste
- 1/4 cup fish sauce
- 28 oz. water
- 14 oz. chicken broth
- 14 oz. coconut milk

DIRECTION

- Add coconut milk, basil, ginger, lime juice, coconut aminos, chili garlic paste, fish sauce, water, and broth into the stockpot. Stir well and bring to boil over medium-high heat.
- Add chicken and stir well. Turn heat to medium-low and simmer for 30 minutes.
- Stir well and serve.

NUTRITIONAL

- Calories 357
- Fat 23.4 g
- Carbohydrates 5.5 g
- Sugar 2.9 g
- Protein 31.7 g
- Cholesterol 87 mg
- Phosphorus: 110mg
- Potassium: 117mg
- Sodium: 75mg

Preparation Time: 10 minutes |Cooking Time: 30 minutes |Servings: 6

Tasty Pumpkin Soup

INGREDIENTS

- 2 cups pumpkin puree
- 1 cup coconut cream
- 4 cups vegetable broth
- 1/2 tsp ground ginger
- 1 tsp curry powder
- 2 shallots, chopped
- 1/2 onion, chopped
- 4 tbsp. butter
- Pepper
- Salt

DIRECTION

- Melt butter in a saucepan over medium heat.
- Add shallots and onion and sauté until softened.
- Add ginger and curry powder and stir well.
- Add broth, pumpkin puree, and coconut cream and stir well. Simmer for 10 minutes. Puree the soup using an immersion blender until smooth.
- Season with pepper and salt.
- Serve and enjoy.

NUTRITIONAL

- Calories 229
- Fat 18.4 g
- Carbohydrates 13 g
- Sugar 4.9 g
- Protein 5.6 g
- Cholesterol 20 mg
- Phosphorus: 120mg
- Potassium: 137mg
- Sodium: 95mg

Preparation Time: 10 minutes |Cooking Time: 30 minutes |Servings: 6

Easy Zucchini Soup

INGREDIENTS

- 5 zucchinis, sliced
- 8 oz. cream cheese, softened
- 5 cups vegetable stock
- Pepper
- Salt

DIRECTION

- Add zucchini and stock into the stockpot and bring to boil over high heat.
- Turn heat to medium and simmer for 20 minutes.
- Add cream cheese and stir until cheese is melted.
- Puree soup using an immersion blender until smooth.
- Season with pepper and salt.
- Serve and enjoy.

NUTRITIONAL

- Calories 245
- Fat 20.3 g
- Carbohydrates 10.9 g
- Sugar 5.2 g
- Protein 7.7 g
- Cholesterol 62 mg
- Phosphorus: 110mg
- Potassium: 117mg
- Sodium: 75mg

Preparation Time: 10 minutes |Cooking Time: 25 minutes |Servings: 4

Quick Tomato Soup

INGREDIENTS

- 28 oz. can tomato, diced
- 1 tbsp. balsamic vinegar
- 1 tbsp. dried basil
- 1 tbsp. dried oregano
- 1 tsp garlic, minced
- 2 tbsp. olive oil
- Pepper
- Salt

DIRECTION

- Heat oil in a saucepan over medium heat.
- Add basil, oregano, and garlic and saute for 30 seconds.
- Add Red bell peppers, vinegar, pepper, and salt and simmer for 3 minutes.
- Stir well and serve hot.

NUTRITIONAL

- Calories 108
- Fat 7.1 g
- Carbohydrates 11.2 g
- Sugar 6.8 g
- Protein 2 g
- Cholesterol 0 mg
- Phosphorus: 130mg
- Potassium: 127mg
- Sodium: 75mg

Preparation Time: 10 minutes |Cooking Time: 5 minutes |Servings: 4

Spicy Chicken Soup

INGREDIENTS

- 2 cups cooked chicken, shredded
- 1/2 cup half and half
- 4 cups chicken broth
- 1/3 cup hot sauce
- 3 tbsp. butter
- 4 oz. cream cheese
- Pepper
- Salt

DIRECTION

- Add half and half, broth, hot sauce, butter, and cream cheese into the blender and blend until smooth.
- Pour blended mixture into the saucepan and cook over medium heat until just hot.
- Add chicken stir well. Season soup with pepper and salt.
- Serve and enjoy.

NUTRITIONAL

- Calories 361
- Fat 25.6 g
- Carbohydrates 3.3 g
- Sugar 1.1 g
- Protein 28.4 g
- Cholesterol 119 mg
- Phosphorus: 110mg
- Potassium: 117mg
- Sodium: 75mg

Preparation Time: 10 minutes |Cooking Time: 5 minutes |Servings: 4

Shredded Pork Soup

INGREDIENTS

- 1 lb. pork loin
- 8 cups chicken broth
- 2 tsp fresh lime juice
- 1 1/2 tsp garlic powder
- 1 1/2 tsp onion powder
- 1 1/2 tsp chili powder
- 1 1/2 tsp cumin
- 1 jalapeno pepper, minced
- 1 cup onion, chopped
- 3 Red bell peppers, chopped

DIRECTION

- Add Red bell peppers, jalapeno, and onion into the slow cooker and stir well.
- Place meat on top of the tomato mixture.
- Pour remaining ingredients on top of the meat.
- Cover slow cooker and cook on low for 8 hours.
- Remove meat from slow cooker and shred using a fork.
- Return shredded

NUTRITIONAL

- Calories 199
- Fat 9.6 g
- Carbohydrates 6.3 g
- Sugar 3.1 g
- Protein 21.2 g
- Cholesterol 45 mg
- Phosphorus: 140mg
- Potassium: 127mg
- Sodium: 95mg

Preparation Time: 10 minutes |Cooking Time: 8 hours |Servings: 8

Creamy Chicken Green lettuce Soup

INGREDIENTS

- 3 cups cooked chicken, shredded
- 1/8 tsp nutmeg
- 4 cup chicken broth
- 1/2 cup parmesan cheese, shredded
- 8 oz. cream cheese
- 1/4 cup butter
- 4 cup baby green lettuce, chopped
- 1 tsp garlic, minced
- Pepper
- Salt

DIRECTION

- Melt butter in a saucepan over medium heat.
- Add green lettuce and garlic and cook until green lettuce is wilted.
- Add parmesan cheese and cream cheese and stir until cheese is melted.
- Add remaining ingredients and stir everything well and cook for 5 minutes.
- Season soup with pepper and salt.
- Serve and enjoy.

NUTRITIONAL

- Calories 361
- Fat 25.6 g
- Carbohydrates 2.8 g
- Sugar 0.6 g
- Protein 29.5 g
- Cholesterol 121 mgP
- hosphorus: 110mg
- Potassium: 117mg
- Sodium: 75mg

Preparation Time: 10 minutes | Cooking Time: 10 minutes | Servings: 6

Creamy Cauliflower Soup

INGREDIENTS

- 6 cups cauliflower florets
- 4 oz. mascarpone cheese
- 1 1/2 cup cheddar cheese, shredded
- 1/4 tsp mustard powder
- 3 cups of water
- 1 tsp garlic, minced
- Pepper
- Salt

DIRECTION

- Add cauliflower, mustard powder, water, and garlic into the slow cooker and stir well.
- Cover and cook on low for 4 hours.
- Stir in cheddar cheese and mascarpone cheese.
- Puree the soup using an immersion blender until smooth.
- Season soup with pepper and salt.
- Serve and enjoy.

NUTRITIONAL

- Calories 208
- Fat 14.3 g
- Carbohydrates 7.7 g
- Sugar 3.1 g
- Protein 13.5 g
- Cholesterol 47 mg
- Phosphorus: 210mg
- Potassium: 157mg
- Sodium: 85mg

Preparation Time: 10 minutes | Cooking Time: 4 hours | Servings: 5

Delicious Curried Chicken Soup

INGREDIENTS

- 5 cups cooked chicken, chopped
- 1/4 cup fresh parsley, chopped
- 1/2 cup sour cream
- 1/4 cup apple cider
- 3 cups celery, chopped
- 1 1/2 tbsp. curry powder
- 10 cups chicken broth
- Pepper
- Salt

DIRECTION

- Add all ingredients except sour cream and parsley into the stockpot and stir well.
- Bring to boil over medium-high heat.
- Turn heat to medium and simmer for 30 minutes.
- Add parsley and sour cream and stir well.
- Season with pepper and salt.
- Serve and enjoy.

NUTRITIONAL

- Calories 180
- Fat 6.1 g
- Carbohydrates 3.7 g
- Sugar 1.9 g
- Protein 28.9 g
- Cholesterol 59 mg
- Phosphorus: 160mg
- Potassium: 107mg
- Sodium: 75mg

Preparation Time: 10 minutes |Cooking Time: 35 minutes |Servings: 10

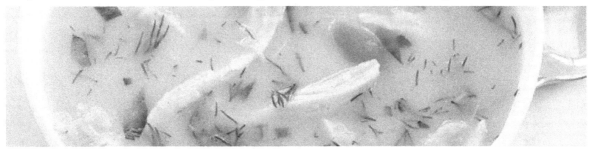

Delicious Tomato Basil Soup

INGREDIENTS

- 28 oz. can tomato, diced
- 1 1/2 cups chicken stock
- 1/2 tsp Italian seasoning
- 1/2 tsp garlic, minced
- 1 onion, chopped
- 1/4 cup fresh basil leaves
- 1/2 cup heavy cream
- 2 tbsp. butter
- Pepper
- Salt

DIRECTION

- Melt butter in a saucepan over medium-high heat.
- Add onion and garlic sauté for 5 minutes.
- Add Red bell peppers, Italian seasoning, and broth. Stir well and bring to boil over high heat.
- Turn heat to medium-low and simmer for 8-10 minutes.
- Blend the soup using an immersion blender until smooth.
- Add heavy cream and basil and stir well. Season soup with pepper and salt.
- Stir and serve.

NUTRITIONAL

- Calories 108
- Fat 7.8 g
- Carbohydrates 9.1 g
- Sugar 5.5 g
- Protein 1.9 g
- Cholesterol 24 mg
- Phosphorus: 110mg P
- otassium: 137mg
- Sodium: 95mg

Preparation Time: 10 minutes |Cooking Time: 20 minutes |Servings: 6

White Fish Stew

INGREDIENTS

- 4 white fish fillets
- 1 cup of water
- 1 onion, sliced
- 1/2 tsp paprika
- 1/4 cup olive oil
- 1/4 tsp pepper
- 1 tsp salt

DIRECTION

- Add olive oil, paprika, onion, water, pepper, and salt into the saucepan. Stir well and bring to boil over medium-high heat.
- Turn heat to medium-low and simmer for 15 minutes.
- Add white fish fillets and cook until fish is cooked.
- Serve and enjoy.

NUTRITIONAL

- Calories 513
- Fat 32.3 g
- Carbohydrates 3.7 g
- Sugar 1.6 g
- Protein 50.7 g
- Cholesterol 158 mg
- Phosphorus: 120mg
- Potassium: 117mg
- Sodium: 75mg

Preparation Time: 10 minutes |Cooking Time: 35 minutes |Servings: 3

Carrot Cauliflower Soup

INGREDIENTS

- 4 carrots, shredded
- 1 cauliflower head, chopped
- 8 cups chicken broth
- 1 onion, diced
- 5 oz. coconut milk
- 1 tbsp. olive oil
- 1 tbsp. curry powder
- 1/2 tsp turmeric powder
- 1/2 tbsp. ginger, grated
- Pepper
- Salt

DIRECTION

- Heat oil in a saucepan over medium heat.
- Add onion and sauté for 5 minutes.
- Add cauliflower, carrots, and broth and bring to boil.
- Turn heat to medium-low and simmer until veggie is softened.
- Add curry powder, turmeric, and ginger and stir well.
- Blend the soup using a blender until smooth.
- Add coconut milk and stir well.
- Season soup with pepper and salt.
- Serve and enjoy.

NUTRITIONAL

- Calories 125
- Fat 7.5 g
- Carbohydrates 8.7 g
- Sugar 4.2 g
- Protein 6.5 g
- Cholesterol 0 mg
- Phosphorus: 210mg
- Potassium: 187mg
- Sodium: 105mg

Preparation Time: 10 minutes |Cooking Time: 25 minutes |Servings: 8

Pumpkin, Coconut and Sage Soup

INGREDIENTS

- 1 cup pumpkin, canned
- 6 cups chicken broth
- 1 cup low fat coconut almond milk
- 1 teaspoon sage, chopped
- 3 garlic cloves, peeled
- Sunflower seeds and pepper to taste

DIRECTION

- Take a stockpot and add all the ingredients except coconut almond milk into it.
- Place stockpot over medium heat.
- Let it bring to a boil.
- Reduce heat to simmer for 30 minutes.
- Add the coconut almond milk and stir.
- Serve bacon and enjoy!

NUTRITIONAL

- Calories: 145
- Fat: 12g
- Carbohydrates: 8g
- Protein: 6g
- Phosphorus: 110mg
- Potassium: 117mg
- Sodium: 75mg

Preparation Time: 10 minutes |Cooking Time: 30 minutes |Servings: 3

The Kale and Green lettuce Soup

INGREDIENTS

- 3 ounces coconut oil
- 8 ounces kale, chopped
- 4 1/3 cups coconut almond milk
- Sunflower seeds and pepper to taste

DIRECTION

- Take a skillet and place it over medium heat.
- Add kale and sauté for 2-3 minutes
- Add kale to blender.
- Add water, spices, coconut almond milk to blender as well.
- Blend until smooth and pour mix into bowl.
- Serve and enjoy!

NUTRITIONAL

- Calories: 124
- Fat: 13g
- Carbohydrates: 7g
- Protein: 4.2g
- Phosphorus: 110mg
- Potassium: 117mg
- Sodium: 105mg

Preparation Time: 5 minutes |Cooking Time: 10 minutes |Servings: 4

Japanese Onion Soup

INGREDIENTS

- ½ stalk celery, diced
- 1 small onion, diced
- ½ carrot, diced
- 1 teaspoon fresh ginger root, grated
- ¼ teaspoon fresh garlic, minced
- 2 tablespoons chicken stock
- 3 teaspoons beef bouillon granules
- 1 cup fresh shiitake, mushrooms
- 2 quarts water
- 1 cup baby Portobello mushrooms, sliced
- 1 tablespoon fresh chives

DIRECTION

- Take a saucepan and place it over high heat, add water, bring to a boil.
- Add beef bouillon, celery, onion, chicken stock, and carrots, half of the mushrooms, ginger, and garlic.
- Put on the lid and reduce heat to medium, cook for 45 minutes.
- Take another saucepan and add another half of mushrooms.
- Once the soup is cooked, strain the soup into the pot with uncooked mushrooms.
- Garnish with chives and enjoy!

NUTRITIONAL

- Calories: 25
- Fat: 0.2g C
- arbohydrates: 5g
- Protein: 1.4g
- Phosphorus: 210mg
- Potassium: 217mg
- Sodium: 75mg

Preparation Time: 15 minutes | Cooking Time: 45 minutes | Servings: 4

Amazing Broccoli and Cauliflower Soup

INGREDIENTS

- 3 cups broccoli florets
- 2 cups cauliflower florets
- 2 garlic cloves, minced
- ½ cup shallots, chopped
- 1 carrot, chopped
- 3 ½ cups low sodium veggie stick
- Pinch of pepper
- 1 cup fat-free milk
- 6 ounces low-fat cheddar, shredded
- 1 cup non-fat Greek yogurt

DIRECTION

- Add broccoli, cauliflower, garlic, shallots, carrot, stock, and pepper to your Slow Cooker.
- Stir well and place lid.
- Cook on LOW for 8 hours.
- Add milk and cheese.
- Use an immersion blender to smooth the soup.
- Add yogurt and blend once more.
- Ladle into bowls and enjoy!

NUTRITIONAL

- Calories: 218
- Fat: 11g
- Carbohydrates: 15g
- Protein: 12g
- Phosphorus: 206mg
- Potassium: 147mg
- Sodium: 75mg

Preparation Time: 10 minutes | Cooking Time: 8 hours | Servings: 4

Amazing Zucchini Soup

INGREDIENTS

- 1 onion, chopped
- 3 zucchinis, cut into medium chunks
- 2 tablespoons coconut milk
- 2 garlic cloves, minced
- 4 cups chicken stock
- 2 tablespoons coconut oil
- Pinch of salt
- Black pepper to taste

DIRECTION

- Take a pot and place over medium heat.
- Add oil and let it heat up.
- Add zucchini, garlic, onion and stir.
- Cook for 5 minutes.
- Add stock, salt, pepper and stir.
- Bring to a boil and reduce the heat.
- Simmer for 20 minutes.
- Remove from heat and add coconut milk.
- Use an immersion blender until smooth.
- Ladle into soup bowls and serve.
- Enjoy!

NUTRITIONAL

- Calories: 160
- Fat: 2g
- Carbohydrates: 4g
- Protein: 7g
- Phosphorus: 110mg
- Potassium: 117mg
- Sodium: 75mg

Preparation Time: 10 minutes |Cooking Time: 20 minutes |Servings: 4

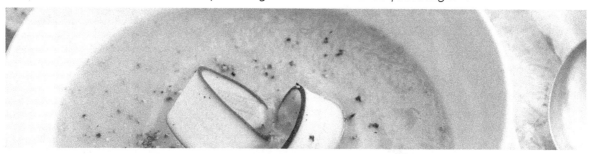

Creamy Broccoli Cheese Salad

INGREDIENTS

- 6 cups broccoli florets, chopped
- 1/2 cup cheddar cheese, shredded
- 3 bacon, cooked and chopped
- 1/2 tsp parsley
- 1 tsp garlic powder
- 1 tsp onion powder
- 1 1/2 tsp dill
- 1/2 cup sour cream
- 3/4 cup mayonnaise
- Pepper
- Salt

DIRECTION

- Add all ingredients into the large mixing bowl and mix everything well.
- Season salad with pepper and salt.
- Serve and enjoy.

NUTRITIONAL

- Add all ingredients into the large mixing bowl and mix everything well.
- Season salad with pepper and salt.
- Serve and enjoy.

Preparation Time: 10 minutes |Cooking Time: 5 minutes |Servings: 8

Healthy Green lettuce Salad

INGREDIENTS

- 5 oz. fresh green lettuce
- 3 tbsp. almonds, toasted and sliced
- 1 small onion, sliced
- 1/3 cup feta cheese, crumbled
- 1 apple, sliced
- For dressing:
- 2 tsp Dijon mustard
- 1/2 tsp garlic, minced
- 3 tbsp. vinegar
- 1/3 cup olive oil
- Pepper
- Salt

DIRECTION

- In a small bowl, whisk together all dressing ingredients and set aside.
- Add green lettuce, almonds, onion, feta cheese, and apple into the large bowl and mix well.
- Pour dressing over salad and toss well.
- Serve and enjoy.

NUTRITIONAL

- Calories 252
- Fat 22.1 g
- Carbohydrates 12.5 g
- Sugar 7.5 g
- Protein 4.2 g
- Cholesterol 11 mg
- Phosphorus: 110mg
- Potassium: 117mg
- Sodium: 75mg

Preparation Time: 10 minutes |Cooking Time: 5 minutes |Servings: 4

Green lettuce Strawberry Salad

INGREDIENTS

- For salad:
- 6 cups baby green lettuce
- 1/4 cup walnuts, toasted and chopped
- 2.5 oz. feta cheese, crumbled
- 1 apple, cored and chopped
- 1/2 cup strawberries, sliced
- 1 1/2 cup cucumbers, sliced
- For dressing:
- 1 tbsp. Dijon mustard
- 1 tbsp. apple cider vinegar
- 1/4 cup olive oil
- Pepper

DIRECTION

- Add all salad ingredients into the large bowl and mix well.
- In a small bowl, whisk together all dressing ingredients and pour over salad.
- Toss well and serve.

NUTRITIONAL

- Clories 258
- Fat 21.5 g
- Carbohydrates 13.9 g
- Sugar 8.4 g
- Protein 6.4 g
- Cholesterol 16 mg
- Phosphorus: 120mg
- Potassium: 137mg
- Sodium: 45mg

Preparation Time: 10 minutes |Cooking Time: 5 minutes |Servings: 4

Flavorful Pesto Chicken Salad

INGREDIENTS

- 2 chicken breasts, cooked and shredded
- 1/2 cup parmesan cheese, shredded
- 1/4 cup mayonnaise
- 1/2 cup basil pesto
- 2 celery stalks, chopped
- Pepper
- Salt

DIRECTION

- Add all ingredients into the mixing bowl and mix until well combined.
- Serve and enjoy.

NUTRITIONAL

- Calories 234
- Fat 12.8 g
- Carbohydrates 4.3 g
- Sugar 1.1 g
- Protein 25 g
- Cholesterol 77 mg
- Phosphorus: 210mg
- Potassium: 107mg
- Sodium: 75mg

Preparation Time: 10 minutes |Cooking Time: 5 minutes |Servings: 4

Pesto Chicken Mozzarella Salad

INGREDIENTS

- 1 lb. cooked chicken, shredded
- 1/2 tbsp. fresh lemon juice
- 3 tbsp. pesto
- 1/2 cup yogurt
- 1/4 cup fresh basil, chopped
- 1/4 cup pine nuts
- 6 mozzarella balls, halved
- 1 cup cherry Red bell peppers, halved
- Pepper
- Salt

DIRECTION

- In a small bowl, whisk together yogurt, lemon juice, pesto, pepper, and salt and set aside.
- Add chicken, basil, pine nuts, mozzarella balls, and cherry Red bell peppers and mix well.
- Pour dressing over salad and toss well and serve.

NUTRITIONAL

- Calories 490
- Fat 28.1 g
- Carbohydrates 5.9 g
- Sugar 4.4 g
- Protein 52.4 g
- Cholesterol 137 mg
- Phosphorus: 110mg
- Potassium: 117mg
- Sodium: 75mg

Preparation Time: 10 minutes |Cooking Time: 5 minutes |Servings: 4

Healthy Cucumber Salad

INGREDIENTS

- 2 cucumbers, cubed
- 2 tbsp. fresh lime juice
- 1 tbsp. lemon juice
- 2 tbsp. green onion, minced
- 1 garlic, minced
- 1/4 cup fresh cilantro, chopped
- Pepper
- Salt

DIRECTION

- In a small bowl, whisk together lime juice, lemon juice, garlic, pepper, and salt.
- Add cucumber, green onion, cilantro, into the medium bowl and mix well.
- Pour dressing over salad and mix.
- Cover and place in the refrigerator for 30 minutes.
- Serve chilled and enjoy.

NUTRITIONAL

- Calories 239
- Fat 19.8 g
- Carbohydrates 17.1 g
- Sugar 3.6 g
- Protein 3.2 g
- Cholesterol 0 mg
- Phosphorus: 130mg
- Potassium: 127mg
- Sodium: 75mg

Preparation Time: 10 minutes |Cooking Time: 5 minutes |Servings: 4

Pesto Cucumber Tomato Salad

INGREDIENTS

- 1 lb. cherry Red bell peppers, halved
- 1 tbsp. fresh lemon juice
- 1/4 cup pesto
- 1/3 cup onion, diced
- 1 cucumber, sliced
- Pepper
- Salt

DIRECTION

- Add all ingredients into the large bowl and mix everything well.
- Serve and enjoy.

NUTRITIONAL

- Calories 206
- Fat 17.6 g
- Carbohydrates 11.9 g
- Sugar 4.2 g
- Protein 3.4 g
- Cholesterol 3 mg
- Phosphorus: 110mg
- Potassium: 137mg
- Sodium: 85mg

Preparation Time: 10 minutes |Cooking Time: 5 minutes |Servings: 6

Egg Tuna Salad

INGREDIENTS

- 8 eggs, hard-boiled, peeled and chopped
- 1/8 tsp paprika
- 1 tsp Dijon mustard
- 2 tbsp. mayonnaise
- 1/3 cup yogurt
- 2 tbsp. chives, minced
- 2 tbsp. onion, minced
- 5 oz. tuna, drain
- Pepper
- Salt

DIRECTION

- In a large bowl, whisk together mustard, mayonnaise, yogurt, pepper, and salt.
- Add eggs, chives, onion, and tuna and mix well.
- Sprinkle with paprika and serve.

NUTRITIONAL

- Calories 159
- Fat 9.6 g
- Carbohydrates 3 g
- Sugar 1.9 g
- Protein 14.6 g
- Cholesterol 228 mg
- Phosphorus: 110mg
- Potassium: 117mg
- Sodium: 75mg

Preparation Time: 10 minutes |Cooking Time: 5 minutes |Servings: 6

Chicken Vegetable Salad

INGREDIENTS

- 1 1/2 lbs. cooked chicken, cubed
- 1 cup cherry Red bell peppers, halved
- 4 small zucchinis, trimmed and sliced
- 8 oz. green beans, trimmed
- 1 tbsp. olive oil
- 1/2 small onion, sliced
- 2 tbsp. pesto
- Pepper
- Salt

DIRECTION

- Add green beans into the boiling water and cook for 2 minutes. Drain well and transfer in large bowl.
- Add remaining ingredients to the bowl and toss well.
- Serve and enjoy.

NUTRITIONAL

- Calories 369
- Fat 12.3 g
- Carbohydrates 11.1 g
- Sugar 4.9 g
- Protein 53 g
- Cholesterol 133 mg
- Phosphorus: 110mg
- Potassium: 117mg
- Sodium: 75mg

Preparation Time: 10 minutes |Cooking Time: 10 minutes |Servings: 4

Protein Packed Shrimp Salad

INGREDIENTS

- 1 lb. shrimp, peeled and deveined
- 1 1/2 tbsp. fresh dill, chopped
- 1 tsp Dijon mustard
- 2 tsp fresh lemon juice
- 2 tbsp. onion, minced
- 1/2 cup celery, diced
- 1/2 cup mayonnaise
- Pepper
- Salt

DIRECTION

- Add shrimp in boiling water and cook for 2 minutes. Drain well and transfer in large bowl.
- Add remaining ingredients into the bowl and mix well.
- Serve and enjoy.

NUTRITIONAL

- Calories 258
- Fat 11.9 g
- Carbohydrates 10.4 g
- Sugar 2.3 g
- Protein 26.5 g
- Cholesterol 246 mg
- Phosphorus: 135mg
- Potassium: 154mg
- Sodium: 75mg

Preparation Time: 10 minutes |Cooking Time: 10 minutes |Servings: 4

Pumpkin and Walnut Puree

INGREDIENTS

- 100 g walnuts, without shell
- 300 g pumpkin
- 30 ml of milk
- 600 ml of water

DIRECTION

- Peel the walnuts and pound them with the mortar.
- Peel the pumpkin and cut into pieces. Place the pumpkin pieces in a plastic bag and place it in the microwave over a high temperature for five minutes.
- Put the water with the pumpkin and walnuts in the blender and puree.
- Put everything in a saucepan and cook until mushy over low heat.
- Slowly pour in the milk and stir.

NUTRITIONAL

- Calories 53,
- White eggs 2 g,
- Carbohydrates 4 g,
- Fat 4 g,
- Cholesterol 1 mg,
- Sodium 167 mg,
- Potassium 201 mg,
- Calcium 23 mg,
- Phosphorus 59 mg,
- Dietary fiber 1.2 g

Preparation Time: 10mins |Cooking Time: 10mins |Serving: 6

Bean and Pepper Soup with Coriander

INGREDIENTS

- 1 onion
- 2 garlic cloves
- 2 tbsp. olive oil
- 2 red peppers
- 800 ml vegetable broth
- salt
- cayenne pepper
- Tabasco
- curry powder
- 2 cans kidney beans á 240 g
- 200 ml whipped cream at least 30% fat content
- 1 coriander

DIRECTION

- Peel the onion and garlic, diced finely, and sauté in a saucepan with hot oil until translucent. Wash the bell peppers, cut in half, core, dice, and add. Sweat briefly and deglaze with the broth. Season with salt, cayenne pepper, curry, and Tabasco and simmer over medium heat for 10 minutes.
- Pour the beans over a sieve, rinse with cold water and drain well.
- Stir the cream with the beans into the soup and simmer for another 4 minutes.
- Wash the coriander, shake dry, pluck the leaves off, and roughly chop.
- Season the soup to taste, season again if necessary, pour into preheated bowls, and serve sprinkled with the coriander. Serve with a fresh baguette if you like.

NUTRITIONAL

- Calories 357 kcal
- Protein 14 g
- Fat 22 g
- Carbohydrates 26 g

Preparation time 30mins|Cooking time 20mins|Serving 4

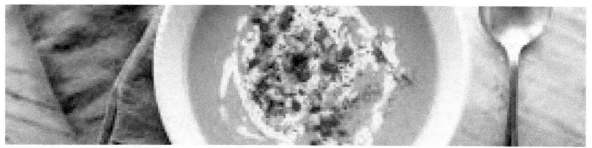

Bean and Ham Soup with Bread

INGREDIENTS

- 1 onion
- 2 garlic cloves
- 1 red chili pepper
- 100 g ham
- 2 tbsp. vegetable oil
- 1 l meat soup
- 100 g dried kidney beans
- 100 g dried white lima bean
- Tabasco
- Salt
- Pepper from the mill
- 4 rye rolls

DIRECTION

- Mix the beans, pour water over them, and leave to soak overnight. The next day, peel and finely chop the onion and garlic. Wash the chili pepper, slit lengthways, core, and chop very finely. Finely dice the ham. Peel the sweet potato and cut into pieces of equal size.
- Heat the oil in a large saucepan, sauté the onions and garlic until translucent. Fry the ham and tomato paste in it, season with salt and pepper. Add the chili and fry briefly. Add the stock and beans (without soaking water), mash the Red bell peppers with a fork, and add to the beans.
- Season with Tabasco and cover and simmer over low heat for about 30-40 minutes. If necessary, add some more broth and season the bean soup to taste. Serve with the rye rolls.

NUTRITIONAL

- Calories/Energy: 181 Kcal,
- Carbs: 33.5 g
- Protein: 10.3 g
- Fibbers: 9.3 g,
- Cholesterol: 4.9 mg,
- Sodium: 0.5 g,
- Calcium: 93.1 mg,
- Phosphorous: 31.9 mg,
- Potassium: 387.1 mg

Preparation Time: 30 mins |Cooking Time: 1h|Serving 4

Hearty Vegetable Soup with Bacon

INGREDIENTS

- 250 g dried kidney beans
- 150 g smoked bacon
- 1 large onion
- 2 garlic cloves
- 3 Red bell peppers
- 1 small savoy cabbage
- 4 potatoes
- 2 tbsp. olive oil
- 1 ½ l meat soup
- salt
- pepper from the mill

DIRECTION

- Soak the beans with cold water and leave overnight.
- Drain the beans and cook them halfway through in fresh cold water for about 30–40 minutes.
- In the meantime, dice the bacon. Peel onion and garlic and chop finely. Scald the Red bell peppers with boiling water for a few seconds, rinse, peel, quarter, core, and chop.
- Clean and wash the cabbage, quarter lengthways, cut off the stalk, and cut the quarters crosswise into strips. Peel the potatoes and cut into bite-sized pieces.
- A sauce pan heats the olive oil and briefly brown the onions, garlic cloves, and bacon. Pour the meat stock. Add Red bell peppers, savoy cabbage strips, and potatoes. Drain the beans and stir into the stock under the vegetables. Salt and pepper and let simmer on low heat for about 30 minutes.

NUTRITIONAL

- Calories 567 kcal
- Protein 17 g
- Fat 40 g
- Carbohydrates 36 g

Preparation time 12h|Cooking Time: 1 h 15 min|Serving 4

Mexican-Style Chicken and Vegetable Soup

INGREDIENTS

- 1 soup chicken
- 3 onions
- 2 carrots
- 150 g celery root
- 1 bay leaf
- 2 cloves
- 1 tsp peppercorns
- 1 tbsp. rapeseed oil
- 2 green peppers
- 1 red chili pepper
- 6 Red bell peppers
- 1 can of kidney beans
- 1 can corn
- salt
- pepper

DIRECTION

- Wash the chicken soup and cover it with cold water in a saucepan that is large enough. Simmer. Boil. Meanwhile, peel 2 onions, carrots, and celery, and roughly dice them.
- Add the bay leaves, cloves, and peppercorns to the chicken and cook for about 2 hours, over medium heat. If necessary, skim off the foam occasionally and add water.
- Take the chicken out of the soup. Strain the stock and measure 1 liter (otherwise use the remainder). Peel the chicken and the skin is removed. Have the meat cut into strips.
- Peel the remaining onion and dice it. In a saucepan, sweat in hot oil until it is translucent. Pour the stock into it and bring it to a boil. In the meantime, wash, cut in half, clean and dice the peppers and chili. Scald the hot-water Red bell peppers, rinse, peel, quarter, core, and dice. Drain the beans and maize and add bell pepper, chili, Red bell peppers, and chicken to the soup.
- For about 15 minutes, let everything simmer together. Season with pepper and salt and serve.

NUTRITIONAL

- Calories/Energy: 69 Kcal,
- Protein: 5.13 g,
- Carbs: 7.87 g,
- Lipids: 2.01 g,
- Sodium: 347 mg,
- Calcium: 11 mg,
- Potassium: 153 mg,
- Phosphorous: 44 mg

Preparation: 40 min, |Cooking Time: 2 h 10 min, |Serving 4

Mexican Bean Soup

INGREDIENTS

- 4 Red bell peppers
- 150 g green beans
- 1 onion
- 1 clove of garlic
- 1 red chili pepper
- 2 tbsp. olive oil
- 2 tbsp. tomato paste
- 1 tsp paprika noble sweet
- 1 tsp ground cumin
- 1 tsp ground coriander
- 1 l vegetable broth
- 240 g kidney beans (can; drained weight)
- 240 g white beans (can; drained weight)
- Salt
- Pepper
- Coriander greens for garnish

DIRECTION

- Scald, quench, peel, remove the stalk and roughly chop the Red bell peppers with hot water. Wash the green beans, clean them, and cut them into small pieces.
- Wash and clean the chili, remove the seeds and, if desired, finely chop it.
- Sauté onion garlic and chilly. Sauté the tomato paste and add paprika, cumin, and cilantro to the mixture. Put the broth in and bring it to a boil. Add the green beans and Red bell peppers and simmer over low heat for about 10 minutes. The kidney and white beans are drained, washed, and added.
- Let it simmer more for 5 minutes. Serve in bowls with coriander leaves and season with salt and pepper.

NUTRITIONAL

- Calories 205 kcal
- Protein 13 g,
- Fat 6 g,
- Carbohydrates 23 g,

Preparation time 20mins |Cooking time 25mins, |Serving 4

Clear Soup with Vegetables

INGREDIENTS

- 200 g waxy potatoes
- 2 poles celery
- 4 spring onions
- 1 onion
- 2 garlic cloves
- 2 yellow peppers
- 2 tbsp. olive oil
- 1 tbsp. tomato paste
- 1 l vegetable broth
- 400 g kidney beans can
- 2 fresh bay leaves
- salt
- pepper

DIRECTION

- Peel and dice the potatoes, clean and wash the celery and spring onions and cut into rings. Peel and chop the onion and garlic. Clean the peppers, cut in half, remove the seeds and white skins, wash and cut into thin strips.
- Heat the oil in a hot saucepan and sauté the vegetables for 2-3 minutes over medium heat.
- Fry the tomato paste briefly, then pour in the stock and bring to the boil once. In the meantime, drain the beans and wash them. Add to the clear soup together with the bay leaf.
- Season
- Simmer over low heat for about 15 minutes.
- Season the soup again to taste and serve in bowls.

NUTRITIONAL

- Calories 227 kcal,
- Protein 12 g,
- Fat 6 g,
- Carbohydrates 30 g,

Preparation time 20mins, |Cooking time 20 mins |Serving 4

Bean Stew with Beef Fillet

INGREDIENTS

- 50 g kidney beans (can; drained weight)
- 50 g small white beans (can; drained weight)
- ½ onion
- 1 small clove of garlic
- ½ red pepper
- 2 tsp olive oil
- 1 branch thyme
- 1 bay leaf
- 200 chunky Red bell peppers (can)
- salt
- pepper
- cayenne pepper
- ¼ tsp ground coriander
- 150 g beef fillet
- 1 stem basil

DIRECTION

- In a sieve, rinse both types of beans and let them drain. Peel the garlic and onion and cut them into fine cubes. Wash, clean, core, and slice the peppers.
- In a casserole, heat one teaspoon of oil. Sauté the onion and garlic in it over medium heat for 2 minutes. Wash the thyme and the bay leaves and add the beans and Red bell peppersto the saucepan, season with salt, pepper, cayenne pepper, and coriander and cook for about 15-17 minutes over medium heat, stirring occasionally.
- Cut the beef into thin strips about 20 minutes before cooking time ends. In a pan, heat the remaining oil. For 2-3 minutes, fry the beef fillet strips over high heat. With salt and pepper, season.
- Wash the basil, shake it dry, and finely chop it. Top the bean stew with the meat and basil.

NUTRITIONAL

- Calories 393 kcal,
- Protein 40 g,
- Fat 17 g,
- Carbohydrates 19 g,

Preparation time 20mins|Cooking time 25mins, |Serving 4

Nutmeg Pumpkin Soup with Kidney Beans

INGREDIENTS

- 1 kg nutmeg pumpkin
- 2 dice vegetable broth
- 1 tbsp. olive oil
- 1 lemon
- 400 g kidney beans (1 can, drained weight)
- 2 stems parsley
- pepper
- salt

DIRECTION

- The pumpkin is cleaned and peeled, the core removed and the pulp cut into cubes. In a saucepan, put the pumpkin cubes in. Add sufficient water just to cover the pumpkin.
- When boiling add 2 cubes of stock. Cook for 20 minutes over medium heat until the pumpkin is tender.
- Squeeze the juice of the lemon.
- In a colander drain the kidney beans and rinse with hot water.
- Wash the parsley, shake it dry and, except for a few leaves, chop finely.
- Add the oil to the pumpkin at the end of the cooking time and finely puree it with a hand blender. Season with lemon juice, pepper, and a little salt if necessary. Distribute the beans and pour hot soup over them on 4 soup plates. Serve with parsley, sprinkled.

NUTRITIONAL

- Calories 197 kcal,
- Protein 12 g,
- Fat 4 g,
- Carbohydrates 27 g,

Preparation Time: 20 mins|Cooking Time: 0 mins|Serving 4

Zucchini Soup

INGREDIENTS

- 2 large zucchinis
- 1 onion
- 2 potatoes
- 2 carrots
- 1 tbsp. (sesame oil, coconut fat, refined rapeseed or olive oil) frying oil
- 500 ml vegetable broth
- 100 g (natural, 15% fat in dry matter) cream cheese
- ½ bunch of parsley
- Salt and pepper

DIRECTION

- Wash and dice the zucchini. Peel the onion, potatoes, and carrots, then dice them.
- Heat the oil in a pot. Sweat the onion cubes in it until they are golden yellow. Add the rest of the vegetables and fry briefly.
- Deglaze with the vegetable stock
- Simmer for about 10 minutes.
- Puree the soup.
- Stir the cream cheese into the warm soup and season with salt and pepper. Wash and finely chop the parsley and serve on top of the soup.

NUTRITIONAL

- Calories/Energy: 36.04 Kcal,
- Carbs: 4.07 g
- Lipids: 1.68 g
- Protein: 2.38 g

Preparation time 20mins|Cooking time 20mins|Servings 4

Quick Pea Soup

INGREDIENTS

- 300 g Potatoes
- 1 onion
- 1 toe garlic
- 30 g butter
- 200 g cream
- 1 Bay leaf
- 400 g frozen peas
- Salt
- Pepper
- Nutmeg
- Cumin
- As required: smoked salmon

DIRECTION

- Peel the potatoes, onion, and garlic and cut into cubes.
- Melt the butter and sauté potatoes, onions, and garlic in it.
- Deglaze with cream, fill the cup twice with water and add this as well. Season with salt, pepper, freshly grated nutmeg, and cumin.
- Add the bay leaf and cook everything until the potatoes are done. Take out the bay leaf and add the peas.
- Bring to the boil again and then puree with a hand blender. If the soup is still too thick, add 1 more shot of water.
- Season again to taste and serve. Add smoked salmon strips to the soup to taste.

NUTRITIONAL

- Calories/Energy: 61 Kcal,
- Protein: 3.2 g
- Carbs: 9.88 g
- Calcium: 12 mg,
- Phosphorous: 47 mg,
- Potassium: 71 mg,
- Sodium: 336 mg

Preparation Time: 5 mins|Cooking time 15 mins|Serving 3

Tomato Soup Made from Fresh Red bell peppers

INGREDIENTS

- 1 kg of Red bell peppers
- 200 ml of water
- ½ teaspoon salt
- 1 sprig of rosemary
- 1 sprig of thyme
- 2 tbsp. cream
- 2 tbsp. sour cream

DIRECTION

- Wash the Red bell peppers and put them in a saucepan with water and salt. Bring to a boil. Simmer for until the peel starts to peel off the Red bell peppers and the Red bell peppers are soft.
- In the meantime, wash the herbs and let them dry on kitchen paper.
- Drain the Red bell peppers, collecting the cooking water if necessary. Strain or strain the soft Red bell peppers through a sieve. Let the pureed Red bell peppers simmer for about 10 minutes. Then stir with the cream until smooth. Dilute with some of the collected cooking water as desired.
- Strip off the rosemary and thyme needles and chop finely. Pour the soup into two bowls, put a dollop of sour cream on top and sprinkle everything with the herbs.

NUTRITIONAL

- Calories186 kcal,
- Protein 6g
- Fat 8 g
- Carbohydrates 21g

Preparation Time: 20mins|Cooking Time: 20mins|Servings 2

Chickpea Soup with Croutons

INGREDIENTS

- Dried chickpeas 60 g
- Common bread without salt 80 g
- Extra virgin olive oil 20 g
- Rosemary
- Sage
- Garlic
- Bay leaf
- Chili

DIRECTION

- Soak the chickpeas the night before.
- Bring to a boil to pots of water.
- Meanwhile, prepare a sauté with chopped rosemary, a bit of garlic, oil, sage, a few bay leaves, and a little chili. When the garlic is golden, it should be removed.
- Pour the chickpeas into boiling water, drain them after a quarter of an hour and dip them back into the second pot of boiling water. Leave to cook for another quarter of an hour.
- Add some chickpeas to the mixture and place them in a small pan with some of their water. The others must be blended to create a cream that we can make more or less thick with your water. Add the whole chickpeas, bring to the boil again and add the common pasta.
- Serve accompanied with common wood baked toasted bread, adding a drizzle of extra virgin olive oil.

NUTRITIONAL

- Protein: 23 g,
- Phosphorous: 241mg,
- Potassium: 609 mg,
- Carbs: 81 g,
- Sodium: 8 mg,
- Calories: 594 kcal

Preparation time 20 mins|Cooking time 45 mins|Serving: 1 – 4

Chicken Wild Rice Soup

INGREDIENTS

- 2/3 cup wild rice, un-cooked
- 1 tbsp. onion, chopped finely
- 1 tbsp. fresh parsley, chopped
- 1 cup carrots, chopped
- 8 oz. chicken breast, cooked
- 2 tbsp. butter
- 1/4 cup all-purpose white flour
- 5 cups low-sodium chicken broth
- 1 tbsp. slivered almonds

DIRECTION

- Start by adding rice and 2 cups broth along with ½ cup water to a cooking pot.
- Cook until the rice soft and set it aside.
- Melt butter in a saucepan.
- Stir in onion and sauté until soft then add the flour and the remaining broth.
- Cook while stirring for 1 minute then add the chicken, cooked rice, and carrots.
- Cook for 5 minutes on simmer.
- Garnish with almonds.
- Serve fresh.

NUTRITIONAL

- Calories 287
- Protein 21 g.
- Carbohydrates 35 g.
- Fat 7 g.
- Cholesterol 42 mg.
- Sodium 182 mg.
- Potassium 384 mg.
- Phosphorus 217 mg.
- Calcium 45 mg.

Preparation Time:10minutes |Cooking Time:15 minutes |Servings:6

Chicken Noodle Soup

INGREDIENTS

- 1 1/2 cups low-sodium vegetable broth
- 1 cup of water
- 1/4 tsp poultry season-ing
- 1/4 tsp black pepper
- 1 cup chicken strips
- 1/4 cup carrot
- 2 oz. egg noodles, un-cooked

DIRECTION

- Cook soup on high heat for 25 minutes in a slow cooker.
- Serve warm.

NUTRITIONAL

- Calories 103.
- Protein 8 g.
- Carbohydrates 11 g.
- Fat 3 g.
- Cholesterol 4 mg.
- Sodium 355 mg.
- Potassium 264 mg.
- Phosphorus 128 mg.
- Calcium 46 mg.

Preparation Time:10minutes |Cooking Time:25 minutes |Servings:2

Spicy Mushroom Stir-Fry

INGREDIENTS

- 1 cup low-sodium vege-table broth
- 2 tablespoons corn-starch
- 1 teaspoon low-sodium soy sauce
- 1/2 teaspoon ground ginger
- 1/8 teaspoon cayenne pepper
- 2 tablespoons olive oil
- 2 (8-ounce) packages sliced button mush-rooms
- 1 red bell pepper, chopped
- 1 jalapeño pepper, minced
- 2 tablespoons sesame

DIRECTION

- In a small bowl, whisk together the broth, cornstarch, soy sauce, ginger, and cayenne pepper and set aside.
- Heat the olive oil in a wok or heavy skillet over high heat.
- Add the mushrooms and peppers and stir-fry for 3 to 5 minutes or until the vegetables are ten-der-crisp.
- Stir the broth mixture and add it to the wok; stir-fry for 3 to 5 min-utes longer or until the vegeta-bles are tender and the sauce has thickened.
- Serve

NUTRITIONAL

- Calories: 361
- Fat: 16g
- Carbohydrates: 49g
- Protein: 8g
- Sodium: 95mg
- Phosphorus: 267mg
- Potassium: 582mg

Preparation Time: 10 minutes|Cooking Time: 10 minutes|Servings: 4

Curried Veggies and Rice

INGREDIENTS

- 1/4 cup olive oil
- 1 cup long-grain white basmati rice
- 4 garlic cloves, minced
- 2 1/2 teaspoons curry powder
- 1/2 cup sliced shiitake mushrooms
- 1 red bell pepper, chopped
- 1 cup frozen, shelled edamame
- 2 cups low-sodium vegetable broth
- 1/8 teaspoon freshly ground black pepper

DIRECTION

- Heat the olive oil on medium heat.
- Add the rice, garlic, curry powder, mushrooms, bell pepper, and edamame; cook, stirring, for 2 minutes.
- Add the broth and black pepper and bring to a boil.
- Reduce the heat to low, partially cover the pot, and simmer for 15 to 18 minutes or until the rice is tender. Stir and serve.

NUTRITIONAL

- Calories: 347
- Fat: 16g
- Carbohydrates: 44g
- Protein: 8g
- Sodium: 114mg
- Phosphorus: 131mg
- Potassium: 334mg

Preparation Time: 12 minutes|Cooking Time: 18 minutes|Servings: 4

Spicy Veggie Pancakes

INGREDIENTS

- 3 tablespoons olive oil, divided
- 2 small onions, finely chopped
- 1 jalapeño pepper, minced
- 3/4 cup carrot, grated
- 3/4 cup cabbage, finely chopped
- 11/2 cups quick-cooking oats
- 3/4 cup of water
- ½ cup whole-wheat flour
- 1 large egg
- 1 large egg white
- 1 teaspoon baking soda
- 1/4 teaspoon cayenne pepper

DIRECTION

- In a skillet, heat 2 teaspoons oil over medium heat.
- Sauté the onion, jalapeño, carrot, and cabbage for 4 minutes.
- While the veggies are cooking, combine the oats, rice, water, flour, egg, egg white, baking soda, and cayenne pepper in a medium bowl until well mixed.
- Add the cooked vegetables to the mixture and stir to combine.
- Heat the remaining oil in a large skillet over medium heat.
- Drop the mixture into the skillet, about 1/3 cup per pancake. Cook for 4 minutes, or until bubbles form on the pancakes' surface and the edges look cooked, then carefully flip them over.
- Repeat with the remaining mixture and serve.

NUTRITIONAL

- Calories: 323
- Fat: 11g
- Carbohydrates: 48g
- Protein: 10g
- Sodium: 366mg
- Potassium: 381mg
- Phosphorus: 263mg

Preparation Time: 10 minutes|Cooking Time: 10 minutes|Servings: 4

Egg and Veggie Fajitas

INGREDIENTS

- 3 large eggs
- 3 egg whites
- 2 teaspoons chili powder
- 1 tablespoon unsalted butter
- 1 onion, chopped
- 2 garlic cloves, minced
- 1 jalapeño pepper, minced
- 1 red bell pepper, chopped
- 1 cup frozen corn, thawed and drained
- 8 (6-inch) corn tortillas

DIRECTION

- Whisk the eggs, egg whites, and chili powder in a small bowl until well combined. Set aside.
- Prepare a large skillet and melt the butter on medium heat.
- Sauté the onion, garlic, jalapeño, bell pepper, and corn until the vegetables are tender, 3 to 4 minutes.
- Add the beaten egg mixture to the skillet. Cook, occasionally stirring, until the eggs form large curds and are set, 3 to 5 minutes.
- Meanwhile, soften the corn tortillas as directed on the package.
- Divide the egg mixture evenly among the softened corn tortillas. Roll the tortillas up and serve.

NUTRITIONAL

- Calories: 316
- Fat 14g
- Carbohydrates: 35g
- Protein: 14g
- Sodium: 167mg
- Potassium: 408mg
- Phosphorus: 287mg

Preparation Time: 15 minutes|Cooking Time: 10 minutes|Servings: 4

Vegetable Biryani

INGREDIENTS

- 2 tablespoons olive oil
- 1 onion, diced
- 4 garlic cloves, minced
- 1 tbsp. peeled and grated fresh ginger root
- 1 cup carrot, grated
- 2 cups chopped cauliflower
- 1 cup thawed frozen baby peas
- 2 teaspoons curry powder
- 1 cup low-sodium vegetable broth
- 3 cups of frozen cooked white rice

DIRECTION

- Get a skillet and heat the olive oil on medium heat.
- Add onion, garlic, and ginger root. Sauté, frequently stirring, until tender-crisp, 2 minutes.
- Add the carrot, cauliflower, peas, and curry powder and cook for 2 minutes longer.
- Put vegetable broth. Cover the skillet partially, and simmer on low for 6 to 7 minutes or until the vegetables are tender.
- Meanwhile, heat the rice as directed on the package.
- Stir the rice into the vegetable mixture and serve.

NUTRITIONAL

- Calories: 378
- Fat 16g
- Carbohydrates: 53g
- Protein: 8g
- Sodium: 113mg
- Potassium: 510mg
- Phosphorus: 236mg

Preparation Time: 10 minutes|Cooking Time: 15 minutes|Servings: 4

Pesto Pasta Salad

INGREDIENTS

- 1 cup fresh basil leaves
- ½ cup packed fresh flat-leaf parsley leaves
- ½ cup arugula, chopped
- 2 tablespoons Parmesan cheese, grated
- ¼ cup extra-virgin olive oil
- 3 tablespoons mayonnaise
- 2 tablespoons water
- 12 ounces whole-wheat rotini pasta
- 1 red bell pepper, chopped
- 1 medium yellow summer squash, sliced
- 1 cup frozen baby peas

DIRECTION

- Boil water in a large pot.
- Meanwhile, combine the basil, parsley, arugula, cheese, and olive oil in a blender or food processor. Process until the herbs are finely chopped. Add the mayonnaise and water, then process again. Set aside.
- Prepare the pasta to the pot of boiling water; cook according to package directions, about 8 to 9 minutes. Drain well, reserving ¼ cup of the cooking liquid.
- Combine the pesto, pasta, bell pepper, squash, and peas in a large bowl and toss gently, adding enough reserved pasta cooking liquid to make a sauce on the salad. Serve immediately or cover and chill, then serve.
- Store covered in the refrigerator for up to 3 days.

NUTRITIONAL

- Calories: 378
- Fat: 24g
- Carbohydrates: 35g
- Protein: 9g
- Sodium: 163mg
- Potassium: 472mg
- Phosphorus: 213mg

Preparation Time: 15 minutes|Cooking Time: 15 minutes|Servings: 4

Barley Blueberry Salad

INGREDIENTS

- 1 cup quick-cooking barley
- 3 cups low-sodium vegetable broth
- 3 tablespoons extra-virgin olive oil
- 2 tablespoons freshly squeezed lemon juice
- 1 teaspoon yellow mustard
- 1 teaspoon honey
- 2 cups blueberries
- ¼ cup crumbled feta cheese

DIRECTION

- Combine the barley and vegetable broth in a medium saucepan and bring to a simmer.
- Reduce the heat to low, partially cover the pan, and simmer for 10 to 12 minutes or until the barley is tender.
- Meanwhile, whisk together the olive oil, lemon juice, mustard, and honey in a serving bowl until blended.
- Drain the barley if necessary and add to the bowl; toss to combine.
- Add the blueberries, and feta and toss gently. Serve.

NUTRITIONAL

- Calories: 345
- Fat 16g
- Carbohydrates: 44g
- Protein: 7g
- Sodium: 259mg
- Potassium: 301mg
- Phosphorus: 152mg

Preparation Time: 15 minutes|Cooking Time: 15 minutes|Servings: 4

Pasta with Creamy Broccoli Sauce

INGREDIENTS

- 2 tablespoons olive oil
- 1-pound broccoli florets
- 3 garlic cloves, halved
- 1 cup low-sodium vegetable broth
- ½ pound whole-wheat spaghetti pasta
- 4 ounces cream cheese
- 1 teaspoon dried basil leaves
- ½ cup grated Parmesan cheese

DIRECTION

- Prepare a large pot of water to a boil.
- Put olive oil in a large skillet. Sauté the broccoli and garlic for 3 minutes.
- Add the broth to the skillet and bring to a simmer. Reduce the heat to low, partially cover the skillet, and simmer until the broccoli is tender about 5 to 6 minutes.
- Cook the pasta according to package directions. Drain when al dente, reserving 1 cup pasta water.
- When the broccoli is tender, add the cream cheese and basil—purée using an immersion blender.
- Put mixture into a food processor, about half at a time, and purée until smooth and transfer the sauce back into the skillet.
- Add the cooked pasta to the broccoli sauce. Toss, adding enough pasta water until the sauce coats the pasta completely. Sprinkle with the Parmesan and serve.

NUTRITIONAL

- Calories: 302
- Fat 14g
- Carbohydrates: 36g
- Protein: 11g
- Sodium: 260mg
- Potassium: 375mg
- Phosphorus: 223mg

Preparation Time: 15 minutes|Cooking Time: 15 minutes|Servings: 4

Asparagus Fried Rice

INGREDIENTS

- 3 large eggs, beaten
- ½ teaspoon ground ginger
- 2 teaspoons low-sodium soy sauce
- 2 tablespoons olive oil
- 1 onion, diced
- 4 garlic cloves, minced
- 1 cup sliced cremini mushrooms
- 1 (10-ounce) package frozen white rice, thawed
- 8 ounces fresh asparagus, about 15 spears, cut into 1-inch pieces
- 1 teaspoon sesame oil

DIRECTION

- Whisk the eggs, ginger, and soy sauce in a small bowl and set aside.
- Heat the olive oil in a medium skillet or wok over medium heat.
- Add the onion and garlic and sauté for 2 minutes until tender crisp.
- Add the mushrooms and rice; stir-fry for 3 minutes longer.
- Put asparagus and cook for 2 minutes.6.
- Pour in the egg mixture. Stir the eggs until cooked through, 2 to 3 minutes, and stir into the rice mixture.
- Sprinkle the fried rice with the sesame oil and serve.

NUTRITIONAL

- Calories: 247
- Fat: 13g
- Carbohydrates: 25g
- Protein: 9g
- Sodium: 149mg
- Potassium: 367mg
- Phosphorus: 206mg

Preparation Time: 10 minutes|Cooking Time: 10 minutes|Servings: 1

Vegetarian Taco Salad

INGREDIENTS

- 1½ cups canned low-sodium or no-salt-added pinto beans, rinsed and drained
- 1 (10-ounce) package frozen white rice, thawed
- 1 red bell pepper, chopped
- 3 scallions, white and green parts, chopped
- 1 jalapeño pepper, minced
- 1 cup frozen corn, thawed and drained
- 1 tablespoon chili powder
- 1 cup chopped romaine lettuce
- 2 cups chopped butter lettuce
- ½ cup Powerhouse Salsa
- ½ cup grated pepper Jack cheese

DIRECTION

- In a medium bowl, combine the beans, rice, bell pepper, scallions, jalapeño, and corn.
- Sprinkle with the chili powder and stir gently.
- Stir in the romaine and butter lettuce.
- Serve topped with Powerhouse Salsa and cheese.

NUTRITIONAL

- Calories: 254
- Fat: 7g
- Carbohydrates: 39g
- Protein: 11g
- Sodium: 440mg
- Potassium: 599mg
- Phosphorus: 240mg

Preparation Time: 15 minutes|Cooking Time: 15 minutes|Servings: 2

Sautéed Green Beans

INGREDIENTS

- 2 cup frozen green beans
- ½ cup red bell pepper
- 4 tsp margarine
- ¼ cup onion
- 1 tsp dried dill weed
- 1 tsp dried parsley
- ¼ tsp black pepper

DIRECTION

- Cook green beans in a large pan of boiling water until tender, then drain.
- While the beans are cooking, melt the margarine in a skillet and fry the other vegetables.
- Add the beans to sautéed vegetables.
- Sprinkle with freshly ground pepper and serve with meat and fish dishes.

NUTRITIONAL

- Calories 67
- Carbs 8g
- Protein 4g
- Sodium 5mg
- Potassium 179mg
- Phosphorous 32mg

Preparation Time: 10 minutes|Cooking Time: 15 minutes|Servings: 4

Garlicky Penne Pasta with Asparagus

INGREDIENTS

- 2 tbsp. butter
- 1lb asparagus, cut into 2-inch pieces
- 2 tsp lemon juice
- 4 cup whole wheat penne pasta, cooked
- ¼ cup shredded Parmesan cheese
- ¼ tsp Tabasco® hot sauce

DIRECTION

1. Add olive oil and butter in a skillet over medium heat.
2. Fry garlic and red pepper flakes for 2-3 minutes.
3. Add asparagus, Tabasco sauce, lemon juice, and black pepper to skillet and cook for a further 6 minutes.
4. Add hot pasta and cheese. Toss and serve.

NUTRITIONAL

- Calories 387
- Carbs 49g
- Protein 13g
- Sodium 93
- Potassium 258mg
- Phosphorous 252mg

Preparation Time: 10 minutes|Cooking Time: 10 minutes|Servings: 4

Garlic Mashed Potatoes

INGREDIENTS

- 2 medium potatoes, peeled and sliced
- ¼ cup butter
- ¼ cup 1% low-fat milk
- 2 garlic cloves

DIRECTION

- Double-boil or soak the potatoes to reduce potassium if you are on a low potassium diet.
- Boil potatoes and garlic until soft. Drain.
- Beat the potatoes and garlic with butter and milk until smooth.

NUTRITIONAL

- Calories 168
- Carbs 29g
- Protein 5g
- Sodium 59
- Potassium 161g
- Phosphorous 57mg

Preparation Time: 5 minutes|Cooking Time: 20 minutes|Servings: 4

Ginger Glazed Carrots

INGREDIENTS

- 2 cups carrots, sliced into 1-inch pieces
- ¼ cup apple juice
- 2 tbsp. margarine, melted
- ¼ cup boiling water
- 1 tbsp. sugar
- 1 tsp cornstarch
- ¼ tsp salt
- ¼ tsp ground ginger

DIRECTION

- Cook carrots until tender.
- Mix sugar, cornstarch, salt, ginger, apple juice, and margarine together
- Pour mixture over carrots and cook for 10 minutes until thickened.

NUTRITIONAL

- Calories 101
- Fat 3
- Carbs 14g
- Protein 1g
- Sodium 87
- Potassium 202g
- Phosphorous 26mg

Preparation Time: 10 minutes|Cooking Time: 20 minutes|Servings: 4

Carrot-Apple Casserole

INGREDIENTS

- 6 large carrots, peeled and sliced
- 4 large apples, peeled and sliced
- 3 tbsp. butter
- ½ cup apple juice
- 5 tbsp. all-purpose flour
- 2 tbsp. brown sugar
- ½ tsp ground nutmeg

DIRECTION

- Preheat oven to 350° F.
- Let the carrots boil for 5 minutes or until tender. Drain.
- Arrange the carrots and apples in a large casserole dish.
- Mix the flour, brown sugar, and nutmeg in a small bowl.
- Rub in butter to make a crumb topping.
- Sprinkle the crumb over the carrots and apples, then drizzle with juice.
- Bake until bubbling and golden brown.

NUTRITIONAL

- Calories 245
- Fat 6g
- Carbs 49g
- Protein 1g
- Sodium 91mg
- Potassium 169mg
- Phosphorous 17mg

Preparation Time: 15 minutes|Cooking Time: 50 minutes|Servings: 8

Creamy Shells with Peas and Bacon

INGREDIENTS

- 1 cup part-skim ricotta cheese
- ½ cup grated Parmesan cheese
- 3 slices bacon, cut into strips
- 1 cup onion, chopped
- ¾ cup of frozen green peas
- 1 tbsp. olive oil
- ¼ tsp black pepper
- 3 garlic cloves, minced
- 3 cup cooked whole-wheat small shell pasta
- 1 tbsp. lemon juice
- 2 tbsp. unsalted butter

DIRECTION

- Place ricotta, Parmesan cheese, butter, and pepper in a large bowl.
- Cook bacon in a skillet until crisp. Set aside.
- Add the garlic and onion to the same skillet and fry until soft. Add to bowl with ricotta.
- Cook the peas and add to the ricotta.
- Add half a cup of the reserved cooking water and lemon juice to the ricotta mixture and mix well.
- Add the pasta, bacon, and peas to the bowl and mix well.
- Put freshly ground black pepper and serve.

NUTRITIONAL

- Calories 429
- Fat 14g
- Carbs 27g
- Protein 13g
- Sodium 244mg
- Potassium 172mg
- Phosphorous 203mg

Preparation Time: 15 minutes|Cooking Time: 15 minutes|Servings: 4

Double-Boiled Stewed Potatoes

INGREDIENTS

- 2 cup potatoes, diced into ½ inch cubes
- ½ cup hot water
- ½ cup liquid non-dairy creamer
- ¼ tsp garlic powder
- ¼ tsp black pepper
- 2 tbsp. margarine
- 2 tsp all-purpose white flour

DIRECTION

- Soak or double boil the potatoes if you are on a low potassium diet.
- Boil potatoes for 15 minutes.
- Drain potatoes and return to pan. Add half a cup of hot water, the creamer, garlic powder, pepper, and margarine. Heat to a boil.
- Mix the flour with a tablespoon of water and then stir this into the potatoes. Cook for 3 minutes until the mixture has thickened and the flour has cooked.

NUTRITIONAL

- Calories 184
- Carbs 25g
- Protein 2g
- Potassium 161mg
- Phosphorous 65mg

Preparation Time: 20 minutes|Cooking Time: 30 minutes|Servings: 4

Double-Boiled Country Style Fried Potatoes

INGREDIENTS

- ½ cup canola oil
- ¼ tsp ground cumin
- ¼ tsp paprika
- ¼ tsp white pepper
- 3 tbsp. ketchup

DIRECTION

- Soak or double boil the potatoes if you are on a low potassium diet.
- Heat oil over medium heat in a skillet.
- Fry the potatoes for around 10 minutes until golden brown.
- Drain potatoes, then sprinkle with cumin, pepper, and paprika.
- Serve with ketchup or mayo.

NUTRITIONAL

- Calories 156
- Fat 0.1g
- Carbs 21g
- Protein 2g
- Sodium 3mg
- Potassium 296mg
- Phosphorous 34mg

Preparation Time: 20 minutes|Cooking Time: 20 minutes|Servings: 4

Broccoli-Onion Latkes

INGREDIENTS

- 3 cups broccoli florets, diced
- ½ cup onion, chopped
- 2 large eggs, beaten
- 2 tbsp. all-purpose white flour
- 2 tbsp. olive oil

DIRECTION

- Cook the broccoli for around 5 minutes until tender. Drain.
- Mix the flour into the eggs.
- Combine the onion, broccoli, and egg mixture and stir through.
- Prepare olive oil in a skillet on medium-high heat.
- Drop a spoon of the mixture onto the pan to make 4 latkes.
- Cook each side until golden brown.
- Drain on a paper towel and serve.

NUTRITIONAL

- Calories 140
- Fat
- Carbs 7g
- Protein 6g
- Sodium 58mg
- Potassium 276mg
- Phosphorous 101mg

Preparation Time: 15 minutes|Cooking Time: 20 minutes|Servings: 4

Cranberry Cabbage

INGREDIENTS

- 10 ounces canned whole-berry cranberry sauce
- 1 tablespoon fresh lemon juice
- 1 medium head red cabbage
- 1/4 teaspoon ground cloves

DIRECTION

- Place the cranberry sauce, lemon juice, and cloves in a large pan and bring to the boil.
- Add the cabbage and reduce it to a simmer.
- Cook until the cabbage is tender, occasionally stirring to make sure the sauce does not stick.
- Delicious served with beef, lamb, or pork.

NUTRITIONAL

- Calories 73
- Fat 0g
- Carbs 18g
- Protein 1g
- Sodium 32mg
- Potassium 138mg
- Phosphorous 18mg

Preparation Time: 10 minutes|Cooking Time: 20 minutes|Servings: 8

Cauliflower Rice

INGREDIENTS

- 1 small head cauliflower cut into florets
- 1 tbsp. butter
- ¼ tsp black pepper
- ¼ tsp garlic powder
- ¼ tsp salt-free herb seasoning blend

DIRECTION

- Blitz cauliflower pieces in a food processor until it has a grain-like consistency.
- Melt butter in a saucepan and add spices.
- Add the cauliflower rice grains and cook over low-medium heat for approximately 10 minutes.
- Use a fork to fluff the rice before serving.
- Serve as an alternative to rice with curries, stews, and starch to accompany meat and fish dishes.

NUTRITIONAL

- Calories 47
- Fat
- Carbs 4g
- Protein 1g
- Sodium 300mg
- Potassium 206mg
- Phosphorous 31mg

Preparation Time: 5 minutes|Cooking Time: 10 minutes|Servings: 1

Rutabaga Latkes

INGREDIENTS

- 1 teaspoon hemp seeds
- 1 teaspoon ground black pepper
- 7 oz. rutabaga, grated
- ½ teaspoon ground paprika
- 2 tablespoons coconut flour
- 1 egg, beaten
- 1 teaspoon olive oil

DIRECTION

- Mix up together hemp seeds, ground black pepper, ground paprika, and coconut flour.
- Then add grated rutabaga and beaten egg.
- With the help of the fork combine together all the ingredients into the smooth mixture.
- Preheat the skillet for 2-3 minutes over the high heat.
- Then reduce the heat till medium and add olive oil.
- With the help of the fork, place the small amount of rutabaga mixture in the skillet. Flatten it gently in the shape of latkes.
- Cook the latkes for 3 minutes from each side.
- After this, transfer them in the plate and repeat the same steps with remaining rutabaga mixture.

NUTRITIONAL

- Calories 64,
- Fat 3.1,
- Fiber 3,
- Carbs 7.1,
- Protein 2.8

Preparation Time: 15 minutes |Cooking Time: 7 minutes |Servings: 4

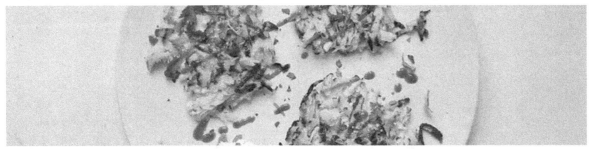

Glazed Snap Peas

INGREDIENTS

- 1 cup snap peas
- 2 teaspoon Erythritol
- 1 teaspoon butter, melted
- ¾ teaspoon ground nutmeg
- ¼ teaspoon salt
- 1 cup water, for cooking

DIRECTION

- Pour water in the pan. Add snap peas and bring them to boil.
- Boil the snap peas for 5 minutes over the medium heat.
- Then drain water and chill the snap peas.
- Meanwhile, whisk together ground nutmeg, melted butter, salt, and Erythritol.
- Preheat the mixture in the microwave oven for 5 seconds.
- Pour the sweet butter liquid over the snap peas and shake them well.
- The side dish should be served only warm.

NUTRITIONAL

- Calories 80,
- Fat 2.5,
- Fiber 3.9,
- Carbs 10.9,
- Protein 4

Preparation Time: 10 minutes |Cooking Time: 5 minutes |Servings: 2

Steamed Collard Greens

INGREDIENTS

- 2 cups Collard Greens
- 1 tablespoon lime juice
- 1 teaspoon olive oil
- 1 teaspoon sesame seeds
- ½ teaspoon chili flakes
- 1 cup water, for the steamer

DIRECTION

- Chop collard greens roughly.
- Pour water in the steamer and insert rack.
- Place the steamer bowl, add collard greens, and close the lid.
- Steam the greens for 5 minutes.
- After this, transfer the steamed collard greens in the salad bowl.
- Sprinkle it with the lime juice, olive oil, sesame seeds, and chili flakes.
- Mix up greens with the help of 2 forks and leave to rest for 10 minutes before serving.

NUTRITIONAL

- Calories 43,
- Fat 3.4,
- Fiber 1.7,
- Carbs 3.4,
- Protein 1.3

Preparation Time: 10 minutes |Cooking Time: 5 minutes |Servings: 2

Baked Eggplants Slices

INGREDIENTS

- 1 large eggplant, trimmed
- 1 tablespoon butter, softened
- 1 teaspoon minced garlic
- 1 teaspoon salt

DIRECTION

- Slice the eggplant season it with salt. Mix up well and leave for 10 minutes to make the vegetable "give" bitter juice.
- After this, dry the eggplant with the paper towel.
- In the shallow bowl, mix up together minced garlic and softened butter.
- Brush every eggplant slice with the garlic mixture.
- Line the baking tray with baking paper. Preheat the oven to 355F.
- Place the sliced eggplants in the tray to make 1 layer and transfer it in the oven.
- Bake the eggplants for 15 minutes. The cooked eggplants will be tender but not soft!

NUTRITIONAL

- Calories 81,
- Fat 4.2,
- Fiber 6.5,
- Carbs 11.1,
- Protein 1.9

Preparation Time: 15 minutes |Cooking Time: 15 minutes |Servings: 3

Vegetable Masala

INGREDIENTS

- 2 cups green beans, chopped
- 1 cup white mushroom, chopped
- ¾ cup Red bell peppers, crushed
- 1 teaspoon minced garlic
- 1 teaspoon minced ginger
- 1 teaspoon chili flakes
- 1 tablespoon garam masala
- 1 tablespoon olive oil
- 1 teaspoon salt

DIRECTION

- Line the tray with parchment and preheat the oven to 360F.
- Place the green beans and mushrooms in the tray.
- Sprinkle the vegetables with crushed Red bell peppers, minced garlic and ginger, chili flakes, garam masala, olive oil, and salt.
- Mix up well and transfer in the oven.
- Cook vegetable masala for 18 minutes.

NUTRITIONAL

- Calories 60,
- Fat 30.7,
- Fiber 2.5,
- Carbs 6.4,
- Protein 2

Preparation Time: 10 minutes |Cooking Time: 18 minutes |Servings: 4

Fast Cabbage Cakes

INGREDIENTS

- 1 cup cauliflower, shredded
- 1 egg, beaten
- 1 teaspoon salt
- 1 teaspoon ground black pepper
- 2 tablespoons almond flour
- 1 teaspoon olive oil

DIRECTION

- Blend the shredded cabbage in the blender until you get cabbage rice.
- Then, mix up cabbage rice with the egg, salt, ground black pepper, and almond flour.
- Pour olive oil in the skillet and preheat it.
- Then make the small cakes with the help of 2 spoons and place them in the hot oil.
- Roast the cabbage cakes for 4 minutes from each side over the medium-low heat.

NUTRITIONAL

- Calories 227,
- Fat 18.6,
- Fiber 4.5,
- Carbs 9.5,
- Protein 9.9

Preparation Time: 15 minutes |Cooking Time: 10 minutes |Servings: 2

Cilantro Chili Burgers

INGREDIENTS

- 1 cup red cabbage
- 3 tablespoons almond flour
- 1 tablespoon cream cheese
- 1 oz. scallions, chopped
- ½ teaspoon salt
- ½ teaspoon chili powder
- ½ cup fresh cilantro

DIRECTION

- Chop red cabbage roughly and transfer in the blender.
- Add fresh cilantro and blend the mixture until very smooth.
- After this, transfer it in the bowl.
- Add cream cheese, scallions, salt, chili powder, and almond flour.
- Stir the mixture well.
- Make 3 big burgers from the cabbage mixture or 6 small burgers.
- Line the baking tray with baking paper.
- Place the burgers in the tray.
- Bake the cilantro burgers for 15 minutes at 360F.
- Flip the burgers onto another side after 8 minutes of cooking.

NUTRITIONAL

- Calories 182,
- Fat 15.3,
- Fiber 4.1,
- Carbs 8.5,
- Protein 6.8

Preparation Time: 10 minutes |Cooking Time: 15 minutes |Servings: 3

Jicama Noodles

INGREDIENTS

- 1-pound jicama, peeled
- 2 tablespoons butter
- 1 teaspoon chili flakes
- 1 teaspoon salt
- ¾ cup of water

DIRECTION

- Spiralize jicama with the help of spiralizer and place in jicama spirals in the saucepan.
- Add butter, chili flakes, and salt.
- Then add water and preheat the ingredients until the butter is melted.
- Mix up it well.
- Close the lid and cook noodles for 4 minutes over the medium heat.
- Stir the jicama noodles well before transferring them in the serving plates.

NUTRITIONAL

- Calories 63,
- Fat 3.9,
- Fiber 3.7,
- Carbs 6.7,
- Protein 0.6

Preparation Time: 15 minutes |Cooking Time: 7 minutes |Servings: 6

Crack Slaw

INGREDIENTS

- 1 cup cauliflower rice
- 1 tablespoon sriracha
- 1 teaspoon tahini paste
- 1 teaspoon sesame seeds
- 1 tablespoon lemon juice
- 1 teaspoon olive oil
- 1 teaspoon butter
- ½ teaspoon salt
- 2 cups coleslaw

DIRECTION

- Toss the butter in the skillet and melt it.
- Add cauliflower rice and sprinkle it with sriracha and tahini paste.
- Mix up the vegetables and cook them for 10 minutes over the medium heat. Stir them from time to time.
- When the cauliflower is cooked, transfer it into the big plate.
- Add coleslaw and stir gently.
- Then sprinkle the salad with sesame seeds, lemon juice, olive oil, and salt.
- Mix up well.

NUTRITIONAL

- Calories 76,
- Fat 5.8,
- Fiber 0.6,
- Carbs 6,
- Protein 1.1

Preparation Time: 15 minutes |Cooking Time: 10 minutes |Servings: 6

Vegan Chili

INGREDIENTS

- 1 cup cremini mushrooms, chopped
- 1 zucchini, chopped
- 1 bell pepper, diced
- 1/3 cup crushed Red bell peppers
- 1 oz. celery stalk, chopped
- 1 teaspoon chili powder
- 1 teaspoon salt
- ½ teaspoon chili flakes
- ½ cup of water
- 1 tablespoon olive oil
- ½ teaspoon diced garlic
- ½ teaspoon ground black pepper
- 1 teaspoon of cocoa powder
- 2 oz. Cheddar cheese, grated

DIRECTION

- Pour olive oil in the pan and preheat it.
- Add chopped mushrooms and roast them for 5 minutes. Stir them from time to time.
- After this, add chopped zucchini and bell pepper.
- Sprinkle the vegetables with the chili powder, salt, chili flakes, diced garlic, and ground black pepper.
- Stir the vegetables and cook them for 5 minutes more.
- After this, add crushed Red bell peppers. Mix up well.
- Bring the mixture to boil and add water and cocoa powder.
- Then add celery stalk.
- Mix up the chili well and close the lid.
- Cook the chili for 10 minutes over the medium-low heat.
- Then transfer the cooked vegan chili in the bowls and top with the grated cheese.

NUTRITIONAL

- Calories 123,
- Fat 8.6,
- Fiber 2.3,
- Carbs 7.6,
- Protein 5.6

Preparation Time: 10 minutes |Cooking Time: 20 minutes |Servings: 4

Chow Mein

INGREDIENTS

- 7 oz. kelp noodles
- 5 oz. broccoli florets
- 1 tablespoon tahini sauce
- ¼ teaspoon minced ginger
- 1 teaspoon Sriracha
- ½ teaspoon garlic powder
- 1 cup of water

DIRECTION

- Boil water in a sauce pan.
- Add broccoli and boil for 4 minutes over the high heat.
- Then drain water into the bowl and chill it tills the room temperature.
- Soak the kelp noodles in the "broccoli water".
- Meanwhile, place tahini sauce, sriracha, minced ginger, and garlic in the saucepan.
- Bring the mixture to boil. Add oil if needed.
- Then add broccoli and soaked noodles.
- Add 3 tablespoons of "broccoli water".
- Mix up the noodles and bring to boil.
- Switch off the heat and transfer chow Mein in the serving bowls.

NUTRITIONAL

- Calories 18,
- Fat 0.8,
- Fiber 0.7,
- Carbs 2.8,
- Protein 0.9

Preparation Time: 10 minutes |Cooking Time: 10 minutes |Servings: 6

Mushroom Tacos

INGREDIENTS

- 6 collard greens leave
- 2 cups mushrooms, chopped
- 1 white onion, diced
- 1 tablespoon Taco seasoning
- 1 tablespoon coconut oil
- ½ teaspoon salt
- ¼ cup fresh parsley
- 1 tablespoon mayonnaise

DIRECTION

- Put the coconut oil in the skillet and melt it.
- Add chopped mushrooms and diced onion. Mix up the ingredients.
- Close the lid and cook them for 10 minutes.
- After this, sprinkle the vegetables with Taco seasoning, salt, and add fresh parsley.
- Mix up the mixture and cook for 5 minutes more.
- Then add mayonnaise and stir well.
- Chill the mushroom mixture little.
- Fill the collard green leaves with the mushroom mixture and fold up them.

NUTRITIONAL

- Calories 52,
- Fat 3.3,
- Fiber 1.2,
- Carbs 5.1,
- Protein 1.4

Preparation Time: 10 minutes |Cooking Time: 15 minutes |Servings: 6

Lime Green lettuce and Chickpeas Salad

INGREDIENTS

- 16 ounces canned chickpeas, drained and rinsed
- 2 cups baby green lettuce leaves
- ½ tablespoon lime juice
- 2 tablespoons olive oil
- 1 teaspoon cumin, ground
- Sea salt and black pepper
- ½ teaspoon chili flakes

DIRECTION

- In a bowl, mix the chickpeas with the green lettuce and the rest of the ingredients, toss and serve cold.

NUTRITIONAL

- Calories 240,
- Fat 8.2,
- Fiber 5.3,
- Carbs 11.6,
- Protein 12

Preparation Time: 10 minutes |Cooking Time: 0 minutes |Servings: 4

Fried Rice with Kale

INGREDIENTS

- 2 tbsp. Extra virgin oil
- 8 oz. Tofu, chopped
- 6 Scallion, white and green parts, thinly sliced
- 2 cups Kale, stemmed and chopped
- 3 cups Cooked white rice
- ¼ cup Stir fry sauce

DIRECTION

- In a huge skillet on medium-high heat, warm the oil until it shimmers.
- Add the tofu, scallions, and kale. Cook for 5 to 7 minutes, frequently stirring, until the vegetables are soft.
- Add the white rice and stir-fry sauce. Cook for 3 to 5 minutes, occasionally stirring, until heated through.

NUTRITIONAL

- Calories: 301
- Total Fat: 11g
- Total Carbs: 36g
- Sugar: 1g
- Fiber: 3g
- Protein: 16g
- Sodium: 2,535mg

Preparation Time: 10 minutes |Cooking Time: 12 minutes|Servings: 4

Stir-Fried Gingery Veggies

INGREDIENTS

- 1 tablespoon oil
- 3 cloves of garlic, minced
- 1 onion, chopped
- 1 thumb-size ginger, sliced
- 1 tablespoon water
- 1 large carrots, peeled and julienned and seedless
- 1 large green bell pepper, julienned and seedless
- 1 large yellow bell pepper, julienned and seedless
- 1 large red bell pepper, julienned and seedless
- 1 zucchini, julienned
- Salt and pepper to taste

DIRECTION

- Heat oil in a nonstick saucepan over a high flame and sauté the garlic, onion, and ginger until fragrant.
- Stir in the rest of the ingredients. Keep on stirring for at least 5 minutes until vegetables are tender.
- Serve and enjoy.

NUTRITIONAL

- Calories 70
- Total Fat 4g
- Saturated Fat 1g
- Total Carbs 9g
- Net Carbs 7g
- Protein 1g
- Sugar: 4g
- Fiber 2g
- Sodium 173mg
- Potassium 163mg

Preparation Time: 10 minutes |Cooking Time: 10 minutes|Servings: 4

Chapter 17.
Salad Recipes

Pear & Brie Salad

INGREDIENTS

- 1 tablespoon olive oil
- 1 cup arugula
- ½ lemon
- ½ cup canned pears
- ¼ cucumber
- ¼ cup chopped brie

DIRECTION

- Peel and dice the cucumber.
- Dice the pear.
- Wash the arugula.
- Combine salad in a serving bowl and crumble the brie over the top.
- Whisk the olive oil and lemon juice together.
- Drizzle over the salad.
- Season with a little black pepper to taste and serve immediately.

NUTRITIONAL

- Calories 54,
- Protein 1 g,
- Carbs 12 g,
- Fat 7 g,
- Sodium 57mg,
- Potassium 115 mg,
- Phosphorus 67 mg

Preparation Time: 5 minutes |Cooking Time: 0 minutes|Servings: 4

Caesar Salad

INGREDIENTS

- 1 head romaine lettuce
- ¼ cup mayonnaise
- 1 tablespoon lemon juice
- 4 anchovy fillets
- 1 teaspoon Worcestershire sauce
- Black pepper
- 5 garlic cloves
- 4 tablespoons. Parmesan cheese
- 1 teaspoon mustard

DIRECTION

- In a bowl mix all ingredients and mix well
- Serve with dressing

NUTRITIONAL

- Calories 44,
- Fat 2.1 g,
- Sodium 83 mg,
- Potassium 216 mg,
- Carbs 4.3 g,
- Protein 3.2 g,
- Phosphorus 45.6mg
- Calcium 19mg,
- Potassium 27mg
- Sodium: 121 mg

Preparation Time: 5 minutes|Cooking Time: 5 minutes|Servings: 4

Thai Cucumber Salad

INGREDIENTS

- ¼ cup chopped peanuts
- ¼ cup white sugar
- ½ cup cilantro
- ¼ cup rice wine vinegar
- 3 cucumbers
- 2 jalapeno peppers

DIRECTION

- Add all ingredients in a small basin and combine well
- Serve with dressing

NUTRITIONAL

- Calories 20,
- Fat 0g,
- Sodium 85mg,
- Carbs 5g,
- Protein 1g,
- Potassium 190.4 mg,
- Phosphorus 46.8mg

Preparation Time: 5 minutes |Cooking Time: 5 minutes |Servings: 2

Barb's Asian Slaw

INGREDIENTS

- 1 cabbage head, shredded
- 4 chopped green onions
- ½ cup slivered or sliced almonds
- Dressing:
- ½ cup olive oil
- ¼ cup tamari or soy sauce
- 1 tablespoon honey or maple syrup
- 1 tablespoon baking stevia

DIRECTION

- Heat up dressing ingredients in a saucepan on the stove until thoroughly mixed.
- Mix all ingredients when you are ready to serve.

NUTRITIONAL

- Calories: 205
- Protein: 27g
- Carbohydrate: 12g
- Fat: 10 g
- Calcium 29mg,
- Phosphorous 76mg,
- Potassium 27mg
- Sodium: 111 mg

Preparation Time: 5 minutes|Cooking Time: 5 minutes|Servings: 2

Green Bean and Potato Salad

INGREDIENTS

- ½ cup basil
- ¼ cup olive oil
- 1 tablespoon mustard
- ¾ lb. green beans
- 1 tablespoon lemon juice
- ½ cup balsamic vinegar
- 1 red onion
- 1 lb. red potatoes
- 1 garlic clove

DIRECTION

- Place potatoes in a pot with water and bring to a boil for 15-18 minutes or until tender
- Thrown in green beans after 5-6 minutes
- Drain and cut into cubes
- In a bowl add all ingredients and mix well
- Serve with dressing

NUTRITIONAL

- Calories 153.2,
- Fat 2.0 g,
- Sodium 77.6 mg,
- Potassium 759.0 mg,
- Carbs 29.0 g,
- Protein 6.9 g,
- Phosphorus 49 mg

Preparation Time: 5 minutes|Cooking Time: 5 minutes|Servings: 4

Italian Cucumber Salad

INGREDIENTS

- 1/4 cup rice vinegar
- 1/8 teaspoon stevia
- 1/2 teaspoon olive oil
- 1/8 teaspoon black pepper
- 1/2 cucumber, sliced
- 1 cup carrots, sliced
- 2 tablespoons green onion, sliced
- 2 tablespoons red bell pepper, sliced
- 1/2 teaspoon Italian seasoning blend

DIRECTION

- Put all the salad ingredients into a suitable salad bowl.
- Toss them well and refrigerate for 1 hour.
- Serve.

NUTRITIONAL

- Calories 112
- Total Fat 1.6g
- Cholesterol 0mg
- Sodium 43mg
- Protein 2.3g
- Phosphorous 198mg
- Potassium 529mg

Preparation Time: 5 minutes |Cooking Time: 0 minutes|Servings: 2

Grapes Jicama Salad

INGREDIENTS

- 1 jicama, peeled and sliced
- 1 carrot, sliced
- 1/2 medium red onion, sliced
- 1 ¼ cup seedless grapes
- 1/3 cup fresh basil leaves
- 1 tablespoon apple cider vinegar
- 1 ½ tablespoon lemon juice
- 1 ½ tablespoon lime juice

DIRECTION

- Put all the salad ingredients into a suitable salad bowl.
- Toss them well and refrigerate for 1 hour.
- Serve.

NUTRITIONAL

- Calories 203
- Total Fat 0.7g
- Sodium 44mg
- Protein 3.7g
- Calcium 79mg
- Phosphorous 141mg
- Potassium 429mg

Preparation Time: 5 minutes |Cooking Time: 0 minutes|Servings: 2

Cucumber Couscous Salad

INGREDIENTS

- 1 cucumber, sliced
- ½ cup red bell pepper, sliced
- ¼ cup sweet onion, sliced
- ¼ cup parsley, chopped
- ½ cup couscous, cooked
- 2 tablespoons olive oil
- 2 tablespoons rice vinegar
- 2 tablespoons feta cheese crumbled
- 1 ½ teaspoon dried basil
- 1/4 teaspoon black pepper

DIRECTION

- Put all the salad ingredients into a suitable salad bowl.
- Toss them well and refrigerate for 1 hour.
- Serve.

NUTRITIONAL

- Calories 202
- Total Fat 9.8g
- Sodium 258mg
- Protein 6.2g
- Calcium 80mg
- Phosphorous 192mg
- Potassium 209mg

Preparation Time: 5 minutes |Cooking Time: 0 minutes|Servings: 4

Carrot Jicama Salad

INGREDIENTS

- 2 cup carrots, julienned
- 1 1/2 cups jicama, juli-enned
- 2 tablespoons lime juice
- 1 tablespoon olive oil
- ½ tablespoon apple cider
- ½ teaspoon brown Swerve

DIRECTION

- Put all the salad ingredients into a suitable salad bowl.
- Toss them well and refrigerate for 1 hour.
- Serve.

NUTRITIONAL

- Calories 173
- Total Fat 7.1g
- Sodium 80mg
- Protein 1.6g
- Calcium 50mg
- Phosphorous 96mg
- Potassium 501mg

Preparation Time: 5 minutes |Cooking Time: 0 minutes|Servings: 2

Butterscotch Apple Salad

INGREDIENTS

- 3 cups jazz apples, chopped
- 8 oz. canned crushed pineapple
- 8 oz. whipped topping
- 1/2 cup butterscotch topping
- 1/3 cup almonds
- 1/4 cup butterscotch

DIRECTION

- Put all the salad ingredients into a suitable salad bowl.
- Toss them well and refrigerate for 1 hour.
- Serve.

NUTRITIONAL

- Calories 293
- Total Fat 12.7g
- Sodium 52mg
- Protein 4.2g
- Calcium 65mg
- Phosphorous 202mg
- Potassium 296mg

Preparation Time: 5 minutes |Cooking Time: 0 minutes|Servings: 6

Cranberry Cabbage Slaw

INGREDIENTS

- 1/2 medium cabbage head, shredded
- 1 medium red apple, shredded
- 2 tablespoons onion, sliced
- 1/2 cup dried cranberries
- 1/4 cup almonds, toasted sliced
- 1/2 cup olive oil
- ¼ teaspoon stevia
- 1/4 cup cider vinegar
- 1/2 tablespoon celery seed
- 1/2 teaspoon dry mustard
- ½ cup cream

DIRECTION

- Take a suitable salad bowl.
- Start tossing in all the ingredients.
- Mix well and serve.

NUTRITIONAL

- Calories 308
- Total Fat 24.5g
- Sodium 23mg
- Protein 2.6g
- Calcium 69mg
- Phosphorous 257mg
- Potassium 219mg

Preparation Time: 5 minutes |Cooking Time: 0 minutes|Servings: 4

Chestnut Noodle Salad

INGREDIENTS

- 8 cups cabbage, shredded
- 1/2 cup canned chestnuts, sliced
- 6 green onions, chopped
- 1/4 cup olive oil
- 1/4 cup apple cider vinegar
- 3/4 teaspoon stevia
- 1/8 teaspoon black pepper
- 1 cup chow Mein noodles, cooked

DIRECTION

- Take a suitable salad bowl.
- Start tossing in all the ingredients.
- Mix well and serve.

NUTRITIONAL

- Calories 191
- Total Fat 13g
- Cholesterol 1mg
- Sodium 78mg
- Protein 4.2g
- Calcium 142mg
- Phosphorous 188mg
- Potassium 302mg

Preparation Time: 5 minutes |Cooking Time: 0 minutes|Servings: 6

Chapter 18.
Fish and Seafood

Shrimp Paella

INGREDIENTS

- 1 cup cooked whiterice
- 1 chopped red onion
- 1 tsp. paprika
- 1 chopped garlic clove
- 1 tbsp. olive oil
- 6 oz. frozen cooked shrimp
- 1 deseeded and sliced chili pepper
- 1 tbsp. oregano

DIRECTION

- Warm-up olive oil in a large pan on medium-high heat. Add the onion and garlic and sauté for 2-3 minutes until soft. Now add the shrimp and sauté for a further 5 minutes or until hot through.
- Now add the herbs, spices, chili, and rice with 1/2 cup boiling water. Stir until everything is warm, and the water has been absorbed. Plate up and serve.

NUTRITIONAL

- Calories 221
- Protein 17 g
- Carbs 31 g
- Fat 8 g
- Sodium 235 mg
- Potassium 176 mg
- Phosphorus 189 mg

Preparation Time: 5 minutes |Cooking Time: 10 minutes|Servings: 2

Salmon & Pesto Salad

INGREDIENTS

- For the pesto:
- 1 minced garlic clove
- ½ cup fresh arugula
- ¼ cup extra virgin olive oil
- ½ cup fresh basil
- 1 tsp black pepper
- For the salmon:
- 4 oz. skinless salmon fillet
- 1 tbsp. coconut oil
- For the salad:
- ½ juiced lemon
- 2 sliced radishes
- ½ cup iceberg lettuce
- 1 tsp black pepper

DIRECTION

- Prepare the pesto by blending all the fixing for the pesto in a food processor or grinding with a pestle and mortar. Set aside.
- Add a skillet to the stove on medium-high heat and melt the coconut oil. Add the salmon to the pan. Cook for 7-8 minutes and turn over.
- Cook within 3-4 minutes or until cooked through. Remove fillets from the skillet and allow to rest.
- Mix the lettuce and the radishes and squeeze over the juice of ½ lemon. Shred the salmon using a fork and mix through the salad. Toss to coat and sprinkle with a little black pepper to serve.

NUTRITIONAL

- Calories 221
- Protein 13 g
- Carbs 1 g
- Fat 34 g
- Sodium 80 mg
- Potassium 119 mg
- Phosphorus 158 mg

Preparation Time: 5 minutes |Cooking Time: 15 minutes|Servings: 2

Baked Fennel & Garlic Sea Bass

INGREDIENTS

- 1 lemon
- ½ sliced fennel bulb
- 6 oz. sea bass fillets
- 1 tsp black pepper
- 2 garlic cloves

DIRECTION

- Preheat the oven to 375°F. Sprinkle black pepper over the Sea Bass. Slice the fennel bulb and garlic cloves. Add 1 salmon fillet and half the fennel and garlic to one sheet of baking paper or tin foil.
- Squeeze in 1/2 lemon juices. Repeat for the other fillet. Fold and add to the oven for 12-15 minutes or until fish is thoroughly cooked through.
- Meanwhile, add boiling water to your couscous, cover, and allow to steam. Serve with your choice of rice or salad.

NUTRITIONAL

- Calories 221
- Protein 14 g
- Carbs 3 g
- Fat 2 g
- Sodium 119 mg
- Potassium 398 mg
- Phosphorus 149 mg

Preparation Time: 5 minutes|Cooking Time: 15 minutesServings: 2

Lemon, Garlic, Cilantro Tuna and Rice

INGREDIENTS

- ½ cup arugula
- 1 tbsp. extra virgin olive oil
- 1 cup cooked rice
- 1 tsp black pepper
- ¼ finely diced red onion
- 1 juiced lemon
- 3 oz. canned tuna
- 2 tbsp. Chopped fresh cilantro

DIRECTION

- Mix the olive oil, pepper, cilantro, and red onion in a bowl. Stir in the tuna, cover, then serve with the cooked rice and arugula!

NUTRITIONAL

- Calories 221
- Protein 11 g
- Carbs 26 g
- Fat 7 g
- Sodium 143 mg
- Potassium 197 mg
- Phosphorus 182 mg

Preparation Time: 5 minutes|Cooking Time: 0 minutes|Servings: 2

Cod & Green Bean Risotto

INGREDIENTS

- ½ cup arugula
- 1 finely diced white onion
- 4 oz. cod fillet
- 1 cup white rice
- 2 lemon wedges
- 1 cup boiling water
- ¼ tsp. black pepper
- 1 cup low-sodium chicken broth
- 1 tbsp. extra virgin olive oil
- ½ cup green beans

DIRECTION

- Warm-up oil in a large pan on medium heat. Sauté the chopped onion for 5 minutes until soft before adding in the rice and stirring for 1-2 minutes.
- Combine the broth with boiling water. Add half of the liquid to the pan and stir. Slowly add the rest of the liquid while continuously stirring for up to 20-30 minutes.
- Stir in the green beans to the risotto. Place the fish on top of the rice, cover, and steam for 10 minutes.
- Use your fork to break up the fish fillets and stir into the rice. Sprinkle with freshly ground pepper to serve and a squeeze of fresh lemon. Serve with the lemon wedges and the arugula.

NUTRITIONAL

- Calories 221
- Protein 12 g
- Carbs 29 g
- Fat 8 g
- Sodium 398 mg
- Potassium 347 mg
- Phosphorus 241 mg

Preparation Time: 4 minutes |Cooking Time: 40 minutes|Servings: 2

Sardine Fish Cakes

INGREDIENTS

- 11 oz. sardines, canned, drained
- 1/3 cup shallot, chopped
- 1 teaspoon chili flakes
- ½ teaspoon salt
- 2 tablespoon wheat flour, whole grain
- 1 egg, beaten
- 1 tablespoon chives, chopped
- 1 teaspoon olive oil
- 1 teaspoon butter

DIRECTION

- Put the butter in your skillet and dissolve it. Add shallot and cook it until translucent. After this, transfer the shallot to the mixing bowl.
- Add sardines, chili flakes, salt, flour, egg, chives, and mix up until smooth with the fork's help. Make the medium size cakes and place them in the skillet. Add olive oil.
- Roast the fish cakes for 3 minutes from each side over medium heat. Dry the cooked fish cakes with a paper towel if needed and transfer to the serving plates.

NUTRITIONAL

- Calories 221
- Fat 12.2g
- Fiber 0.1g
- Carbs 5.4g
- Protein 21.3 g
- Phosphorus 188.7 mg
- Potassium 160.3 mg
- Sodium 452.6 mg

Preparation Time: 10 minutes |Cooking Time: 10 minutes |Servings: 4

4-Ingredients Salmon Fillet

INGREDIENTS

- 4 oz. salmon fillet
- ½ teaspoon salt
- 1 teaspoon sesame oil
- ½ teaspoon sage

DIRECTION

- Rub the fillet with salt and sage. Put the fish in the tray, then sprinkle it with sesame oil. Cook the fish for 25 minutes at 365F. Flip the fish carefully onto another side after 12 minutes of cooking. Serve.

NUTRITIONAL

- Calories 191
- Fat 11.6g
- Fiber 0.1g
- Carbs 0.2g
- Protein 22g
- Sodium 70.5 mg
- Phosphorus 472 mg
- Potassium 636.3 mg

Preparation Time: 5 minutes |Cooking Time: 25 minutes |Servings: 1

Spanish Cod in Sauce

INGREDIENTS

- 1 teaspoon tomato paste
- 1 teaspoon garlic, diced
- 1 white onion, sliced
- 1 jalapeno pepper, chopped
- 1/3 cup chicken stock
- 7 oz. Spanish cod fillet
- 1 teaspoon paprika
- 1 teaspoon salt

DIRECTION

- Pour chicken stock into the saucepan. Add tomato paste and mix up the liquid until homogenous. Add garlic, onion, jalapeno pepper, paprika, and salt.
- Bring the liquid to boil and then simmer it. Chop the cod fillet and add it to the tomato liquid. Simmer the fish for 10 minutes over low heat. Serve the fish in the bowls with tomato sauce.

NUTRITIONAL

- Calories 113
- Fat 1.2g
- Fiber 1.9g
- Carbs 7.2g
- Protein 18.9g
- Potassium 659 mg
- Sodium 597 mg
- Phosphorus 18 mg

Preparation Time: 10 minutes | Cooking Time: 5 1/2 hours | Servings: 2

Salmon Baked in Foil with Fresh Thyme

INGREDIENTS

- 4 fresh thyme sprigs
- 4 garlic cloves, peeled, roughly chopped
- 16 oz. salmon fillets (4 oz. each fillet)
- ½ teaspoon salt
- ½ teaspoon ground black pepper
- 4 tablespoons cream
- 4 teaspoons butter
- ¼ teaspoon cumin seeds

DIRECTION

- Line the baking tray with foil. Sprinkle the fish fillets with salt, ground black pepper, cumin seeds, and arrange them in the tray with oil.
- Add thyme sprig on the top of every fillet. Then add cream, butter, and garlic. Bake the fish for 30 minutes at 345F. Serve.

NUTRITIONAL

- Calories 198
- Fat 11.6g
- Carbs 1.8g
- Protein 22.4g
- Phosphorus 425 mg
- Potassium 660.9 mg
- Sodium 366 mg

Preparation Time: 10 minutes | Cooking Time: 30 minutes | Servings: 4

Poached Halibut in Orange Sauce

INGREDIENTS

- 1-pound halibut
- 1/3 cup butter
- 1 rosemary sprig
- ½ teaspoon ground black pepper
- 1 teaspoon salt
- 1 teaspoon honey
- ¼ cup of orange juice
- 1 teaspoon cornstarch

DIRECTION

- Put butter in the saucepan and melt it. Add rosemary sprig. Sprinkle the halibut with salt and ground black pepper. Put the fish in the boiling butter and poach it for 4 minutes.
- Meanwhile, pour orange juice into the skillet. Add honey and bring the liquid to boil. Add cornstarch and whisk until the liquid starts to be thick. Then remove it from the heat.
- Transfer the poached halibut to the plate and cut it on 4. Place every fish serving in the serving plate and top with orange sauce.

NUTRITIONAL

- Calories 349
- Fat 29.3g
- Fiber 0.1g
- Carbs 3.2g
- Protein 17.8g
- Phosphorus 154 mg
- Potassium 388.6 mg
- Sodium 29.3 mg

Preparation Time: 10 minutes |Cooking Time: 10 minutes |Servings: 4

Fish En' Papillote

INGREDIENTS

- 10 oz. snapper fillet
- 1 tablespoon fresh dill, chopped
- 1 white onion, peeled, sliced
- ½ teaspoon tarragon
- 1 tablespoon olive oil
- 1 teaspoon salt
- ½ teaspoon hot pepper
- 2 tablespoons sour cream

DIRECTION

- Make the medium size packets from parchment and arrange them in the baking tray. Cut the snapper fillet into 3 and sprinkle them with salt, tarragon, and hot pepper.
- Put the fish fillets in the parchment packets. Then top the fish with olive oil, sour cream, sliced onion, and fresh dill. Bake the fish for 20 minutes at 355F. Serve.

NUTRITIONAL

- Calories 204
- Fat 8.2g
- Carbs 4.6g
- Protein 27.2g
- Phosphorus 138.8 mg
- Potassium 181.9 mg
- Sodium 59.6 mg

Preparation Time: 15 minutes |Cooking Time: 20 minutes |Servings: 3

Tuna Casserole

INGREDIENTS

- ½ cup Cheddar cheese, shredded
- 2 Red bell peppers, chopped
- 7 oz. tuna filet, chopped
- 1 teaspoon ground coriander
- ½ teaspoon salt
- 1 teaspoon olive oil
- ½ teaspoon dried oregano

DIRECTION

- Brush the casserole mold with olive oil. Mix up together chopped tuna fillet with dried oregano and ground coriander.
- Place the fish in the mold and flatten well to get the layer. Then add chopped Red bell peppers and shredded cheese. Cover the casserole with foil and secure the edges. Bake the meal for 35 minutes at 355F. Serve.

NUTRITIONAL

- Calories 260
- Fat 21.5g
- Carbs 2.7g
- Protein 14.6g
- Phosphorus 153 mg
- Potassium 311 mg
- Sodium 600 mg

Preparation Time: 15 minutes |Cooking Time: 35 minutes |Servings: 4

Fish Chili with Lentils

INGREDIENTS

- 1 red pepper, chopped
- 1 yellow onion, diced
- 1 teaspoon ground black pepper
- 1 teaspoon butter
- 1 jalapeno pepper, chopped
- ½ cup lentils
- 3 cups chicken stock
- 1 teaspoon salt
- 1 tablespoon tomato paste
- 1 teaspoon chili pepper
- 3 tablespoons fresh cilantro, chopped
- 8 oz. cod, chopped

DIRECTION

- Place butter, red pepper, onion, and ground black pepper in the saucepan. Roast the vegetables for 5 minutes over medium heat. Then add chopped jalapeno pepper, lentils, and chili pepper. Mix up the mixture well and add chicken stock and tomato paste. Stir until homogenous. Add cod. Close the lid and cook chili for 20 minutes over medium heat.

NUTRITIONAL

- Calories 187
- Fat 2.3g
- Carbs 21.3g
- Protein 20.6g
- Phosphorus 50 mg
- Potassium 281 mg
- Sodium 43.8 mg

Preparation Time: 10 minutes |Cooking Time: 30 minutes |Servings: 4

Chili Mussels

INGREDIENTS

- 1-pound mussels
- 1 chili pepper, chopped
- 1 cup chicken stock
- ½ cup milk
- 1 teaspoon olive oil
- 1 teaspoon minced garlic
- 1 teaspoon ground coriander
- ½ teaspoon salt
- 1 cup fresh parsley, chopped
- 4 tablespoons lemon juice

DIRECTION

- Pour milk into the saucepan. Add chili pepper, chicken stock, olive oil, minced garlic, ground coriander, salt, and lemon juice.
- Bring the liquid to boil and add mussels. Boil the mussel for 4 minutes or until they will open shells. Then add chopped parsley and mix up the meal well. Remove it from the heat.

NUTRITIONAL

- Calories 136
- Fat 4.7g
- Fiber 0.6g
- Carbs 7.5g
- Protein 15.3g
- Phosphorus 180.8 mg
- Potassium 312.5 mg
- Sodium 319.6 mg

Preparation Time: 7 minutes |Cooking Time: 10 minutes |Servings: 4

Grilled Cod

INGREDIENTS

- 2 (8 ounce) fillets cod, cut in half
- 1 tablespoon oregano
- ½ teaspoon lemon pepper
- ¼ teaspoon ground black pepper
- 2 tablespoons olive oil
- 1 lemon, juiced
- 2 tablespoons chopped green onion (white part only)

DIRECTION

- Season both sides of cod with oregano, lemon pepper, and black pepper. Set fish aside on a plate. Heat butter in a small saucepan over medium heat, stir in lemon juice and green onion, and cook until onion is softened, about 3 minutes.
- Place cod onto oiled grates and grill until fish is browned and flakes easily, about 3 minutes per side; baste with olive oil mixture frequently while grilling. Allow cod to rest off the heat for about 5 minutes before serving.

NUTRITIONAL

- Calories 92,
- Total Fat 7.4g,
- Saturated Fat 1g,
- Cholesterol 14mg,
- Sodium 19mg,
- Total Carbohydrate 2.5g,
- Dietary Fiber 1g,
- Total Sugars 0.5g,
- Protein 5.4g,
- Calcium 25mg, Iron 1mg,
- Potassium 50mg,
- Phosphorus 36 mg

Preparation Time: 10 min |Cooking Time: 10 minutes |Servings: 4

Cod and Green Bean Curry

INGREDIENTS

- 1/2-pound green beans, trimmed and cut into bite-sized pieces
- 1 white onion, sliced
- 2 cloves garlic, minced
- 1 tablespoon olive oil, or more as needed
- Ground black pepper to taste
- Curry Mixture:
- 2 tablespoons water, or more as needed
- 2 teaspoons curry powder
- 2 teaspoons ground ginger
- 1 1/2 (6 ounce) cod fillets

DIRECTION

- Preheat the oven to 400 degrees F.
- Combine green beans, onion, and garlic in a large glass baking dish. Toss with olive oil to coat; season with the pepper.
- Bake in the preheated oven, stirring occasionally, until edges of onion are slightly charred and green beans start to look dry, about 40 minutes. In the meantime, mix water, curry powder, and ginger together.
- Remove dish and stir the vegetables; stir in curry mixture. Increase oven temperature to 450 degrees F.
- Lay cod over the bottom of the dish and coat with vegetables. Continue baking until fish is opaque, 25 to 30 minutes depending on thickness.

NUTRITIONAL

- Calories 64,
- Total Fat 3.8g,
- Saturated Fat 0.5g,
- Cholesterol 0mg,
- Sodium 5mg,
- Total Carbohydrate 7.7g,
- Dietary Fiber 2.9g,
- Total Sugars 2g,
- Protein 1.6g,
- Calcium 35mg,
- Iron 1mg,
- Potassium 180mg,
- Phosphorus 101 mg

Preparation Time: 15 min |Cooking Time: 60 minutes |Servings: 4

White Fish Soup

INGREDIENTS

- 2 tablespoons olive oil
- 1 onion, finely diced
- 1 green bell pepper, chopped
- 1 rib celery, thinly sliced
- 3 cups chicken broth, or more to taste
- 1/4 cup chopped fresh parsley
- 1 1/2 pounds cod, cut into 3/4-inch cubes
- Pepper to taste
- 1 dash red pepper flakes

DIRECTION

- Heat oil in a soup pot over medium heat.
- Add onion, bell pepper, and celery and cook until wilted, about 5 minutes.
- Add broth and bring to a simmer, about 5 minutes.
- Cook 15 to 20 minutes.
- Add cod, parsley, and red pepper flakes and simmer until fish flakes easily with a fork, 8 to 10 minutes more.
- Season with black pepper.

NUTRITIONAL

- Calories 117,
- Total Fat 7.2g,
- Saturated Fat 1.4g,
- Cholesterol 18mg,
- Sodium 37mg,
- Total Carbohydrate 5.4g,
- Dietary Fiber 1.3g,
- Total Sugars 2.8g,
- Protein 8.1g,
- Calcium 23mg,
- Iron 1mg,
- Potassium 122mg,
- Phosphorus 111 mg

Preparation Time: 15 min |Cooking Time: 20 minutes |Servings: 4

Onion Dijon Crusted Catfish

INGREDIENTS

- 1 onion, finely chopped
- 1/4 cup honey Dijon mustard
- 4 (6 ounce) fillets catfish fillets
- Pepper to taste
- Dried parsley flakes

DIRECTION

- Preheat the oven to 350 degrees F.
- In a small bowl, mix together the onion and mustard. Season the catfish fillets with pepper. Place on a baking tray and coat with the onion and honey. Sprinkle parsley flakes over the top.
- Bake for 20 minutes in the preheated oven, then turn the oven to broil. Broil until golden, 3 to 5 minutes.

NUTRITIONAL

- Calories 215,
- Total Fat 6.1g,
- Saturated Fat 1.7g,
- Cholesterol 87mg,
- Sodium 86mg,
- Total Carbohydrate 10.4g,
- Dietary Fiber 0.6g,
- Total Sugars 4.2g,
- Protein 31.6g,
- Calcium 8mg,
- Iron 0mg,
- Potassium 46mg,
- Phosphorus 30 mg

Preparation Time: 05 min |Cooking Time: 25 minutes |Servings: 4

Herb Baked Tuna

INGREDIENTS

- 4 (6 ounce) tuna fillets
- 2 tablespoons dried parsley
- 3/4 teaspoon paprika
- 1/2 teaspoon dried thyme
- 1/2 teaspoon dried oregano
- 1/2 teaspoon dried basil
- 1/2 teaspoon ground black pepper
- 2 tablespoons lemon juice
- 1 tablespoon olive oil
- 1/4 teaspoon garlic powder

DIRECTION

- Preheat oven to 350 degrees F.
- Arrange tuna fillets in a 9x13-inch baking dish. Combine parsley, paprika, thyme, oregano, basil, and black pepper in a small bowl; sprinkle herb mixture over fish. Mix lemon juice, olive oil, and garlic powder in another bowl; drizzle olive oil mixture over fish.
- Bake in preheated oven until fish is easily flaked with a fork, about 20 minutes.

NUTRITIONAL

- Calories 139,
- Total Fat 12.5g,
- Saturated Fat 0.6g
- Cholesterol 0mg,
- Sodium 3mg,
- Total Carbohydrate 1g,
- Dietary Fiber 0.5g,
- Total Sugars 0.3g,
- Protein 6.2g,
- Calcium 11mg,
- Iron 1mg,
- Potassium 39mg,
- Phosphorus 20 mg

Preparation Time: 10 min |Cooking Time: 20 minutes |Servings: 4

Cilantro Lime Salmon

INGREDIENTS

- ¼ cup olive oil
- ¼ cup chopped fresh cilantro
- ½ teaspoon chopped garlic
- 5 (5 ounce) fillets salmon
- Ground black pepper to taste
- ½ lemon, juiced
- ½ lime, juiced

DIRECTION

- Heat the olive oil in a skillet over medium heat.
- Stir cilantro and garlic into the oil; cook about 1 minute.
- Season salmon fillets with black pepper; lay gently into the oil mixture.
- Place a cover on the skillet. Cook fillets 10 minutes, turn, and continue cooking until the fish flakes easily with a fork and is lightly browned, about 10 minutes more.
- Squeeze lemon juice and lime juice over the fillets to serve.

NUTRITIONAL

- Calories 249,
- Total Fat 18.7g,
- Saturated Fat 3.3g,
- Cholesterol 18mg, Sodium 48mg,
- Total Carbohydrate 1.7g,
- Dietary Fiber 0.5g,
- Total Sugars 0.3g,
- Protein 20.7g,
- Calcium 6mg,
- Iron 0mg,
- Potassium 26mg,
- Phosphorus 20 mg

Preparation Time: 10 min |Cooking Time: 20 minutes |Servings: 4

Asian Ginger tuna

INGREDIENTS

- 1 cup water
- 1 tablespoon minced fresh ginger root
- 1 tablespoon minced garlic
- 2 tablespoons soy sauce
- 1 1/4 pounds thin tuna fillets
- 6 large white mushrooms, sliced
- 1/4 cup sliced green onion
- 1 tablespoon chopped fresh cilantro (optional)

DIRECTION

- Put water, ginger, and garlic in a wide pot with a lid.
- Bring the water to a boil, reduce heat to medium-low, and simmer 3 to 5 minutes.
- Stir soy sauce into the water mixture; add tuna fillets.
- Place cover on the pot, bring water to a boil, and let cook for 3 minutes more.
- Add mushrooms, cover, and cook until the fish loses pinkness and begins to flake, about 3 minutes more.
- Sprinkle green onion over the fillets, cover, and cook for 30 seconds.
- Garnish with cilantro to serve.

NUTRITIONAL

- Calories 109,
- Total Fat 7.9g,
- Saturated Fat 0g,
- Cholesterol 0mg,
- Sodium 454mg,
- Total Carbohydrate 3.1g,
- Dietary Fiber 0.6g,
- Total Sugars 0.9g,
- Protein 7.1g,
- Calcium 10mg,
- Iron 1mg,
- Potassium 158mg,
- Phosphorus 120 mg

Preparation Time: 10 min |Cooking Time: 20 minutes |Servings:

Cheesy Tuna Chowder

INGREDIENTS

- 2 tablespoons olive oil
- 1/2 small onion, chopped
- 1 cup water
- 1/2 cup chopped celery
- 1 cup sliced baby carrots
- 3 cups soy milk, divided
- 1/3 cup all-purpose flour
- 1/2 teaspoon ground black pepper
- 1 1/2 pounds tuna fillets, cut into 1-inch pieces
- 1 1/2 cups shredded Cheddar cheese

DIRECTION

- In a Dutch oven over medium heat, heat olive oil and sauté the onion until tender. Pour in water. Mix in celery, carrots, cook 10 minutes, stirring occasionally, until vegetables are tender.
- In a small bowl, whisk together 1 1/2 cups milk and all-purpose flour. Mix into the Dutch oven.
- Mix remaining milk, and pepper into the Dutch oven. Stirring occasionally, continue cooking the mixture about 10 minutes, until thickened.
- Stir tuna into the mixture, and cook 5 minutes, or until fish is easily flaked with a fork. Mix in Cheddar cheese, and cook another 5 minutes, until melted.

NUTRITIONAL

- Calories 228,
- Total Fat 15.5g,
- Saturated Fat 6.5g,
- Cholesterol 30mg,
- Sodium 206mg,
- Total Carbohydrate 10.8g,
- Dietary Fiber 1g,
- Total Sugars 4.1g,
- Protein 11.6g,
- Calcium 183mg,
- Iron 1mg,
- Potassium 163mg,
- Phosphorus 150 mg

Preparation Time: 10 min |Cooking Time: 20 minutes |Servings: 4

Marinated Salmon Steak

INGREDIENTS

- ¼ cup lime juice
- ¼ cup soy sauce
- 2 tablespoons olive oil
- 1 tablespoon lemon juice
- 2 tablespoons chopped fresh parsley
- 1 clove garlic, minced
- ½ teaspoon chopped fresh oregano
- ½ teaspoon ground black pepper
- 4 (4 ounce) salmon steaks

DIRECTION

- In a large non-reactive dish, mix together the lime juice, soy sauce, olive oil, lemon juice, parsley, garlic, oregano, and pepper. Place the salmon steaks in the marinade and turn to coat. Cover, and refrigerate for at least 30 minutes.
- Preheat grill for high heat.
- Lightly oil grill grate. Cook the salmon steaks for 5 to 6 minutes, then salmon and baste with the marinade. Cook for an additional 5 minutes, or to desired doneness. Discard any remaining marinade.

NUTRITIONAL

- Calories 108,
- Total Fat 8.4g,
- Saturated Fat 1.2g,
- Cholesterol 9mg,
- Sodium 910mg,
- Total Carbohydrate 3.6g,
- Dietary Fiber 0.4g,
- Total Sugars 1.7g,
- Protein 5.4g,
- Calcium 19mg,
- Iron 1mg,
- Potassium 172mg,
- Phosphorus 165 mg

Preparation Time: 10 min |Cooking Time: 10 minutes |Servings: 4

Tuna with honey Glaze

INGREDIENTS

- 1/4 cup honey
- 2 tablespoons Dijon mustard
- 4 (6 ounce) boneless tuna fillets
- Ground black pepper to taste

DIRECTION

- Preheat the oven's broiler and set the oven rack at about 6 inches from the heat source; prepare the rack of a broiler pan with cooking spray.
- Season the tuna with pepper and arrange onto the prepared broiler pan. Whisk together the honey and Dijon mustard in a small bowl; spoon mixture evenly onto top of salmon fillets.
- Cook under the preheated broiler until the fish flakes easily with a fork, 10 to 15 minutes.

NUTRITIONAL

- Calories 160,
- Total Fat 8.1g,
- Saturated Fat 0g,
- Cholesterol 0mg,
- Sodium 90mg,
- Total Carbohydrate 17.9g,
- Dietary Fiber 0.3g,
- Total Sugars 17.5g,
- Protein 5.7g,
- Calcium 6mg,
- Iron 0mg,
- Potassium 22mg,
- Phosphorus 16 mg

Preparation Time: 10 min |Cooking Time: 10 minutes |Servings: 4

Stuffed Mushrooms

INGREDIENTS

- 12 large fresh mushrooms, stems removed
- ½ pound crabmeat, flaked
- 2 cups olive oil
- 2 cloves garlic, peeled and minced
- Garlic powder to taste
- Crushed red pepper to taste

DIRECTION

- Arrange mushroom caps on a medium baking sheet, bottoms up. Chop and reserve mushroom stems.
- Preheat oven to 350 degrees F.
- In a medium saucepan over medium heat, heat oil. Mix in garlic and cook until tender, about 5 minutes.
- In a medium bowl, mix together reserved mushroom stems, and crab meat. Liberally stuff mushrooms with the mixture. Drizzle with the garlic. Season with garlic powder and crushed red pepper.
- Bake uncovered in the preheated oven 10 to 12 minutes, or until stuffing is lightly browned.

NUTRITIONAL

- Calories 312,
- Total Fat 33.8g,
- Saturated Fat 4.8g,
- Cholesterol 4mg,
- Sodium 160mg,
- Total Carbohydrate 3.8g,
- Dietary Fiber 0.3g,
- Total Sugars 1.6g,
- Protein 2.2g,
- Calcium 3mg,
- Iron 1mg,
- Potassium 93mg,
- Phosphorus 86 mg

Preparation Time: 10 min |Cooking Time: 10 minutes |Servings: 4

Easy Salmon and Brussels sprouts

INGREDIENTS

- 6 deboned medium salmon fillets
- 1 tsp. onion powder
- 1 ¼ lbs. halved Brussels sprouts
- 3 tbsps. Extra virgin extra virgin olive oil
- 2 tbsps. Brown sugar
- 1 tsp. garlic powder
- 1 tsp. smoked paprika

DIRECTION

- In a bowl, mix sugar with onion powder, garlic powder, smoked paprika as well as a number of tablespoon olive oil and whisk well.
- Spread Brussels sprouts about the lined baking sheet, drizzle the rest in the essential extra virgin olive oil, toss to coat, introduce in the oven at 450 0F and bake for 5 minutes.
- Add salmon fillets brush with sugar mix you've prepared, introduce inside the oven and bake for 15 minutes more.
- Divide everything between plates and serve.
- Enjoy!

NUTRITIONAL

- Calories: 212,
- Fat: 5 g,
- Carbs: 12 g,
- Protein: 8 g,
- Sugars: 3.7 g,
- Sodium: 299.1 mg

Preparation Time: 10 minutes|Cooking Time: 10 minutes|Servings: 6

Salmon in Dill Sauce

INGREDIENTS

- 6 salmon fillets
- 1 c. low-fat, low-sodium chicken broth
- 1 tsp. cayenne pepper
- 2 tbsps. Fresh lemon juice
- 2 c. water
- ¼ c. chopped fresh dill

DIRECTION

- In a slow cooker, mix together water, broth, lemon juice, lemon juice and dill.
- Arrange salmon fillets on top, skin side down.
- Sprinkle with cayenne pepper.
- Set the slow cooker on low.
- Cover and cook for about 1-2 hours.

NUTRITIONAL

- Calories: 360,
- Fat: 8 g,
- Carbs: 44 g,
- Protein: 28 g,
- Sugars: 0.5 g,
- Sodium: 8 mg

Preparation Time: 10 minutes|Cooking Time: 10 minutes|Servings: 6

Shrimp Lo Mein

INGREDIENTS

- 1 tbsp. cornstarch
- 1 lb. medium-size frozen raw shrimp
- 1 c. frozen shelled edamame
- 3 tbsps. Light teriyaki sauce
- 16 Oz. Drained and rinsed tofu spaghetti noodles
- 18 oz. frozen Szechuan vegetable blend with sesame sauce

DIRECTION

- Microwave noodles for 1 minute; set aside. Place shrimp in a small bowl and toss with 2 tablespoons teriyaki sauce; set aside.
- Place mixed vegetables and edamame in a large nonstick skillet with 1/4 cup water. Cover and cook, stirring occasionally, over medium-high heat for 7 minutes or until cooked through.
- Stir shrimp into vegetable mixture; cover and cook 4 to 5 minutes or until shrimp is pink and cooked through.
- Stir together remaining 1 tablespoon teriyaki sauce and the cornstarch, then stir into the mixture in the skillet until thickened. Gently stir noodles into skillet and cook until warmed through.

NUTRITIONAL

- Calories: 252,
- Fat: 7.1 g,
- Carbs: 35.2 g,
- Protein: 12.1 g,
- Sugars: 2.2 g,
- Sodium: 180 mg

Preparation Time: 10 minutes|Cooking Time: 10 minutes|Servings: 6

Salmon and Potatoes Mix

INGREDIENTS

- 4 oz. chopped smoked salmon
- 1 tbsp. essential olive oil
- Black pepper
- 1 tbsp. chopped chives
- ¼ c. coconut cream
- 1 ½ lbs. chopped potatoes
- 2 tsps. Prepared horseradish

DIRECTION

- Heat up a pan using the oil over medium heat, add potatoes and cook for 10 minutes. Add salmon, chives, horseradish, cream and black pepper, toss, cook for 1 minute more, divide between plates and serve.
- Enjoy!

NUTRITIONAL

- Calories: 233,
- Fat: 6 g,
- Carbs: 9 g,
- Protein: 11 g,
- Sugars: 3.3 g,
- Sodium: 97 mg

Preparation Time: 10 minutes|Cooking Time: 10 minutes|Servings: 4

Smoked Salmon and Radishes

INGREDIENTS

- ½ c. drained and chopped capers
- 1 lb. skinless, de-boned and flaked smoked salmon
- 4 chopped radishes
- 3 tbsps. Chopped chives
- 3 tbsps. Prepared beet horseradish
- 2 tsps. Grated lemon zest
- 1/3 c. roughly chopped red onion

DIRECTION

- In a bowl, combine the salmon while using the beet horseradish, lemon zest, radish, capers, onions and chives, toss and serve cold.
- Enjoy!

NUTRITIONAL

- Calories: 254,
- Fat: 2 g, Carbs: 7 g,
- Protein: 7 g,
- Sugars: 1.4 g,
- Sodium: 660 mg

Preparation Time: 10 minutes|Cooking Time: 10 minutes|Servings: 8

Parmesan Baked Fish

INGREDIENTS

- ½ tsp. Worcestershire sauce
- 1/3 c. mayonnaise
- 3 tbsps. Freshly grated parmesan cheese
- 4 oz. cod fish fillets
- 1 tbsp. snipped fresh chives

DIRECTION

- Preheat oven to 450°C.
- Rinse fish and pat dry with paper towels; spray an 8x8x2 baking dish with non-stick pan spray, set aside.
- In small bowl stir mayo, grated cheese, chives, and Worcestershire sauce; spread mixture over fish fillets.
- Bake, uncovered, 12-15 minutes or until fish flakes easily with a fork

NUTRITIONAL

- Calories: 850.5,
- Fat: 24.8g,
- Carbs: 44.5 g,
- Protein: 104.6 g, Sugars: 0.6 g,
- Sodium: 307.7 mg

Preparation Time: 10 minutes|Cooking Time: 10 minutes|Servings: 4

Shrimp and Mango Mix

INGREDIENTS

- 3 tbsps. Finely chopped parsley
- 3 tbsps. Coconut sugar
- 1 lb. peeled, deveined and cooked shrimp
- 3 tbsps. Balsamic vinegar
- 3 peeled and cubed mangos

DIRECTION

- In a bowl, mix vinegar with sugar and mayo and whisk.
- In another bowl, combine the mango with the parsley and shrimp, add the mayo mix, toss and serve.
- Enjoy!

NUTRITIONAL

- Calories: 204,
- Fat: 3 g,
- Carbs: 8 g,
- Protein: 8 g,
- Sugars: 12.6 g,
- Sodium: 273.4 mg

Preparation Time: 10 minutes|Cooking Time: 10 minutes|Servings: 4

Roasted hake

INGREDIENTS

- ½ c. tomato sauce
- 2 sliced Red bell peppers
- Fresh parsley
- ½ c. grated cheese
- 4 lbs. deboned hake fish
- 1 tbsp. olive oil
- Salt.

DIRECTION

- Season the fish with salt. Pan-fry the fish until half-done.
- Shape foil into containers according to the number of fish pieces.
- Pour tomato sauce into each foil dish; arrange the fish, then the tomato slices, again add tomato sauce and sprinkle with grated cheese.
- Bake in the oven at 400 F until there is a golden crust.
- Serve with fresh parsley.

NUTRITIONAL

- Calories: 421,
- Fat: 48.7 g,
- Carbs: 2.4 g,
- Protein: 17.4 g,
- Sugars: 0.5 g,
- Sodium: 94.6 mg

Preparation Time: 20 minutes|Cooking Time: 30 minutes|Servings: 4

Coconut Cream Shrimp

INGREDIENTS

- 1 tbsp. coconut cream
- ½ tsp. lime juice
- ¼ tsp. black pepper
- 1 tbsp. parsley
- 1 lb. cooked, peeled and de-veined shrimp
- ¼ tsp. chopped jalapeno

DIRECTION

- In a bowl, mix the shrimp while using cream, jalapeno, lime juice, parsley and black pepper, toss, divide into small bowls and serve.
- Enjoy!

NUTRITIONAL

- Calories: 183,
- Fat: 5 g,
- Carbs: 12 g,
- Protein: 8 g,
- Sugars: 0.9 g,
- Sodium: 474.9 mg

Preparation Time: 10 minutes|Cooking Time: 20 minutes|Servings: 2

Simple Cinnamon Salmon

INGREDIENTS

- 1 tbsp. organic essential olive oil
- Black pepper
- 1 tbsp. cinnamon powder
- 2 de-boned salmon fillets

DIRECTION

- Heat up a pan with the oil over medium heat, add pepper and cinnamon and stir well.
- Add salmon, skin side up, cook for 5 minutes on both sides, divide between plates and serve by using a side salad.
- Enjoy!

NUTRITIONAL

- Calories: 220,
- Fat: 8 g,
- Carbs: 11 g,
- Protein: 8 g,
- Sugars: 9.3 g,
- Sodium: 250.5 mg

Preparation Time: 10 minutes|Cooking Time: 10 minutes|Servings: 2

Lemon-Herb Grilled Fish

INGREDIENTS

- 4 peeled garlic cloves
- ¼ tsp. salt
- 8 lemon slices
- ¼ tsp. ground black pepper
- Remoulade
- 2 small blue-fish
- 2 sprigs fresh thyme

DIRECTION

- Prepare outdoor grill with medium-low to medium coals, or heat gas grill to medium-low to medium (to broil, see Note below).
- Rinse fish; pat dry. Cut 3 slashes on each side. Season with salt, pepper.
- Stuff 3 lemon slices in cavity of each fish. Add thyme and 2 cloves garlic to each cavity.
- Grill fish 6 inches from heat, covered, 10 to 12 minutes, until just beginning to char, flip over carefully. Cover each eye with one of remaining lemon slices. Grill 12 to 15 minutes more, until flesh is white throughout.
- Transfer fish to platter. For each, pry up top fillet in one piece, flipping over, and skin side down.
- Beginning at tail, carefully pull up end of spine of fish, and lift up, removing whole backbone. Remove any small bones from fish.
- Serve with Remoulade.

NUTRITIONAL

- Calories: 118.1,
- Fat: 6.8 g,
- Carbs: 1 g,
- Protein: 12.9 g,
- Sugars: 12.9 g,
- Sodium: 91.2 mg

Preparation Time: 5 minutes|Cooking Time: 10 minutes|Servings: 4

Scallops and Strawberry Mix

INGREDIENTS

- 1 tbsp. lime juice
- ½ c. Pico de Gallo
- Black pepper
- 4 oz. scallops
- ½ c. chopped strawberries

DIRECTION

- Heat up a pan over medium heat, add scallops, cook for 3 minutes on both sides and take away heat,
- In a bowl, mix strawberries with lime juice, Pico de gallo, scallops and pepper, toss and serve cold.
- Enjoy!

NUTRITIONAL

- Calories: 169,
- Fat: 2 g,
- Carbs: 8 g,
- Protein: 13 g,
- Sugars: 0 g,
- Sodium: 235.7 mg

Preparation Time: 20 minutes|Cooking Time: 30 minutes|Servings: 2

Cod Peas

INGREDIENTS

- 1 c. peas
- 2 tbsps. Capers
- 4 de-boned medium cod fillets
- 3 tbsps. Olive oil
- ¼ tsp. black pepper
- 2 tbsps. Lime juice
- 2 tbsps. Chopped shallots
- 1 ½ tbsps. Chopped oregano

DIRECTION

- Heat up 1 tbsp. olive oil in a saucepan over medium flame
- Add the fillets, cook for 5 minutes on each side; set aside.
- In a bowl of large size, thoroughly mix the oregano, shallots, lime juice, peas, capers, black pepper, and 2 tbsp. olive oil.
- Toss and serve with the cooked fish.

NUTRITIONAL

- Calories: 224,
- Fat: 11 g,
- Carbs: 7 g,
- Protein: 24 g,
- Sugars: 2 g,
- Sodium: 485 mg

Preparation Time: 18-20 minutes|Cooking Time: 40 minutes|Servings: 4-5

Chipotle Spiced Shrimp

INGREDIENTS

- ½ tsp. minced garlic
- 2 tbsps. Tomato paste
- ½ tsp. chopped fresh oregano
- 1 ½ tsps. Water
- ¾ lb. peeled, deveined and uncooked shrimp
- ½ tsp. chipotle chili powder
- ½ tsp. extra-virgin olive oil

DIRECTION

- In cold water, rinse shrimp.
- Pat dry with a paper towel. Set aside on a plate.
- Whisk together the tomato paste, water and oil in a small bowl to make the marinade. Add garlic, chili powder and oregano and mix well.
- Spread the marinade (it will be thick) on both sides of the shrimp using a brush and place in the refrigerator.
- Heat a gas grill or broiler, or prepare a hot fire in a charcoal grill.
- Coat the grill rack or broiler pan with cooking spray lightly.
- Put the cooking rack 4 to 6 inches from the heat source.
- Thread the shrimp onto skewers or lay them in a grill basket, to place on the grill.
- After 3 to 4 minutes turn the shrimp.
- When the shrimp is fully cooked, take it off the heat and serve immediately.

NUTRITIONAL

- Calories: 151.9,
- Fat: 2.8 g,
- Carbs: 5.1 g,
- Protein: 24.2 g,
- Sugars: 2.3 g,
- Sodium: 283.1 mg

Preparation Time: 10 minutes|Cooking Time: 10 minutes|Servings: 4

Baked Haddock

INGREDIENTS

- 1 tsp. chopped dill
- 3 tsps. Water
- ¼ tsp. black pepper and salt
- Cooking spray
- 1 lb. chopped haddock
- 2 tbsps. Fresh lemon juice

DIRECTION

- Spray a baking dish with a few oils, add fish, water, freshly squeezed lemon juice, salt, black pepper, mayo and dill, toss, introduce inside the oven and bake at 350 0F for the half-hour.
- Divide between plates and serve.
- Enjoy!

NUTRITIONAL

- Calories: 264,
- Fat: 4 g, Carbs: 7 g,
- Protein: 12 g,
- Sugars: 0 g,
- Sodium: 71.4 mg

Preparation Time: 10 minutes|Cooking Time: 10 minutes|Servings: 4

Crispy Fish Fillets

INGREDIENTS

- 1 egg
- 2 tablespoons prepared yellow mustard
- 1/4 cup oil for frying
- ½ cup graham crakes
- 4 (6 ounce) fish fillets

DIRECTION

- In a shallow dish, whisk together the egg, mustard, set aside. Place the graham crakes in another shallow dish.
- Heat oil in a large heavy skillet over medium-high heat.
- Dip fish fillets in the egg mixture. Dredge the fillets in the graham crakes, making sure to coat the fish completely. For extra crispy, dip into egg and graham crakes again.
- Fry fish fillets in oil for 3 to 4 minutes on each side, or until golden brown.

NUTRITIONAL

- Calories 194,
- Total Fat 17.8g,
- Saturated Fat 2.8g,
- Cholesterol 49mg,
- Sodium 225mg,
- Total Carbohydrate 4.4g,
- Dietary Fiber 0.4g,
- Total Sugars 0.2g,
- Protein 5.1g,
- Calcium 14mg,
- Iron 1mg,
- Potassium 98mg,
- Phosphorus 76 mg

Preparation Time: 10 min |Cooking Time: 10 minutes |Servings: 4

Simple Soup

INGREDIENTS

- 2 teaspoons tuna
- 4 cups water
- 1 (8 ounce) package silken tofu, diced
- 2 green onions, sliced diagonally into 1/2-inch pieces

DIRECTION

- In a medium saucepan over medium-high heat, combine tuna and water; bring to a boil.
- Reduce heat to medium, Stir in tofu.
- Separate the layers of the green onions, and add them to the soup.
- Simmer gently for 2 to 3 minutes before serving.

NUTRITIONAL

- Calories 77,
- Total Fat 3.3g,
- Saturated Fat 0.6g
- , Cholesterol 7mg,
- Sodium 39mg,
- Total Carbohydrate 1.9g,
- Dietary Fiber 0.3g,
- Total Sugars 0.9g,
- Protein 9.7g,
- Calcium 32mg,
- Iron 1mg,
- Potassium 104mg,
- Potassium 88mg

Preparation Time: 05 min |Cooking Time: 15 minutes |Servings: 4

Lime-Marinated Salmon

INGREDIENTS

- ¼ cup olive oil
- 1 clove garlic, minced
- 1/8 teaspoon ground black pepper
- 1/2 teaspoon cayenne pepper
- 2 tablespoons lime juice
- 1/8 teaspoon grated lime zest
- 2 (4 ounce) salmon fillets

DIRECTION

- Preheat an outdoor grill for medium heat, and lightly oil the grate.
- Whisk the olive oil, minced garlic, black pepper, cayenne pepper, lime juice, and grated lime zest together in a bowl to make the marinade.
- Place the salmon fillets in the marinade and turn to coat; allow to marinate at least 15 minutes.
- Cook on the preheated grill until the fish flakes easily with a fork and is lightly browned, 3 to 4 minutes per side.
- Garnish with the twists of lime zest to serve.

NUTRITIONAL

- Calories 126,
- Total Fat 9.7g,
- Saturated Fat 1.4g,
- Cholesterol 19mg,
- Sodium 20mg,
- Total Carbohydrate 2.7g,
- Dietary Fiber 0.3g,
- Total Sugars 0.5g,
- Protein 8.5g,
- Calcium 22mg,
- Iron 0mg,
- Potassium 206mg
- Potassium 108mg

Preparation Time: 05 min |Cooking Time: 15 minutes |Servings: 4

Ginger Glazed Tuna

INGREDIENTS

- 3 tablespoons honey
- 3 tablespoons soy sauce
- 3 tablespoons vinegar
- 1 teaspoon grated fresh ginger root
- 1 clove garlic, crushed or to taste
- 4 (6 ounce) tuna fillets
- Pepper to taste
- 2 tablespoons olive oil

DIRECTION

- In a shallow glass dish, stir together the honey, soy sauce, vinegar, ginger, garlic and 2 teaspoons olive oil. Season fish fillets with pepper, and place them into the dish. If the fillets have skin on them, place them skin side down. Cover, and refrigerate for 20 minutes to marinate.
- Heat remaining olive oil in a large skillet over medium-high heat. Remove fish from the dish, and reserve marinade. Fry fish for 4 to 6 minutes on each side, turning only once, until fish flakes easily with a fork. Remove fillets to a serving platter and keep warm.
- Pour reserved marinade into the skillet, and heat over medium heat until the mixture reduces to a glaze consistently. Spoon glaze over fish, and serve immediately.

NUTRITIONAL

- Calories 181,
- Total Fat 11.1g,
- Saturated Fat 0.3g,
- Cholesterol 0mg,
- Sodium 678mg,
- Total Carbohydrate 14.3g,
- Dietary Fiber 0.2g,
- Total Sugars 13.2g,
- Protein 6.8g,
- Calcium 6mg,
- Iron 0mg,
- Potassium 47mg,
- Potassium 18mg

Preparation Time: 05 min |Cooking Time: 12 minutes |Servings: 4

Tuna with Pineapple

INGREDIENTS

- 2 tablespoons olive oil
- 1 tablespoon minced fresh garlic
- 1 tablespoon chopped onion
- 1/2 red bell pepper, diced
- 1 cup pineapple - peeled, seeded and cubed
- 1 teaspoon corn-starch
- 1 tablespoon water
- 2 tablespoons lime juice
- 1 tablespoon lime juice
- 1 tablespoon melted butter
- 3 (4 ounce) fillets tuna

DIRECTION

- Preheat the oven's broiler and set the oven rack about 6 inches from the heat source.
- Heat olive oil in a saucepan over medium heat. Stir in the garlic and onion; cook and stir until the onion begins to soften, about 2 minutes. Add the red bell pepper and pineapple. Continue cooking a few more minutes until the bell pepper begins to soften. Stir together the corn-starch, water, and 2 tablespoons of lime juice. Stir into the pineapple sauce until thickened, stirring constantly. Keep the sauce warm over very low heat.
- Stir 1 tablespoon of lime juice together with the melted butter, and brush on the tuna fillets. Place onto a broiler pan.
- Cook under the preheated broiler for 4 minutes, then turn the fish over, and continue cooking for 4 minutes more. Season to taste with salt and serve with the pineapple sauce.

NUTRITIONAL

- Calories 98,
- Total Fat 7.1g,
- Saturated Fat 1g,
- Cholesterol 0mg,
- Sodium 2mg,
- Total Carbohydrate 10.1g,
- Dietary Fiber 1g,
- Total Sugars 5.3g
- Protein 0.6g,
- Calcium 14mg,
- Iron 0mg,
- Potassium 111mg,
- Potassium 101mg

Preparation Time: 25 min |Cooking Time: 15 minutes |Servings: 4

Tangy Glazed Black Cod

INGREDIENTS

- 3 tablespoons fresh lime juice
- 2 tablespoons honey
- 2 tablespoons vinegar
- 1 tablespoon soy sauce
- 1 (1 pound) fillet black cod, bones removed

DIRECTION

- Preheat oven to 425 degrees F. Spray the bottom of a Dutch oven or covered casserole dish with cooking spray.
- Combine lime juice, honey, vinegar, and soy sauce in a saucepan over medium heat; cook and stir until sauce is thickened, about 5 minutes.
- Place cod in the prepared Dutch oven. Pour sauce over fish Cover dish with an oven-safe lid.
- Bake in the preheated oven until fish flakes easily with a fork, about 10 minutes.

NUTRITIONAL

- Calories 44,
- Total Fat 0g,
- Saturated Fat 0g,
- Cholesterol 0mg,
- Sodium 127mg,
- Total Carbohydrate 11.8g,
- Dietary Fiber 0.2g,
- Total Sugars 9.3g,
- Protein 0.5g,
- Calcium 6mg,
- Iron 0mg,
- Potassium 58mg, P
- otassium 40mg

Preparation Time: 10 min |Cooking Time: 15 minutes |Servings: 4

Marinated Fried Fish

INGREDIENTS

- 2 (4 ounce) Salmon fillets
- 2 tablespoons lemon juice
- 2 tablespoons garlic powder
- 2 teaspoons ground cumin
- 1 teaspoon paprika
- 1/2 cup all-purpose flour
- 1 teaspoon dried rosemary
- 1/4 teaspoon cayenne pepper, or to taste
- 1 egg, beaten
- 1 tablespoon water
- ½ cup olive oil for frying

DIRECTION

- Place salmon fillets in a small glass dish. Mix lemon juice, garlic powder, cumin, and paprika in a small bowl; pour over salmon fillets. Cover dish with plastic wrap and marinate salmon in refrigerator for 2 hours.
- Mix flour, rosemary, and cayenne pepper together on a piece of waxed paper.
- Beat egg and water together in a wide bowl.
- Heat oil in a large skillet over medium heat.
- Gently press the salmon fillets into the flour mixture to coat; shake to remove excess flour. Dip into the beaten egg to coat and immediately return to the flour mixture to coat.
- Fry flounder in hot oil until the fish flakes easily with a fork, about 5 minutes per side.

NUTRITIONAL

- Calories 139,
- Total Fat 4.7g,
- Saturated Fat 0.9g,
- Cholesterol 50mg,
- Sodium 30mg,
- Total Carbohydrate 16.3g,
- Dietary Fiber 1.4g,
- Total Sugars 1.4g,
- Protein 8.2g,
- Calcium 34mg,
- Iron 2mg,
- Potassium 203mg,
- Potassium 140mg

Preparation Time: 15 min |Cooking Time: 10 minutes |Servings: 4

Spicy Lime and Basil Grilled Fish

INGREDIENTS

- 2 pounds salmon fillets, each cut into thirds
- 6 tablespoons butter, melted
- 1 lime, juiced
- 1 tablespoon dried basil
- 1 teaspoon red pepper flakes
- 1 onion, sliced crosswise 1/8-inch thick

DIRECTION

- Preheat grill for medium heat and lightly oil the grate.
- Lay 4 8x10-inch pieces of aluminum foil onto a flat work surface and spray with cooking spray.
- Arrange equal amounts of the salmon into the center of each foil square.
- Stir butter, lime juice, basil, and red pepper flakes together in a small bowl; drizzle evenly over each portion of fish. Top each portion with onion slices.
- Bring opposing ends of the foil together and roll together to form a seam. Roll ends toward fish to seal packets.
- Cook packets on the preheated grill until fish flakes easily with a fork, 5 to 7 minutes per side.

NUTRITIONAL

- Calories 151,
- Total Fat 13.4g,
- Saturated Fat 7.6g,
- Cholesterol 43mg,
- Sodium 95mg,
- Total Carbohydrate 3.1g,
- Dietary Fiber 0.8g,
- Total Sugars 1g,
- Protein 6g,
- Calcium 23mg,
- Iron 0mg,
- Potassium 158mg,
- Potassium 137mg

Preparation Time: 30 min |Cooking Time: 30 minutes |Servings: 4

Steamed Fish with Garlic

INGREDIENTS

- 2 (6 ounce) fillets cod fillets
- 3 tablespoons olive oil
- 1 onion, chopped
- 4 cloves garlic, minced
- 3 pinches dried rosemary
- Ground black pepper to taste
- 1 lemon, halved

DIRECTION

- Preheat oven to 350 degrees F.
- Place cod fillets on an 18x18-inch piece of aluminum foil; top with oil. Sprinkle onion, garlic, rosemary, and pepper over oil and cod. Squeeze juice from ½ lemon evenly on top.
- Lift up bottom and top ends of the aluminum foil towards the center; fold together to 1 inch above the cod. Flatten short ends of the aluminum foil; fold over to within 1 inch of the sides of the cod. Place foil package on a baking sheet.
- Bake in the preheated oven until haddock flakes easily with a fish, about 45 minutes. Let sit, about 5 minutes. Open ends of the packet carefully; squeeze juice from the remaining 1/2 lemon on top.

NUTRITIONAL

- Calories 171,
- Total Fat 11.3g,
- Saturated Fat 1.6g,
- Cholesterol 95mg,
- Sodium 308mg,
- Total Carbohydrate 5g,
- Dietary Fiber 1.1g,
- Total Sugars 1.6g,
- Protein 14.3g,
- Calcium 31mg,
- Iron 1mg,
- Potassium 76mg,
- Potassium 67mg

Preparation Time: 15 min |Cooking Time: 45 minutes |Servings: 4

Honey Fish

INGREDIENTS

- 3/4 cup olive oil, divided
- 1 1/2 pounds haddock, patted dry
- 1/2 cup honey
- 1 teaspoon dried basil

DIRECTION

- Preheat oven to 400 degrees F.
- Place 1/2 cup oil in a shallow microwave-safe bowl. Heat in the microwave until hot, about 30 seconds. Dip haddock in cracker mixture until coated on both sides. Transfer to a shallow baking dish.
- Bake haddock in the preheated oven until flesh flakes easily with a fork, about 25 minutes.
- Place remaining 1/4 cup oil in a small microwave-safe bowl. Heat in the microwave until hot, about 15 seconds. Stir in honey and basil until blended.
- Remove haddock from the oven; drizzle honey oil on top.
- Continue baking until top is browned, about 5 minutes more.

NUTRITIONAL

- Calories 347,
- Total Fat 25.9g,
- Saturated Fat 3.6g,
- Cholesterol 16mg,
- Sodium 46mg,
- Total Carbohydrate 27.5g,
- Dietary Fiber 0.2g,
- Total Sugars 24.5g
- , Protein 5.6g,
- Calcium 11mg,
- Iron 4mg,
- Potassium 108mg,
- Potassium 97mg

Preparation Time: 15 min |Cooking Time: 30 minutes |Servings: 4

Salmon and Sweet Potato Chowder

INGREDIENTS

- 1 tbsp. Butter
- 1 minced clove of Garlic
- 1 chopped Onion
- 2 tsp. Dill Weed
- 3 tbsp. o all-purpose Flour
- Ground Black Pepper
- 2 cups Milk
- 2 cups Chicken Broth
- 1 ½ cups Corn Kernels
- 1 tsp. Lemon Zest
- 12 ounces sliced Salmon Fillets
- 3 tbsp. Lemon Juice

DIRECTION

- Sauté pepper, dill, garlic and onion in butter in a pan.
- Add in the flour and cook for 2 mins.
- Pour broth and then milk to the pan. Simmer.
- Cook on "low" for 4 hrs.
- Add in the salmon and cook again on "low" for 20 more mins.
- Now, stir in the lemon zest, lemon juice along with the pepper.
- Serve hot in heated bowls.

NUTRITIONAL

- Calories 391
- Total Fat 27 g
- Cholesterol 94 mg
- Sodium 320 mg
- Carbohydrates 39 mg
- Dietary Fiber 7 g
- Protein 37 g

Preparation Time: 1hrs. |Cooking Time: 4 hrs. |Servings: 4

Sesame Salmon Fillets

INGREDIENTS

- 2 tbsp. Sesame Oil
- ¼ tsp. Sea Salt
- ¼ tsp. Black Pepper (cracked)
- 1 tbsp. Vinegar
- 4 tsp. Sesame Seeds (black)
- ¼ tsp. Ginger (ground)
- 4 skinless Salmon fillets

DIRECTION

- Coat the slow cooker with oil. Set the cooker on "high".
- Place the salmon in the cooker. Drizzle the sesame seeds, pepper, salt and ginger on the salmon.
- Turn after 3 mins and repeat the procedure.
- Add vinegar and cook on "high" for 20 mins.
- Transfer the salmon to a plate. Serve immediately

NUTRITIONAL

- Calories 319
- Total Fat 21g
- Cholesterol 81mg
- Sodium 204mg
- Carbohydrates 31g
- Dietary Fiber 1g
- Protein 31g

Preparation Time: 10 minutes|Cooking Time: 30 minutes|Servings: 4

Peppered Balsamic Cod

INGREDIENTS

- 1 1/2 pounds cod filets
- 2 teaspoons olive oil
- 1 teaspoon lemon zest
- 1/2 teaspoon cracked black peppercorns
- 2 tablespoons balsamic vinegar, reduced to a syrup

DIRECTION

- Cut a piece of foil large enough to wrap completely around the fish, or cut 4 smaller pieces to wrap the fish into individual packets. Brush the foil with 1 teaspoon of the oil. Arrange the fish in the center of the foil and brush with the remaining oil. Season evenly with the lemon zest and pepper. Drizzle with the balsamic vinegar. Fold the foil completely around the fish and crimp the edges to seal the package(s) completely.
- Set the package in the slow cooker, cover with a lid, cook on HIGH for 2 hours, or until the fish is completely cooked.
- Serve at once.

NUTRITIONAL

- Calories 201;
- Total Fat 5g;
- Saturated Fat 1g;
- Cholesterol 101mg;
- Sodium 121mg;
- Total Carbohydrates 1g;
- Dietary Fiber 1g;
- Protein 39g;
- Sugars 1g

Preparation Time: 10 minutes|Cooking Time: 2 hours|Servings: 4

Seafood Gumbo

INGREDIENTS

- 2 teaspoons olive oil
- 1/4 cup minced turkey ham (low sodium)
- 2 stalks celery, sliced
- 1 medium onion, sliced
- 1 green bell pepper, chopped
- 2 cloves garlic, minced
- 2 cups chicken broth (low sodium)
- 1 (14-ounce) can diced Red bell peppers, including juices
- 1 teaspoon Worcestershire sauce
- 1/4 teaspoon kosher salt
- 1 teaspoon dried thyme
- 1-pound shrimp (16/20), cleaned
- 1 pound fresh or frozen crabmeat, picked to remove cartilage
- 1 (10-ounce) package frozen okra, thawed

DIRECTION

- Heat the oil in a sauté pan over medium-high heat. Add the ham and cook until crisp.
- Transfer the ham to a slow cooker.
- Add the celery, onion, green pepper, and garlic to the sauté pan and cook over medium heat, stirring frequently, until the vegetables are tender, about 10 minutes. Transfer to the cooker and add the broth, Red bell peppers, juices, Worcestershire, salt, and thyme.
- Cover and cook on LOW for 4 hours. Add the shrimp, crabmeat, and okra, and cook on HIGH for 20 minutes or until the shrimp is bright pink and firm.
- Serve at once in heated soup bowls.

NUTRITIONAL

- Saturated Fat 3g;
- Cholesterol 207mg;
- Sodium 313mg;
- Total Carbohydrates 16g;
- Dietary Fiber 5g;
- Protein 22g;
- Sugars 2g
- Calories 155;
- Total Fat

Preparation Time: 25 minutes|Cooking Time: 5 hours|Servings: 6

Salmon Chowder with and Corn

INGREDIENTS

- 1 tablespoon butter
- 1 onion, finely chopped
- 1 clove garlic, minced
- 2 teaspoons dill weed
- Freshly ground black pepper
- 3 tablespoons all-purpose flour
- 2 cups chicken broth (low sodium)
- 2 cups milk
- 1 1/2 cups of corn kernels
- 12 ounces salmon fillet, cut into chunks
- 1 teaspoon grated lemon zest
- 3 tablespoons lemon juice

DIRECTION

- Melt the butter on medium heat. Add the onion, garlic, dill, and a pinch of pepper; sauté, stirring frequently, until the onion is tender.
- Add the flour and stir until thick and pasty, about 2 minutes.
- Whisk in the broth until there are no lumps, then stir in the milk, and bring to a simmer.
- Pour into the slow cooker and add the corn.
- Stir in the salmon, replace the lid, cook on LOW for 20 minutes, or until the salmon is cooked (145°F) and very hot.
- Stir in the lemon zest and season to taste with lemon juice and additional pepper.
- Serve in heated soup bowls.

NUTRITIONAL

- Calories 391;
- Total Fat 18g;
- Saturated Fat 9g;
- Cholesterol 94mg;
- Sodium 320mg;
- Total Carbohydrates 39g;
- Dietary Fiber 7g;
- Protein 37g;
- Sugars 17g

Preparation Time: 10 minutes|Cooking Time: 4 hours|Servings: 4

Mediterranean Fish Stew

INGREDIENTS

- 1 onion, sliced
- 1 leek, white and light green portion, sliced thin
- 4 cloves garlic, minced
- 1/2 cup dry white wine
- 1/4 cup water
- 4 bay leaves
- 1-piece orange peel, 2 inches, pith removed
- 1/2 teaspoon cracked black peppercorns
- 1 1/2 pounds haddock fillets
- 12 ounces shrimp (16/20), peeled and deveined
- 2 teaspoons extra-virgin olive oil for serving
- 2 tablespoons chopped parsley, flat leaf

DIRECTION

- Make a bed of the onion, leek, and garlic in the slow cooker. Add the wine and water to the cooker. Scatter the bay leaves, orange peel, and peppercorns on top.
- Cover the cooker and cook on HIGH for 2 hours. Add the fish and the shrimp, replace the cover, and cook on HIGH for an additional 2 hours or until the fish is cooked through and the shrimps are bright pink and opaque. Remove and discard the bay leaves and orange peel.
- Serve the fish and shrimp in heated soup bowls topped with the cooking liquid and vegetables. Drizzle with olive oil and garnish with parsley.

NUTRITIONAL

- Calories 207;
- Total Fat 4g;
- Saturated Fat 0g;
- Cholesterol 168mg;
- Sodium 536mg;
- Total Carbohydrates 5g;
- Dietary Fiber 1g;
- Protein 32g;
- Sugars 0g

Preparation Time: 15 minutes|Cooking Time: 4 hours|Servings: 6

Tuna and Red Pepper Stew

INGREDIENTS

- 1 tablespoon olive oil
- 1 onion, chopped
- 1 garlic clove, minced
- 1/4 teaspoon red pepper flakes, or more to taste
- 1/2 cup dry white wine
- 1 (14-ounce) can diced Red bell peppers
- 1-pound baby red potatoes, scrubbed
- 1 teaspoon paprika
- 2 pounds tuna fillet
- 2 roasted red bell peppers, seeded and cut into strips
- 3 tablespoons chopped cilantro for garnish

DIRECTION

- Combine the oil, onions, garlic, red pepper flakes, wine, Red bell peppers, and potatoes, in a slow cooker.
- Cover and cook on HIGH for 2 hours.
- Add the tuna and the roasted peppers, season with the paprika, and replace the cover.
- Continue to cook on HIGH for another 2 hours or until the tuna is fully cooked.
- Serve at once, topped with the cilantro.

NUTRITIONAL

- Calories 107;
- Total Fat 3g;
- Saturated Fat 0g;
- Cholesterol 8mg;
- Sodium 200mg;
- Total Carbohydrates 15g;
- Dietary Fiber 2g;
- Protein 5g;
- Sugars 0g

Preparation Time: 15 minutes|Cooking Time: 4 hours|Servings: 6

Sweet and Sour Shrimp

INGREDIENTS

- 1 cup Chinese pea pods, thawed
- 1 14oz can pineapple chunks
- 2 tablespoons cornstarch
- 3 tbsp. sugar
- 1 cup chicken stock (see recipe)
- ½ cup reserved pineapple juice
- 1 tbsp. low-sodium soy sauce
- ½ tsp ground ginger
- 1lb large cooked shrimp
- 2 tbsp. cider vinegar
- 1 cup of rice, cooked

DIRECTION

- Place the pea pods and pineapple in a 4 to 6-quart slow cooker.
- Blend the cornstarch and sugar with the chicken stock and pineapple juice and heat in a small saucepan until thickened.
- Pour only the sauce into the slow cooker and add the ginger and soy sauce.
- Cover and cook on LOW for 3 to 4 hours.
- Add the shrimp and vinegar and cook for a further 15 minutes.
- Serve with the hot cooked rice.

NUTRITIONAL

- Calories 395,
- Fat 2g,
- Carbs 61g,
- Protein 33g,
- Fiber 5g,
- Potassium 796mg,
- Sodium 215 mg

Preparation Time: 10 minutes |Cooking Time: 5.5 hours |Servings 3-4

Salmon with Caramelized Onions

INGREDIENTS

- 1lb salmon fillet, cut into small fillets
- 1 tbsp. extra-virgin olive oil
- ½ large onion, thinly sliced
- ¼ tsp ground ginger
- ¼ tsp dried dill
- ¼ tsp low-sodium salt
- ¼ tsp black pepper
- ½ lemon, thinly sliced

DIRECTION

- Arrange the onions in the base of the slow cooker.
- Place each piece of salmon in an aluminum foil packet and sprinkle with spices and top with lemon slices.
- Place the salmon packets on top of the onions in the slow cooker and cover.
- Cook on LOW for 6 to 8 hours.
- Serve the salmon on top of the onions.

NUTRITIONAL

- Calories 215,
- Fat 11g,
- Carbs 7g,
- Protein 24g,
- Fiber 2g,
- Potassium 520mg,
- Sodium 200mg

Preparation Time: 25 minutes |Cooking Time: 6 hours |Servings 6

Fisherman's Stew

INGREDIENTS

- 1 fillet of seabass, cod or other white fish, cubed
- 1 dozen each large shrimp, scallops, mussels & clams
- 1 28 ounces no-added salt crushed Red bell peppers with juice
- 1 8oz no-added salt tomato sauce
- ½ cup onion, chopped
- 1 cup dry white wine
- 1/3 cup olive oil
- 3 garlic cloves, minced
- ½ cup parsley, chopped
- 1 green pepper, chopped
- 1 hot pepper, chopped
- ½ tsp low sodium salt
- 1 tsp thyme
- 2 tsp basil
- 1 tsp oregano
- ½ tsp paprika
- ½ tsp cayenne pepper

DIRECTION

- Place all ingredients except seafood in a 4 to 6-quart slow cooker and cover.
- Cook (low) for 6-8 hours.
- Add the fish about 30 minutes towards the end of the cooking time and turn up the heat to HIGH.

NUTRITIONAL

- Calories 434,
- Fat 16g,
- Carbs 27g,
- Protein 39g,
- Fiber 4g,
- Potassium 714mg,
- Sodium 378mg

Preparation Time: 15 minutes|Cooking Time: 6-8 hours |Servings: 8

Fish Chowder

INGREDIENTS

- 2lb white fish fillets, cut into 1-inch pieces
- ¼lb low-sodium bacon, diced
- 1 medium onion, chopped
- 4 medium red-skinned potatoes, peeled and cubed
- 2 cup water
- 1 low sodium salt
- ¼ tsp black pepper
- 1 12oz can evaporated milk

DIRECTION

- Fry the bacon in a skillet for a few minutes with the onion.
- Add the bacon to the slow cooker with the remaining ingredients except for the evaporated milk.
- Cover and cook on HIGH for 5 to 6 hours.
- Add the milk during the last hour of cooking.

NUTRITIONAL

- Calories 311,
- Fat 13g,
- Carbs 27g,
- Protein 14g,
- Fiber 12g,
- Potassium 911mg,
- Sodium 600mg

Preparation Time: 10 minutes|Cooking Time: 6 hours|Servings: 6

Shrimp Creole

INGREDIENTS

- 1½ cup celery, diced
- 1¼ cup onion, chopped
- 1 cup bell pepper, chopped
- 1 8oz can no-added salt tomato sauce
- 1 28oz no-added salt can whole Red bell peppers
- 1 garlic clove, minced
- ½ tsp low-sodium salt
- ½ tsp salt-free Creole seasoning
- ¼ tsp freshly ground black pepper
- 6 drops Tabasco sauce
- 1lb shrimp, deveined and shelled

DIRECTION

- Place all the ingredients into a 3-quart slow cooker except the shrimp.
- Cook (high) 3 to 4 hours.
- Add shrimp during last 30 minutes of cooking.
- Serve over hot cooked rice

NUTRITIONAL

- Calories 388,
- Fat 3g,
- Carbs 42g,
- Protein 52g,
- Fiber 8g,
- Potassium 874mg,
- Sodium 600mg

Preparation Time: 20 minutes|Cooking Time: 4 hours|Servings: 3

Cajun Catfish

INGREDIENTS

- 16 oz. catfish steaks (4 oz. each fish steak)
- 1 tablespoon Cajun spices
- 1 egg, beaten
- 1 tablespoon sunflower oil

DIRECTION

- Pour sunflower oil in the skillet and preheat it until shimmering.
- Meanwhile, dip every catfish steak in the beaten egg and coat in Cajun spices.
- Place the fish steaks in the hot oil and roast them for 4 minutes from each side.
- The cooked catfish steaks should have a light brown crust.

NUTRITIONAL

- Calories 263,
- Fat 16.7,
- Fiber 0,
- Carbs 0.1,
- Protein 26.3

Preparation Time: 10 minutes|Cooking Time: 10 minutes|Servings: 4

Teriyaki Tuna

INGREDIENTS

- 3 tuna fillets
- 3 teaspoons teriyaki sauce
- ½ teaspoon minced garlic
- 1 teaspoon olive oil

DIRECTION

- Whisk together teriyaki sauce, minced garlic, and olive oil.
- Brush every tuna fillet with teriyaki mixture.
- Preheat grill to 390F.
- Grill the fish for 3 minutes from each side.

NUTRITIONAL

- Calories 382,
- Fat 32.6,
- Fiber 0,
- Carbs 1.1,
- Protein 21.4

Preparation Time: 10 minutes|Cooking Time: 6 minutes|Servings: 3

Cod Curry

INGREDIENTS

- 4 cod fillets, boneless
- ½ teaspoon mustard seeds
- Salt and black pepper to the taste
- 2 green chilies, chopped
- 1 teaspoon fresh grated ginger
- 1 teaspoon curry powder
- ¼ teaspoon ground cumin
- 1 small red onion, chopped
- 1 teaspoon ground turmeric
- ¼ cup chopped parsley
- 1½ cups coconut cream
- 3 garlic cloves, minced

DIRECTION

- Heat a pot with half of the oil over medium heat. Add mustard seeds and cook for 2 minutes. Add ginger, onion, garlic, turmeric, curry powder, chilies, and cumin, stir and cook for 10 minutes more. Add coconut milk, salt and pepper then stir. Bring to a boil, cook for 10 minutes and take off the heat. Warm another pan with the rest of the oil over medium heat, add fish, and then cook for 4 minutes. Transfer the fish on top of the curry mix, toss gently then cook for 6 more minutes. Divide between plates, sprinkle the parsley on top and serve.
- Enjoy!

NUTRITIONAL

- Calories 210
- Fat 14
- Fiber 7
- Carbs 6
- Protein 16

Preparation Time: 10 minutes |Cooking Time: 25 minutes |Servings: 4

Chapter 19
Meat Recipes

Beef and Chili Stew

INGREDIENTS

- 1/2 medium red onion, sliced thinly
- 1/2 tablespoon vegetable oil
- 10ounce of flat-cut beef brisket, whole
- ½ cup low sodium stock
- ¾ cup of water
- ½ tablespoon honey
- ½ tablespoon chili powder
- ½ teaspoon smoked paprika
- ½ teaspoon dried thyme
- 1 teaspoon black pepper
- 1 tablespoon corn starch

DIRECTION

- Throw the sliced onion into the slow cooker first. Add a splash of oil to a large hot skillet and briefly seal the beef on all sides.
- Remove the beef, then place it in the slow cooker. Add the stock, water, honey, and spices to the same skillet you cooked the beef meat.
- Allow the juice to simmer until the volume is reduced by about half. Pour the juice over beef in the slow cooker. Cook on low within 7 hours.
- Transfer the beef to your platter, shred it using two forks. Put the rest of the juice into a medium saucepan. Bring it to a simmer.
- Whisk the cornstarch with two tablespoons of water. Add to the juice and cook until slightly thickened.
- For a thicker sauce, simmer and reduce the juice a bit more before adding cornstarch. Put the sauce on the meat and serve.

NUTRITIONAL

- Calories: 128
- Protein: 13g
- Carbohydrates: 6g
- Fat: 6g
- Sodium: 228mg
- Potassium: 202mg
- Phosphorus: 119mg

Preparation Time: 15 minutes |Cooking Time: 7 hours |Servings: 6

Sticky Pulled Beef Open Sandwiches

INGREDIENTS

- ½ cup of green onion, sliced
- 2 garlic cloves
- 2 tablespoons of fresh parsley
- 2 large carrots
- 7 ounce of flat-cut beef brisket, whole
- 1 tablespoon of smoked paprika
- 1 teaspoon dried parsley
- 1 teaspoon of brown sugar
- ½ teaspoon of black pepper
- 2 tablespoon of olive oil
- ¼ cup of red wine
- 8 tablespoon of cider vinegar
- 3 cups of water
- 5 slices white bread
- 1 cup of arugula to garnish

DIRECTION

- Finely chop the green onion, garlic, and fresh parsley. Grate the carrot. Put the beef in to roast in a slow cooker.
- Add the chopped onion, garlic, and remaining ingredients, leaving the rolls, fresh parsley, and arugula to one side. Stir in the slow cooker to combine.
- Cover and cook on low within 8 1/2 to 10 hours or on high for 4 to 5 hours until tender. Remove the meat from the slow cooker. Shred the meat using two forks.
- Return the meat to the broth to keep it warm until ready to serve. Lightly toast the bread and top with shredded beef, arugula, fresh parsley, and ½ spoon of the broth. Serve.

NUTRITIONAL

- Calories: 273
- Protein: 15g
- Carbohydrates: 20g
- Fat: 11g
- Sodium: 308mg
- Potassium: 399mg
- Phosphorus: 159mg

Preparation Time: 15 minutes |Cooking Time: 5 hours |Servings: 5

Herby Beef Stroganoff and Fluffy Rice

INGREDIENTS

- ½ cup onion
- 2 garlic cloves
- 9 ounce of flat-cut beef brisket, cut into 1" cubes
- ½ cup of reduced-sodium beef stock
- 1/3 cup red wine
- ½ teaspoon dried oregano
- ¼ teaspoon freshly ground black pepper
- ½ teaspoon dried thyme
- ½ teaspoon of saffron
- ½ cup almond milk (un-enriched)
- ¼ cup all-purpose flour
- 1 cup of water
- 2 ½ cups of white rice

DIRECTION

- Dice the onion, then mince the garlic cloves. Mix the beef, stock, wine, onion, garlic, oregano, pepper, thyme, and saffron in your slow cooker.
- Cover and cook on high within 4-5 hours. Combine the almond milk, flour, and water. Whisk together until smooth.
- Add the flour mixture to the slow cooker. Cook for another 15 to 25 minutes until the stroganoff is thick.
- Cook the rice using the package instructions, leaving out the salt. Drain off the excess water. Serve the stroganoff over the rice.

NUTRITIONAL

- Calories: 241
- Protein: 15g
- Carbohydrates: 29g
- Fat: 5g
- Sodium: 182mg
- Potassium: 206mg
- Phosphorus: 151mg

Preparation Time: 15 minutes |Cooking Time: 5 hours |Servings: 6

Chunky Beef and Potato Slow Roast

INGREDIENTS

- 3 cups of peeled potatoes, chunked
- 1 cup of onion
- 2 garlic cloves, chopped
- 1 ¼ pound flat-cut beef brisket, fat trimmed
- 2 cups of water
- 1 teaspoon of chili powder
- 1 tablespoon of dried rosemary
- For the sauce:
- 1 tablespoon of freshly grated horseradish
- ½ cup of almond milk (unenriched)
- 1 tablespoon lemon juice (freshly squeezed)
- 1 garlic clove, minced
- A pinch of cayenne pepper

DIRECTION

- Double boil the potatoes to reduce their potassium content. Chop the onion and the garlic. Place the beef brisket in a slow cooker. Combine water, chopped garlic, chili powder, and rosemary.
- Pour the mixture over the brisket. Cover and cook on high within 4-5 hours until the meat is very tender. Drain the potatoes and add them to the slow cooker.
- Adjust the heat to high and cook covered until the potatoes are tender. Prepare the horseradish sauce by whisking together horseradish, milk, lemon juice, minced garlic, and cayenne pepper.
- Cover and refrigerate. Serve your casserole with a dash of horseradish sauce on the side.

NUTRITIONAL

- Calories: 199
- Protein: 21g
- Carbohydrates: 12g
- Fat: 7g
- Sodium: 282mg
- Potassium: 317
- Phosphorus: 191mg

Preparation Time: 15 minutes |Cooking Time: 5-6 hours |Servings: 12

Spiced Lamb Burgers

INGREDIENTS

- 1 tablespoon extra-virgin olive oil
- 1 teaspoon cumin
- ½ finely diced red onion
- 1 minced garlic clove
- 1 teaspoon harissa spices
- 1 cup arugula
- 1 juiced lemon
- 6-ounce lean ground lamb
- 1 tablespoon parsley
- ½ cup low-fat plain yogurt

DIRECTION

- Preheat the broiler on medium to high heat. Mix the ground lamb, red onion, parsley, Harissa spices, and olive oil until combined.
- Shape 1-inch thick patties using wet hands. Add the patties to a baking tray and place under the broiler for 7-8 minutes on each side. Mix the yogurt, lemon juice, and cumin and serve over the lamb burgers with arugula's side salad.

NUTRITIONAL

- Calories 306
- Fat 20g
- Carbs 10g
- Phosphorus 269mg
- Potassium 492mg
- Sodium 86mg
- Protein 23g

Preparation Time: 10 minutes |Cooking Time: 20 minutes |Servings: 2

Pork Loins with Leeks

INGREDIENTS

- 1 sliced leek
- 1 tablespoon mustard seeds
- 6-ounce pork tenderloin
- 1 tablespoon cumin seeds
- 1 tablespoon dry mustard
- 1 tablespoon extra-virgin oil

DIRECTION

- Preheat the broiler to medium-high heat. In a dry skillet, heat mustard and cumin seeds until they start to pop (3-5 minutes). Grind seeds using a pestle and mortar or blender and then mix in the dry mustard.
- Massage the pork on all sides using the mustard blend and add to a baking tray to broil for 25-30 minutes or until cooked through. Turn once halfway through.
- Remove and place to one side, then heat-up the oil in a pan on medium heat and add the leeks for 5-6 minutes or until soft. Serve the pork tenderloin on a bed of leeks and enjoy it!

NUTRITIONAL

- Calories 139
- Fat 5g
- Carbs 2g
- Phosphorus 278mg
- Potassium 45mg
- Sodium 47mg
- Protein 18g

Preparation Time: 10 minutes | Cooking Time: 35 minutes | Servings: 2

Chinese Beef Wraps

INGREDIENTS

- 2 iceberg lettuce leaves
- ½ diced cucumber
- 1 teaspoon canola oil
- 5-ounce lean ground beef
- 1 teaspoon ground ginger
- 1 tablespoon chili flakes
- 1 minced garlic clove
- 1 tablespoon rice wine vinegar

DIRECTION

- Mix the ground meat with the garlic, rice wine vinegar, chili flakes, and ginger in a bowl. Heat-up oil in a skillet over medium heat.
- Put the beef in the pan and cook for 20-25 minutes or until cooked through. Serve beef mixture with diced cucumber in each lettuce wrap and fold.

NUTRITIONAL

- Calories 156
- Fat 2g
- Carbs 4 g
- Phosphorus 1 mg
- Sodium 54mg
- Protein 14g
- Potassium 0mg

Preparation Time: 10 minutes | Cooking Time: 30 minutes | Servings: 2

Spicy Lamb Curry

INGREDIENTS

- 4 teaspoons ground coriander
- 4 teaspoons ground coriander
- 4 teaspoons ground cumin
- ¾ teaspoon ground ginger
- 2 teaspoons ground cinnamon
- ½ teaspoon ground cloves
- ½ teaspoon ground cardamom
- 2 tablespoons sweet paprika
- ½ tablespoon cayenne pepper
- 2 teaspoons chili powder
- 2 teaspoons salt
- 1 tablespoon coconut oil
- 2 pounds boneless lamb, trimmed and cubed into 1-inch size
- Salt
- ground black pepper
- 2 cups onions, chopped
- 1¼ cups water
- 1 cup of coconut milk

DIRECTION

- For spice mixture in a bowl, mix all spices. Keep aside. Season the lamb with salt and black pepper.
- Warm oil on medium-high heat in a large Dutch oven. Add lamb and stir fry for around 5 minutes. Add onion and cook approximately 4-5 minutes.
- Stir in the spice mixture and cook approximately 1 minute. Add water and coconut milk and provide some boil on high heat.
- Adjust the heat to low and simmer, covered for approximately 1-120 minutes or until the lamb's desired doneness. Uncover and simmer for about 3-4 minutes. Serve hot.

NUTRITIONAL

- Calories: 466
- Fat: 10g
- Carbohydrates: 23g
- Protein: 36g
- Potassium 599 mg
- Sodium 203 mg
- Phosphorus 0mg

Preparation Time: 15 minutes |Cooking Time: 2 hours 15 minutes |Servings: 6-8

Roast Beef

INGREDIENTS

- Quality rump or sirloin tip roast
- Pepper & herbs

DIRECTION

- Place in a roasting pan on a shallow rack. Season with pepper and herbs. Insert meat thermometer in the center or thickest part of the roast.
- Roast to the desired degree of doneness. After removing from over for about 15 minutes, let it chill. In the end, the roast should be moister than well done.

NUTRITIONAL

- Calories 158
- Protein 24 g
- Fat 6 g
- Carbs 0 g
- Phosphorus 206 mg
- Potassium 328 mg
- Sodium 55 mg

Preparation Time: 25 minutes |Cooking Time: 55 minutes |Servings: 3

Grilled Skirt Steak

INGREDIENTS

- 2 teaspoons fresh ginger herb, grated finely
- 2 teaspoons fresh lime zest, grated finely
- 1/4 cup coconut sugar
- 2 teaspoons fish sauce
- 2 tablespoons fresh lime juice
- 1/2 cup coconut milk
- 1-pound beef skirt steak, trimmed and cut into 4-inch slices lengthwise
- Salt, to taste

DIRECTION

- In a sizable sealable bag, mix together all ingredients except steak and salt.
- Add steak and coat with marinade generously.
- Seal the bag and refrigerate to marinate for about 4-12 hours.
- Preheat the grill to high heat. Grease the grill grate.
- Remove steak from refrigerator and discard the marinade.
- With a paper towel, dry the steak and sprinkle with salt evenly.
- Cook the steak for approximately 31/2 minutes.
- Flip the medial side and cook for around 21/2-5 minutes or till desired doneness.
- Remove from grill pan and keep side for approximately 5 minutes before slicing.
- With a clear, crisp knife cut into desired slices and serve.

NUTRITIONAL

- Calories: 465,
- Fat: 10g,
- Carbohydrates: 22g,
- Fiber: 0g,
- Protein: 37g

Preparation Time: 15 minutes |Cooking Time: 8-9 minutes |Servings: 4

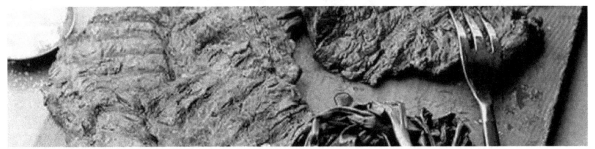

Lamb with Zucchini & Couscous

INGREDIENTS

- ¾ cup couscous
- ¾ cup boiling water
- 1/4 cup fresh cilantro, chopped
- 1 tbsp. olive oil
- 5-ounces lamb leg steak, cubed into ¾-inch size
- 1 medium zucchini, sliced thinly
- 1 medium red onion, cut into wedges
- 1 teaspoon ground cumin
- 1 teaspoon ground coriander
- 1/4 teaspoon red pepper flakes, crushed
- Salt, to taste
- 1/4 cup plain Greek yogurt
- 1 garlic herb, minced

DIRECTION

- In a bowl, add couscous and boiling water and stir to combine.
- Cover whilst aside approximately 5 minutes.
- Add cilantro and with a fork, fluff completely.
- Meanwhile in a substantial skillet, heat oil on high heat.
- Add lamb and stir fry for about 2-3 minutes.
- Add zucchini and onion and stir fry for about 2 minutes.
- Stir in spices and stir fry for about 1 minute
- Add couscous and stir fry approximately 2 minutes.
- In a bowl, mix together yogurt and garlic.
- Divide lamb mixture in serving plates evenly.
- Serve using the topping of yogurt.

NUTRITIONAL

- Calories: 392,
- Fat: 5g,
- Carbohydrates: 2g,
- Fiber: 12g,
- Protein: 35g

Preparation Time: 15 minutes |Cooking Time: 8 minutes |Servings: 2

Ground Lamb with Harissa

INGREDIENTS

- 1 tablespoon extra-virgin olive oil
- 2 red peppers, seeded and chopped finely
- 1 yellow onion, chopped finely
- 2 garlic cloves, chopped finely
- 1 teaspoon ground cumin
- 1/2 teaspoon ground turmeric
- 1/4 teaspoon ground cinnamon
- 1/4 teaspoon ground ginger
- 11/2 pound lean ground lamb
- Salt, to taste
- 1 (141/2-ounce) can diced Red bell peppers
- 2 tablespoons harissa
- 1 cup water
- Chopped fresh cilantro, for garnishing

DIRECTION

- In a sizable pan, heat oil on medium-high heat.
- Add bell pepper, onion and garlic and sauté for around 5 minutes.
- Add spices and sauté for around 1 minute.
- Add lamb and salt and cook approximately 5 minutes, getting into pieces.
- Stir in Red bell peppers, harissa and water and provide with a boil.
- Reduce the warmth to low and simmer, covered for about 1 hour.
- Serve hot while using garnishing of harissa.

NUTRITIONAL

- Calories: 441,
- Fat: 12g,
- Carbohydrates: 24g,
- Fiber: 10g,
- Protein: 36g

Preparation Time: 15 minutes |Cooking Time: one hour 11 minutes |Servings: 4

Broiled Lamb Shoulder

INGREDIENTS

- 2 tablespoons fresh ginger, minced
- 2 tablespoons garlic, minced
- 1/4 cup fresh lemongrass stalk, minced
- 1/4 cup fresh orange juice
- 1/4 cup coconut aminos
- Freshly ground black pepper, to taste
- 2-pound lamb shoulder, trimmed

DIRECTION

- In a bowl, mix together all ingredients except lamb shoulder.
- In a baking dish, squeeze lamb shoulder and coat the lamb with half in the marinade mixture generously.
- Reserve remaining mixture.
- Refrigerate to marinate for overnight.
- Preheat the broiler of oven. Place a rack inside a broiler pan and arrange about 4-5-inches from heating unit.
- Remove lamb shoulder from refrigerator and remove excess marinade.
- Broil approximately 4-5 minutes from both sides.
- Serve with all the reserved marinade like a sauce.

NUTRITIONAL

- Calories: 250,
- Fat: 19g,
- Carbohydrates: 2g,
- Fiber: 0g, P
- rotein: 15g

Preparation Time: 10 minutes |Cooking Time: 8-10 minutes |Servings: 10

Pan-Seared Lamb Chops

INGREDIENTS

- 4 garlic cloves, peeled
- Salt, to taste
- 1 teaspoon black mustard seeds, crushed finely
- 2 teaspoons ground cumin
- 1 teaspoon ground ginger
- 1 teaspoon ground coriander
- 1/2 teaspoon ground cinnamon
- Freshly ground black pepper, to taste
- 1 tablespoon coconut oil
- 8 medium lamb chops, trimmed

DIRECTION

- Place garlic cloves onto a cutting board and sprinkle with salt.
- With a knife, crush the garlic till a paste forms.
- In a bowl, mix together garlic paste and spices.
- With a clear, crisp knife, make 3-4 cuts on both sides in the chops.
- Rub the chops with garlic mixture generously.
- In a large skillet, melt butter on medium heat.
- Add chops and cook for approximately 2-3 minutes per side or till desired doneness.

NUTRITIONAL

- Calories: 443,
- Fat: 11g,
- Carbohydrates: 27g,
- Fiber: 4g,
- Protein: 40g

Preparation Time: 10 minutes |Cooking Time: 4-6 minutes |Servings: 4

Grilled Lamb Chops

INGREDIENTS

- 1 tablespoon fresh ginger, grated
- 4 garlic cloves, chopped roughly
- 1 teaspoon ground cumin
- 1/2 teaspoon red chili powder
- Salt and freshly ground black pepper, to taste
- 1 tbsp. essential olive oil
- 1 tablespoon fresh lemon juice
- 8 lamb chops, trimmed

DIRECTION

- In a bowl, mix together all ingredients except chops.
- With a hand blender, blend till a smooth mixture forms.
- Add chops and coat with mixture generously.
- Refrigerate to marinate for overnight.
- Preheat the barbecue grill till hot. Grease the grill grate.
- Grill the chops for approximately 3 minutes per side.

NUTRITIONAL

- Calories: 227,
- Fat: 12g,
- Carbohydrates: 1g,
- Fiber: 0g,
- Protein: 30g

Preparation Time: 10 min |Cooking Time: 6 minutes |Servings: 4

Lamb & Pineapple Kebabs

INGREDIENTS

- 1 large pineapple, cubed into 11/2-inch size, divided
- 1 (1/2-inch) piece fresh ginger, chopped
- 2 garlic cloves, chopped
- Salt, to taste
- 16-24-ounce lamb shoulder steak, trimmed and cubed into 11/2-inch size
- Fresh mint leaves coming from a bunch
- Ground cinnamon, to taste

DIRECTION

- In a blender, add about 11/2 of pineapple, ginger, garlic and salt and pulse till smooth.
- Transfer the amalgamation right into a large bowl.
- Add chops and coat with mixture generously.
- Refrigerate to marinate for about 1-2 hours.
- Preheat the grill to medium heat. Grease the grill grate.
- Thread lam, remaining pineapple and mint leaves onto pre-soaked wooden skewers.
- Grill the kebabs approximately 10 min, turning occasionally.

NUTRITIONAL

- Calories: 482,
- Fat: 16g,
- Carbohydrates: 22g,
- Fiber: 5g,
- Protein: 377g

Preparation Time: 15 minutes |Cooking Time: 10 minutes |Servings: 4-6

Pork with Bell Pepper

INGREDIENTS

- 1 tablespoon fresh ginger, chopped finely
- 4 garlic cloves, chopped finely
- 1 cup fresh cilantro, chopped and divided
- 1/4 cup plus 1 tbsp. olive oil, divided
- 1-pound tender pork, trimmed, sliced thinly
- 2 onions, sliced thinly
- 1 green bell pepper, seeded and sliced thinly
- 1 tablespoon fresh lime juice

DIRECTION

- In a substantial bowl, mix together ginger, garlic, 1/2 cup of cilantro and 1/4 cup of oil.
- Add pork and coat with mixture generously.
- Refrigerate to marinate approximately a couple of hours.
- Heat a big skillet on medium-high heat.
- Add pork mixture and stir fry for approximately 4-5 minutes.
- Transfer the pork right into a bowl.
- In the same skillet, heat remaining oil on medium heat.
- Add onion and sauté for approximately 3 minutes.
- Stir in bell pepper and stir fry for about 3 minutes.
- Stir in pork, lime juice and remaining cilantro and cook for about 2 minutes.
- Serve hot.

NUTRITIONAL

- Calories: 429,
- Fat: 19g,
- Carbohydrates: 26g,
- Fiber: 9g,
- Protein: 35g

Preparation Time: 15 minutes |Cooking Time: 13 minutes |Servings: 4

Pork with Pineapple

INGREDIENTS

- 2 tablespoons coconut oil
- 11/2 pound pork tenderloin, trimmed and cut into bite-sized pieces
- 1 onion, chopped
- 2 minced garlic cloves
- 1 (1-inch) piece fresh ginger, minced
- 20-ounce pineapple, cut into chunks
- 1 large red bell pepper, seeded and chopped
- 1/4 cup fresh pineapple juice
- 1/4 cup coconut aminos
- Salt and freshly ground black pepper, to taste

DIRECTION

- In a substantial skillet, melt coconut oil on high heat.
- Add pork and stir fry approximately 4-5 minutes.
- Transfer the pork right into a bowl.
- In exactly the same skillet, heat remaining oil on medium heat.
- Add onion, garlic and ginger and sauté for around 2 minutes.
- Stir in pineapple and bell pepper and stir fry for around 3 minutes.
- Stir in pork, pineapple juice and coconut aminos and cook for around 3-4 minutes.
- Serve hot.

NUTRITIONAL

- Calories: 431,
- Fat: 10g,
- Carbohydrates: 22g,
- Fiber: 8g,
- Protein: 33g

Preparation Time: 15 minutes |Cooking Time: 14 minutes |Servings: 4

Ground Pork with Water Chestnuts

INGREDIENTS

- 1 tablespoon plus 1 teaspoon coconut oil
- 1 tablespoon fresh ginger, minced
- 1 bunch scallion (white and green parts separated), chopped
- 1-pound lean ground pork
- Salt, to taste
- 1 tablespoon 5-spice powder
- 1 (18-ounce) can water chestnuts, drained and chopped
- 1 tablespoon organic honey
- 2 tablespoons fresh lime juice

DIRECTION

- In a big heavy bottomed skillet, heat oil on high heat.
- Add ginger and scallion whites and sauté for approximately 1/2-11/2 minutes.
- Add pork and cook for approximately 4-5 minutes.
- Drain the extra Fat from skillet.
- Add salt and 5-spice powder and cook for approximately 2-3 minutes.
- Add scallion greens and remaining ingredients and cook, stirring continuously for about 1-2 minutes.

NUTRITIONAL

- Calories: 520,
- Fat: 30g,
- Carbohydrates: 37g,
- Fiber: 4g,
- Protein: 25g

Preparation Time: fifteen minutes |Cooking Time: 12 minutes |Servings: 4

Baked Pork & Mushroom Meatballs

INGREDIENTS

- 1-pound lean ground pork
- 1 organic egg white, beaten
- 4 fresh shiitake mushrooms, stemmed and minced
- 1 tablespoon fresh parsley, minced
- 1 tablespoon fresh basil leaves, minced
- 1 tablespoon fresh mint leaves, minced
- 2 teaspoons fresh lemon zest, grated finely
- 11/2 teaspoons fresh ginger, grated finely
- Salt and freshly ground black pepper, to taste

DIRECTION

- Preheat the oven to 425 degrees F. Arrange the rack inside center of oven.
- Line a baking sheet with a parchment paper.
- In a sizable bowl, add all ingredients and mix till well combined.
- Make small equal-sized balls from mixture.
- Arrange the balls onto prepared baking sheet in a single layer.
- Bake for approximately 12-15 minutes or till done completely.

NUTRITIONAL

- Calories: 411,
- Fat: 19g,
- Carbohydrates: 27g,
- Fiber: 11g,
- Protein: 35g

Preparation Time: 15 minutes |Cooking Time: fifteen minutes |Servings: 6

Beef Ragu

INGREDIENTS

- 1/4 cup packaged pesto
- 1 teaspoon salt
- 2 large zucchinis, cut into noodle strips
- 1 tablespoon olive oil
- 1/4-pound ground beef
- 4 tablespoons fresh parsley, chopped

DIRECTION

- Heat the oil in a skillet under medium flame and cook the ground beef until thoroughly cooked, around 5 minutes. Discard excess fat.
- Add the packaged pesto sauce and season with salt. Add t
- Thenchopped parsley and cook for three more minutes. Set aside.
- In the same saucepan, place the zucchini noodles and cook for five minutes. Turn off the heat then add the cooked meat. Mix well.
- Serve and enjoy.

NUTRITIONAL

- Calories 353,
- Total Fat 30g,
- Saturated Fat 6g
- Total Carbs 2g,
- Net Carbs 1.3g,
- Protein 19g,
- Sugar: 0.3g,
- Fiber 0.7g,
- Sodium 1481mg,
- Potassium 341mg

Preparation Time: 10 minutes |Cooking Time: 10 minutes |Servings: 2

Stir-Fried Ground Beef

INGREDIENTS

- 1/2 cup broccoli, chopped
- 1/2 of medium-sized onions, chopped
- 1/2 of medium-sized red bell pepper, chopped
- 1 tbsp. cayenne pepper (optional)
- 1 tbsp. Chinese five spices
- 1 tbsp. coconut oil
- 1-lb ground beef
- 2 kale leaves, chopped
- 5 medium-sized mushrooms, sliced

DIRECTION

- In a skillet, heat the coconut oil over medium high heat.
- Sauté the onions for one minute and add the vegetables while stirring constantly.
- Add the ground beef and the spices.
- Cook for two minutes and reduce the heat to medium.
- Cover the skillet and continue to cook the beef and vegetables for another 10 minutes.
- Serve and enjoy.

NUTRITIONAL

- Calories 304,
- Total Fat 17g,
- Saturated Fat 3g,
- Total Carbs 6g,
- Net Carbs 4g,
- Protein 32g,
- Sugar: 2g,
- Fiber 2g,
- Sodium 86mg,
- Potassium 624mg

Preparation Time: 10 minutes |Cooking Time: 15 minutes |Servings: 4

Beef and Three Pepper Stew

INGREDIENTS

- 10ounce of flat cut beef brisket, whole
- 1 teaspoon of dried thyme
- 1 teaspoon of black pepper
- 1 clove garlic
- 1/2 cup of green onion, thinly sliced
- 1/2 cup low sodium chicken stock
- 2 cups water
- 1 large green bell pepper, sliced
- 1 large red bell pepper, sliced
- 1 large yellow bell pepper, sliced
- 1 large red onion, sliced

DIRECTION

- Combine the beef, thyme, pepper, garlic, green onion, stock and water in a slow cooker.
- Leave it all to cook on High for 4-5 hours until tender.
- Remove the beef from the slow cooker and let it cool.
- Shred the beef with two forks and remove any excess fat.
- Place the shredded beef back into the slow cooker.
- Add the sliced peppers and the onion.
- Cook this on High heat for 40-60 minutes until the vegetables are tender.

NUTRITIONAL

- Per Servings:
- Calories: 132
- Protein: 14g
- Carbohydrates: 9g
- Fat: 5g
- Cholesterol: 39mg
- Sodium: 179mg
- Potassium: 390mg
- Phosphorus: 141mg
- Calcium: 33mg
- Fiber: 2g

Preparation Time: 15 minutes |Cooking Time: 6 hours |Servings: 6

Beef Brochettes

INGREDIENTS

- 1 1/2 cups pineapple chunks
- 1 sliced large onion
- 2 pounds thick steak
- 1 sliced medium bell pepper
- 1 bay leaf
- 1/4 cup vegetable oil
- 1/2 cup lemon juice
- 2 crushed garlic cloves

DIRECTION

- Cut beef cubes and place in a plastic bag
- Combine marinade ingredients in small bowl
- Mix and pour over beef cubes
- Seal the bag and refrigerate for 3 to 5 hours
- Divide ingredients onion, beef cube, green pepper, pineapple
- Grill about 9 minutes each side

NUTRITIONAL

- Calories 304
- Protein 35 g
- Fat 15 g
- Carbs 11 g
- Phosphorus 264 mg
- Potassium (K) 388 mg
- Sodium (Na) 70 mg

Preparation Time: 20 minutes |Cooking Time: 1 hour |Servings: 1

Country Fried Steak

INGREDIENTS

- 1 large onion
- 1/2 cup flour
- 3 tablespoons. vegetable oil
- 1/4 teaspoon pepper
- 11/2 pounds round steak
- 1/2 teaspoon paprika

DIRECTION

- Trim excess fat from steak
- Cut into small pieces
- Combine flour, paprika and pepper and mix together
- Preheat skillet with oil
- Cook steak on both sides
- When the color of steak is brown remove to a platter
- Add water (150 ml) and stir around the skillet
- Return browned steak to skillet, if necessary, add water again so that bottom side of steak does not stick

NUTRITIONAL

- Calories 248
- Protein 30 g
- Fat 10 g
- Carbs 5 g
- Phosphorus 190 mg
- Potassium (K) 338 mg
- Sodium (Na) 60 mg

Preparation Time: 10 minutes |Cooking Time: 1 hour and 40 minutes |Servings: 3

Beef Pot Roast

INGREDIENTS

- Round bone roast
- 2 - 4 pounds chuck roast

DIRECTION

- Trim off excess fat
- Place a tablespoon of oil in a large skillet and heat to medium
- Roll pot roast in flour and brown on all sides in a hot skillet
- After the meat gets a brown color, reduce heat to low
- Season with pepper and herbs and add 1/2 cup of water
- Cook slowly for 11/2 hours or until it looks ready

NUTRITIONAL

- Calories 157
- Protein 24 g
- Fat 13 g
- Carbs 0 g
- Phosphorus 204 mg
- Sodium (Na) 50 mg

Preparation Time: 20 minutes |Cooking Time: 1 hour |Servings: 3

Slow-cooked Beef Brisket

INGREDIENTS

- 10-ounce chuck roast
- 1 onion, sliced
- 1 cup carrots, peeled and sliced
- 1 tablespoon mustard
- 1 tablespoon thyme (fresh or dried)
- 1 tablespoon rosemary (fresh or dried)
- 2 garlic cloves
- 2 tablespoon extra-virgin olive oil
- 1 teaspoon black pepper
- 1 cup homemade chicken stock (p.52)
- 1 cup water

DIRECTION

- Preheat oven to 300°f/150°c/Gas Mark 2.
- Trim any fat from the beef and soak vegetables in warm water.
- Make a paste by mixing together the mustard, thyme, rosemary, and garlic, before mixing in the oil and pepper.
- Combine this mix with the stock.
- Pour the mixture over the beef into an oven proof baking dish.
- Place the vegetables onto the bottom of the baking dish with the beef.
- Cover and roast for 3 hours, or until tender.
- Uncover the dish and continue to cook for 30 minutes in the oven.
- Serve hot!

NUTRITIONAL

- Calories: 151
- Fat: 7g
- Carbohydrates: 7g
- Phosphorus: 144mg
- Potassium: 344mg
- Sodium: 279mg
- Protein: 15g

Preparation Time: 10 minutes |Cooking Time: 3 hours and 30 minutes |Servings: 6

Pork Souvlaki

INGREDIENTS

- Olive oil – 3 table-spoons
- Lemon juice – 2 ta-blespoons
- Minced garlic – 1 tea-spoon
- Chopped fresh orega-no – 1 tablespoon
- Ground black pepper – 1/4 teaspoon
- Pork leg – 1 pound, cut in 2-inch cubes

DIRECTION

- In a bowl, stir together the lem-on juice, olive oil, garlic, oregano, and pepper.
- Add the pork cubes and toss to coat.
- Place the bowl in the refrigerator, covered, for 2 hours to marinate.
- Thread the pork chunks onto 8 wooden skewers that have been soaked in water.
- Preheat the barbecue to medi-um-high heat.
- Grill the pork skewers for about 12 minutes, turning once, until just cooked through but still juicy.

NUTRITIONAL

- Calories: 95
- Fat: 4g
- Carb: 0g
- Phosphorus: 125mg
- Potassium: 230mg
- Sodium: 29mg
- Protein: 13g

Preparation Time: 20 minutes |Cooking Time: 12 minutes |Servings: 8

Open-Faced Beef Stir-Up

INGREDIENTS

- 95% Lean ground beef – 1/2 pound
- Chopped sweet onion – 1/2 cup
- Shredded cabbage – 1/2 cup
- Herb pesto – 1/4 cup
- Hamburger buns – 6, bottom halves only

DIRECTION

- Sauté the beef and onion for 6 minutes or until beef is cooked.
- Add the cabbage and sauté for 3 minutes more.
- Stir in pesto and heat for 1 min-ute.
- Divide the beef mixture into 6 portions and serve each on the bottom half of a hamburger bun, open-face.

NUTRITIONAL

- Calories: 120
- Fat: 3g
- Phosphorus: 106mg
- Potassium: 198mg
- Sodium: 134mg
- Protein: 11g

Preparation Time: 10 minutes |Cooking Time: 10 minutes |Servings: 6

Beef Brisket

INGREDIENTS

- Chuck roast – 12 ounces trimmed
- Garlic – 2 cloves
- Thyme – 1 tablespoon
- Rosemary – tablespoon
- Mustard - 1 tablespoon
- Extra virgin olive oil – 1/4 cup
- Black pepper – 1 teaspoon
- Onion – 1, diced
- Carrots – 1 cup, peeled and sliced
- Low salt stock – 2 cups

DIRECTION

- Preheat the oven to 300F.
- Soak vegetables in warm water.
- Make a paste by mixing together the thyme, mustard, rosemary, and garlic. Then mix in the oil and pepper.
- Add the beef to the dish.
- Pour the mixture over the beef into a dish.
- Place the vegetables onto the bottom of the baking dish around the beef.
- Cover and roast for 3 hours, or until tender.
- Uncover the dish and continue to cook for 30 minutes in the oven.
- Serve.

NUTRITIONAL

- Calories: 303
- Fat: 25g
- Carb: 7g
- Phosphorus: 376mg
- Potassium: 246mg
- Sodium: 44mg
- Protein: 18g

Preparation Time: 10 minutes |Cooking Time: 3 1/2 hours |Servings: 6

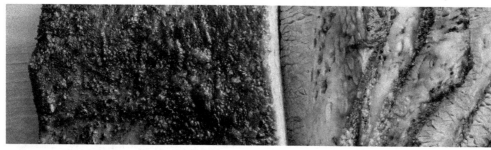

Homemade Burgers

INGREDIENTS

- 4 ounce lean 100% ground beef
- 1 teaspoon black pepper
- 1 garlic clove, minced
- 1 teaspoon olive oil
- 1/4 cup onion, finely diced
- 1 tablespoon balsamic vinegar
- 1/2ounce brie cheese, crumbled
- 1 teaspoon mustard

DIRECTION

- Season ground beef with pepper and then mix in minced garlic.
- Form burger shapes with the ground beef using the palms of your hands.
- Heat a skillet on a medium to high heat, and then add the oil.
- Sauté the onions for 5-10 minutes until browned.
- Then add the balsamic vinegar and sauté for another 5 minutes.
- Remove and set aside.
- Add the burgers to the pan and heat on the same heat for 5-6 minutes before flipping and heating for a further 5-6 minutes until cooked through.
- Spread the mustard onto each burger.
- Crumble the brie cheese over each burger and serve!
- Try with a crunchy side salad!
- Tip: If using fresh beef and not defrosted, prepare double the ingredients and freeze burgers in plastic wrap (after cooling) for up to 1 month.
- Thoroughly defrost before heating through completely in the oven to serve.

NUTRITIONAL

- Calories: 178
- Fat: 10g
- Carbohydrates: 4g
- Phosphorus: 147mg
- Potassium: 272mg
- Sodium: 273 mg
- Protein: 16g

Preparation Time: 10 minutes |Cooking Time: 20 minutes |Servings: 2

Chapter 20. Poultry Recipes

Ground Chicken & Peas Curry

INGREDIENTS

- 3 tablespoons essential olive oil
- 2 bay leaves
- 2 onions grind to some paste
- ½ tablespoon garlic paste
- ½ tablespoon ginger paste
- 2 Red bell peppers, chopped finely
- 1 tablespoon ground cumin
- 1 tablespoon ground coriander
- 1 teaspoon ground turmeric
- 1 teaspoon red chili powder
- Salt, to taste
- 1-pound lean ground chicken
- 2 cups frozen peas
- 1½ cups water
- 1-2 teaspoons garam masala powder

DIRECTION

- Warm oil on medium heat in a deep skillet. Add bay leaves and sauté for approximately half a minute. Add onion paste and sauté for about 3-4 minutes.
- Add garlic and ginger paste and sauté for around 1-1½ minutes. Add Red bell peppers and spices and cook, occasionally stirring, for about 3-4 minutes.
- Stir in chicken and cook for about 4-5 minutes. Stir in peas and water and bring to a boil on high heat.
- Adjust the heat to low and simmer within 5-8 minutes or till the desired doneness. Stir in garam masala and remove from heat. Serve hot.

NUTRITIONAL

- Calories: 450
- Fat: 10g
- Carbohydrates: 19g
- Fiber: 6g
- Protein: 38g
- Phosphorus 268 mg
- Potassium 753.5 mg
- Sodium 17 mg

Preparation Time: 15 minutes |Cooking Time: 6-10 minutes |Servings: 3-4

Chicken Meatballs Curry

INGREDIENTS

- For Meatballs:
- 1-pound lean ground chicken
- 1 tablespoon onion paste
- 1 teaspoon fresh ginger paste
- 1 teaspoon garlic paste
- 1 green chili, chopped finely
- 1 tablespoon fresh cilantro leaves, chopped
- 1 teaspoon ground coriander
- ½ teaspoon cumin seeds
- ½ teaspoon red chili powder
- ½ teaspoon ground turmeric
- Salt, to taste
- For Curry:
- 3 tablespoons extra-virgin olive oil
- ½ teaspoon cumin seeds
- 1 (1-inch) cinnamon stick
- 3 whole cloves
- 3 whole green cardamoms
- 1 whole black cardamom
- 2 onions, chopped
- 1 teaspoon fresh ginger, minced
- 1 teaspoon garlic, minced
- 4 whole Red bell peppers, chopped finely
- 2 teaspoons ground coriander
- 1 teaspoon garam masala powder
- ½ teaspoon ground nutmeg
- ½ teaspoon red chili powder
- ½ teaspoon ground turmeric
- Salt, to taste
- 1 cup of water
- Chopped fresh cilantro for garnishing

DIRECTION

- For meatballs in a substantial bowl, add all ingredients and mix till well combined. Make small equal-sized meatballs from the mixture.
- Warm-up oil on medium heat in a big deep skillet. Add meatballs and fry approximately 3-5 minutes or till browned from all sides. Transfer the meatballs to a bowl.
- In the same skillet, add cumin seeds, cinnamon stick, cloves, green cardamom, and black cardamom and sauté for approximately 1 minute.
- Add onions and sauté for around 4-5 minutes, then put the ginger and garlic paste and sauté within 1 minute. Add tomato and spices and cook, crushing with the back of the spoon for about 2-3 minutes.
- Add water and meatballs and provide to a boil. Reduce heat to low. Simmer for approximately 10 minutes. Serve hot with all the garnishing of cilantro.

NUTRITIONAL

- Calories: 421
- Fat: 8g
- Carbohydrates: 18g
- Fiber: 5g
- Protein: 34g

Preparation Time: 20 min |Cooking Time: 25 minutes |Servings: 3-4

Ground Chicken with Basil

INGREDIENTS

- 2 pounds lean ground chicken
- 3 tablespoons coconut oil, divided
- 1 zucchini, chopped
- 1 red bell pepper, seeded and chopped
- ½ of green bell pepper, seeded and chopped
- 4 garlic cloves, minced
- 1 (1-inch) piece fresh ginger, minced
- 1 (1-inch) piece fresh turmeric, minced
- 1 fresh red chili, sliced thinly
- 1 tablespoon organic honey
- 1 tablespoon coconut aminos
- 1½ tablespoons fish sauce
- ½ cup fresh basil, chopped
- Salt
- ground black pepper
- 1 tablespoon fresh lime juice

DIRECTION

- Heat a large skillet on medium-high heat. Add ground beef and cook for approximately 5 minutes or till browned completely.
- Transfer the beef to a bowl. In a similar pan, melt 1 tablespoon of coconut oil on medium-high heat. Add zucchini and bell peppers and stir fry for around 3-4 minutes.
- Transfer the vegetables inside the bowl with chicken. In precisely the same pan, melt remaining coconut oil on medium heat. Add garlic, ginger, turmeric, and red chili and sauté for approximately 1-2 minutes.
- Add chicken mixture, honey, and coconut aminos and increase the heat to high. Cook within 4-5 minutes or till sauce is nearly reduced. Stir in remaining ingredients and take off from the heat.

NUTRITIONAL

- Calories: 407
- Fat: 7g
- Carbohydrates: 20g
- Fiber: 13g
- Protein: 36g
- Phosphorus 149 mg
- Potassium 706.3 mg
- Sodium 21.3 mg

Preparation Time: 15 minutes |Cooking Time: 16 minutes |Servings: 8

Chicken & Veggie Casserole

INGREDIENTS

- 1/3 cup Dijon mustard
- 1/3 cup organic honey
- 1 teaspoon dried basil
- ¼ teaspoon ground turmeric
- 1 teaspoon dried basil, crushed
- Salt
- ground black pepper
- 1¾ pound chicken breasts
- 1 cup fresh white mushrooms, sliced
- ½ head broccoli, cut into small florets

DIRECTION

- Warm oven to 350 degrees F. Lightly greases a baking dish. In a bowl, mix all ingredients except chicken, mushrooms, and broccoli.
- Put the chicken in your prepared baking dish, then top with mushroom slices. Place broccoli florets around chicken evenly.
- Pour 1 / 2 of honey mixture over chicken and broccoli evenly. Bake for approximately 20 minutes. Now, coat the chicken with the remaining sauce and bake for about 10 minutes.

NUTRITIONAL

- Calories: 427
- Fat: 9g
- Carbohydrates: 16g
- Fiber: 7g
- Protein: 35g
- Phosphorus 353 mg
- Potassium 529.3 mg
- Sodium 1 mg

Preparation Time: 15 minutes |Cooking Time: 30 minutes |Servings: 4

Chicken & Cauliflower Rice Casserole

INGREDIENTS

- 2 tablespoons coconut oil, divided
- 3-pound bone-in chicken thighs and drumsticks
- Salt
- ground black pepper
- 3 carrots, peeled and sliced
- 1 onion, chopped finely
- 2 garlic cloves, chopped finely
- 2 tablespoons fresh cinnamon, chopped finely
- 2 teaspoons ground cumin
- 1 teaspoon ground coriander
- 12 teaspoon ground cinnamon
- ½ teaspoon ground turmeric
- 1 teaspoon paprika
- ¼ tsp red pepper cayenne
- 1 (28-ounce) can diced Red bell peppers with liquid
- 1 red bell pepper, thin strips
- ½ cup fresh parsley leaves, minced
- Salt, to taste
- 1 head cauliflower, grated to some rice-like consistency
- 1 lemon, sliced thinly

DIRECTION

- Warm oven to 375 degrees F. In a large pan, melt 1 tablespoon of coconut oil at high heat. Add chicken pieces and cook for about 3-5 minutes per side or till golden brown.
- Transfer the chicken to a plate. In a similar pan, sauté the carrot, onion, garlic, and ginger for about 4-5 minutes on medium heat.
- Stir in spices and remaining coconut oil. Add chicken, Red bell peppers, bell pepper, parsley plus salt, and simmer for approximately 3-5 minutes.
- In the bottom of a 13x9-inch rectangular baking dish, spread the cauliflower rice evenly. Place chicken mixture over cauliflower rice evenly and top with lemon slices.
- With foil paper, cover the baking dish and bake for approximately 35 minutes. Uncover the baking dish and bake for about 25 minutes.

NUTRITIONAL

- Calories: 412
- Fat: 12g
- Carbohydrates: 23g
- Protein: 34g
- Phosphorus 201 mg
- Potassium 289.4 mg
- Sodium 507.4 mg

Preparation Time: 15 minutes |Cooking Time: 1 hour & 15 minutes |Servings: 8-10

Chicken Meatloaf with Veggies

INGREDIENTS

- Ingredients:
- For Meatloaf:
- ½ cup cooked chickpeas
- 2 egg whites
- 2½ teaspoons poultry seasoning
- Salt
- ground black pepper
- 10-ounce lean ground chicken
- 1 cup red bell pepper, seeded and minced
- 1 cup celery stalk, minced
- 1/3 cup steel-cut oats
- 1 cup tomato puree, divided
- 2 tablespoons dried onion flakes, crushed
- 1 tablespoon prepared mustard
- For Veggies:
- 2-pounds summer squash, sliced
- 16-ounce frozen Brussels sprouts
- 2 tablespoons extra-virgin extra virgin olive oil

DIRECTION

- Warm oven to 350 degrees F. Grease a 9x5-inch loaf pan. In a mixer, add chickpeas, egg whites, poultry seasoning, salt, and black pepper and pulse till smooth.
- Transfer a combination in a large bowl. Add chicken, veggies oats, ½ cup of tomato puree, and onion flakes and mix till well combined.
- Transfer the amalgamation into the prepared loaf pan evenly. With both hands, press down the amalgamation slightly.
- In another bowl, mix mustard and remaining tomato puree. Place the mustard mixture over the loaf pan evenly.
- Bake approximately 1-1¼ hours or till the desired doneness. Meanwhile, in a big pan of water, arrange a steamer basket. Cover and steam for about 10-12 minutes. Drain well and aside.
- Now, prepare the Brussels sprouts according to the package's directions. In a big bowl, add veggies, oil, salt, and black pepper and toss to coat well. Serve the meatloaf with veggies.

NUTRITIONAL

- Calories: 420
- Fat: 9g
- Carbohydrates: 21g
- Protein: 36g
- Phosphorus 237.1 mg
- Potassium 583.6 mg
- Sodium 136 mg

Preparation Time: 20 minutes |Cooking Time: 1-1¼ hours |Servings: 4

Roasted Spatchcock Chicken

INGREDIENTS

- 1 (4-pound) whole chicken
- 1 (1-inch) piece fresh ginger, sliced
- garlic cloves, chopped
- 1 small bunch of fresh thyme
- Pinch of cayenne
- Salt
- ground black pepper
- ¼ cup fresh lemon juice
- tablespoons extra virgin olive oil

DIRECTION

- Arrange chicken, breast side down onto a large cutting board. With a kitchen shear, begin with the thigh, cut along 1 side of the backbone, and turn the chicken around.
- Now, cut along sleep issues and discard the backbone. Change the inside and open it like a book. Flatten the backbone firmly to flatten.
- In a food processor, add all ingredients except chicken and pulse till smooth. In a big baking dish, add the marinade mixture.
- Add chicken and coat with marinade generously. With a plastic wrap, cover the baking dish and refrigerate to marinate overnight.
- Preheat the oven to 450 degrees F. Arrange a rack in a very roasting pan. Remove the chicken from the refrigerator makes onto a rack over the roasting pan, skin side down. Roast for about 50 minutes, turning once in a middle way.

NUTRITIONAL

- Calories: 419
- Fat: 14g
- Carbohydrates: 28g
- Protein: 40g
- Phosphorus 166 mg
- Potassium 196 mg
- Sodium 68 mg

Preparation Time: 20 minutes |Cooking Time: 50 minutes |Servings: 4-6

Roasted Chicken with Veggies & Orange

INGREDIENTS

- 1 teaspoon ground ginger
- ½ teaspoon ground cumin
- ½ teaspoon ground coriander
- 1 teaspoon paprika
- Salt
- ground black pepper
- 1 (3 ½-4-pound) whole chicken
- 1 unpeeled orange, cut into 8 wedges
- 2 medium carrots, peeled and cut into 2-inch pieces
- ½ cup of water

DIRECTION

- Warm oven to 450 degrees F. In a little bowl, mix the spices. Rub the chicken with spice mixture evenly.
- Arrange the chicken in a substantial Dutch oven and put the orange, carrot, and sweet potato pieces around it.
- Add water and cover the pan tightly. Roast for around 30 minutes. Uncover and roast for about half an hour.

NUTRITIONAL

- Calories: 432
- Fat: 10g
- Carbohydrates: 20g
- Protein: 34g
- Potassium 481 mg
- Sodium 418 mg
- Phosphorus 170 mg

Preparation Time: 20 minutes |Cooking Time: 1 hour |Servings: 4

Roasted Chicken Breast

INGREDIENTS

- ½ of a small apple, peeled, cored, and chopped
- 1 bunch scallion, trimmed and chopped roughly
- 8 fresh ginger slices, chopped
- 2 garlic cloves, chopped
- 3 tablespoons essential olive oil
- 12 teaspoon sesame oil, toasted
- 3 tablespoons using apple cider vinegar
- 1 tablespoon fish sauce
- 1 tablespoon coconut aminos
- Salt
- ground black pepper
- 4-pounds chicken thighs

DIRECTION

- Pulse all the fixing except chicken thighs in a blender. Transfer a combination and chicken right into a large Ziploc bag and seal it. Shake the bag to marinade well. Refrigerate to marinate for about 12 hours. Warm oven to 400 degrees F. arranges a rack in foil paper-lined baking sheet.
- Place the chicken thighs on the rack, skin-side down. Roast for about 40 minutes, flipping once within the middle way.

NUTRITIONAL

- Calories: 451
- Fat: 17g
- Carbohydrates: 277g
- Protein: 42g
- Phosphorus 121 mg
- Potassium 324 mg
- Sodium 482.9 mg

Preparation Time: 15 minutes |Cooking Time: 40 minutes |Servings: 4-6

Grilled Chicken

INGREDIENTS

- 1 (3-inch) piece fresh ginger, minced
- 6 small garlic cloves, minced
- 1½ tablespoons tamarind paste
- 1 tablespoon organic honey
- ¼ cup coconut aminos
- 2½ tablespoons extra virgin olive oil
- 1½ tablespoons sesame oil, toasted
- ½ teaspoon ground cardamom
- Salt
- ground white pepper
- 1 (4-5-pound) whole chicken, cut into 8 pieces

DIRECTION

- Mix all ingredients except chicken pieces in a large glass bowl. With a fork, pierce the chicken pieces thoroughly.
- Add chicken pieces in bowl and coat with marinade generously. Cover and refrigerate to marinate for approximately a couple of hours to overnight.
- Preheat the grill to medium heat. Grease the grill grate. Place the chicken pieces on the grill, bone-side down. Grill, covered approximately 20-25 minutes.
- Change the side and grill, covered approximately 6-8 minutes. Change alongside it and grill, covered for about 5-8 minutes. Serve.

NUTRITIONAL

- Calories: 423
- Fat: 12g
- Carbohydrates: 20g
- Protein: 42g
- Sodium 281.9 mg
- Phosphorus 0 mg
- Potassium 0 mg

Preparation Time: 15 minutes |Cooking Time: 41 minutes |Servings: 8

Grilled Chicken with Pineapple & Veggies

INGREDIENTS

- For Sauce:
- 1 garlic oil, minced
- ¾ teaspoon fresh ginger, minced
- ½ cup coconut aminos
- ¼ cup fresh pineapple juice
- 2 tablespoons freshly squeezed lemon juice
- 2 tablespoons balsamic vinegar
- ¼ teaspoon red pepper flakes, crushed
- Salt
- ground black pepper
- For Grilling:
- 4 skinless, boneless chicken breasts
- 1 pineapple, peeled and sliced
- 1 bell pepper, seeded and cubed
- 1 zucchini, sliced
- 1red onion, sliced

DIRECTION

- For sauce in a pan, mix all ingredients on medium-high heat. Bring to a boil reducing the heat to medium-low. Cook approximately 5-6 minutes.
- Remove, then keep aside to cool down slightly. Coat the chicken breasts about ¼ from the sauce. Keep aside for approximately half an hour.
- Preheat the grill to medium-high heat. Grease the grill grate. Grill the chicken pieces for around 5-8 minutes per side.
- Now, squeeze pineapple and vegetables on the grill grate. Grill the pineapple within 3 minutes per side. Grill the vegetables for approximately 4-5 minutes, stirring once inside the middle way.
- Cut the chicken breasts into desired size slices, divide the chicken, pineapple, and vegetables into serving plates. Serve alongside the remaining sauce.

NUTRITIONAL

- Calories: 435
- Fat: 12g
- Carbohydrates: 25g
- Protein: 38g
- Phosphorus 184 mg
- Potassium 334.4 mg
- Sodium 755.6 mg

Preparation Time: 20 or so minutes |Cooking Time: 22 minutes |Servings: 4

Ground Turkey with Veggies

INGREDIENTS

- 1 tablespoon sesame oil
- 1 tablespoon coconut oil
- 1-pound lean ground turkey
- 2 tablespoons fresh ginger, minced
- 2 minced garlic cloves
- 1 (16-ounce) bag vegetable mix (broccoli, carrot, cabbage, kale, and Brussels sprouts)
- ¼ cup coconut aminos
- 2 tablespoons balsamic vinegar

DIRECTION

In a big skillet, heat both oils on medium-high heat. Add turkey, ginger, and garlic and cook approximately 5-6 minutes. Add vegetable mix and cook about 4-5 minutes. Stir in coconut aminos and vinegar and cook for about 1 minute. Serve hot.

NUTRITIONAL

- Calories: 234
- Fat: 9g
- Carbohydrates: 9g
- Protein: 29g
- Phosphorus 14 mg
- Potassium 92.2 mg
- Sodium 114.9 mg

Preparation Time: 15 minutes |Cooking Time: 12 minutes |Servings: 4

Ground Turkey with Asparagus

INGREDIENTS

- 1¾ pound lean ground turkey
- 2 tablespoons sesame oil
- 1 medium onion, chopped
- 1 cup celery, chopped
- 6 garlic cloves, minced
- 2 cups asparagus, cut into 1-inch pieces
- 1/3 cup coconut aminos
- 2½ teaspoons ginger powder
- 2 tablespoons organic coconut crystals
- 1 tablespoon arrowroot starch
- 1 tablespoon cold water
- ¼ teaspoon red pepper

DIRECTION

- Heat a substantial nonstick skillet on medium-high heat. Add turkey and cook for approximately 5-7 minutes or till browned. With a slotted spoon, transfer the turkey inside a bowl and discard the grease from the skillet.
- Heat-up oil on medium heat in the same skillet. Add onion, celery, and garlic and sauté for about 5 minutes. Add asparagus and cooked turkey, minimizing the temperature to medium-low.
- Meanwhile, inside a pan, mix coconut aminos, ginger powder, and coconut crystals n medium heat and convey some boil.
- Mix arrowroot starch and water in a smaller bowl. Slowly add arrowroot mixture, stirring continuously. Cook approximately 2-3 minutes.
- Add the sauce in the skillet with turkey mixture and stir to blend. Stir in red pepper flakes and cook for approximately 2-3 minutes. Serve hot.

NUTRITIONAL

- Calories: 309
- Fat: 20g
- Carbohydrates: 19g
- Protein: 28g
- Potassium 196.4 mg
- Sodium 77.8 mg
- Phosphorus 0 mg

Preparation Time: 15 minutes |Cooking Time: 15 minutes |Servings: 8

Ground Turkey with Peas & Potato

INGREDIENTS

- 3-4 tablespoons coconut oil
- 1-pound lean ground turkey
- 1-2 fresh red chilis, chopped
- 1 onion, chopped
- Salt, to taste
- 2 minced garlic cloves
- 1 (1-inch) piece fresh ginger, grated finely
- 1 tablespoon curry powder
- 1 teaspoon ground coriander
- 1 teaspoon ground cumin
- 1 teaspoon ground turmeric
- 2 large Yukon gold potatoes, cubed into 1-inch size
- ½ cup of water
- 1 cup fresh peas, shelled

DIRECTION

- In a substantial pan, heat oil on medium-high heat. Add turkey and cook for about 4-5 minutes. Add chilis and onion and cook for about 4-5 minutes.
- Add garlic and ginger and cook approximately 1-2 minutes. Stir in spices, potatoes, and water and convey to your boil
- Reduce the warmth to medium-low. Simmer covered around 15-20 or so minutes. Add peas and Red bell peppers and cook for about 2-3 minutes. Serve using the garnishing of cilantro.

NUTRITIONAL

- Calories: 452
- Fat: 14g
- Carbohydrates: 24g
- Fiber: 13g
- Protein: 36g
- Phosphorus 38 mg
- Potassium 99.5 mg
- Sodium 373.4 mg

Preparation Time: 15 minutes |Cooking Time: 35 minutes |Servings: 4

Turkey & Pumpkin Chili

INGREDIENTS

- 2 tablespoons extra-virgin olive oil
- 1 green bell pepper, seeded and chopped
- 1 small yellow onion, chopped
- 2 garlic cloves, chopped finely
- 1-pound lean ground turkey
- 1 (15-ounce) pumpkin puree
- 1 (14 ½-ounce) can diced Red bell peppers with liquid
- 1 teaspoon ground cumin
- ½ teaspoon ground turmeric
- ½ teaspoon ground cinnamon
- 1 cup of water

DIRECTION

- Heat-up oil on medium-low heat in a big pan. Add the bell pepper, onion, and garlic and sauté for approximately 5 minutes. Add turkey and cook for about 5-6 minutes.
- Add Red bell peppers, pumpkin, spices, and water and convey to your boil on high heat. Reduce the temperature to medium-low heat and stir in chickpeas. Simmer, covered for approximately a half-hour, stirring occasionally. Serve hot.

NUTRITIONAL

- Calories: 437
- Fat: 17g
- Carbohydrates: 29g
- Protein: 42g
- Phosphorus 150 mg
- Potassium 652 mg
- Sodium 570 mg

Preparation Time: 15 minutes |Cooking Time: 41 minutes |Servings: 4-6

Chicken curry

INGREDIENTS

- 1lb skinless chicken breasts
- 1 medium onion, thinly sliced
- 1 15 ounce can chickpeas, drained and rinsed well
- ½ cup light coconut milk
- ½ cup chicken stock (see recipe)
- 1 15ounce can sodium-free tomato sauce
- 2 tablespoon curry powder
- 1 teaspoon low-sodium salt
- ½ cayenne powder
- 1 cup green peas
- 2 tablespoon lemon juice

DIRECTION

- Place the chicken breasts, onion, chickpeas into a 4 to 6-quart slow cooker.
- Mix the coconut milk, chicken stock, tomato sauce, curry powder, salt, and cayenne together and pour into the slow cooker, stirring to coat well.
- Cover and cook on low for 8 hours or high for 4 hours.
- Stir in the peas and lemon juice 5 minutes before serving.

NUTRITIONAL

- calories 302,
- fat 5g, carbs 43g,
- protein 24g,
- fiber 9g,
- potassium 573mg, s
- odium 800mg

Preparation Time: 10 minutes|Cooking Time: 4 minutes|Servings: 4

Apple & cinnamon spiced honey pork loin

INGREDIENTS

- 1 2-3lb boneless pork loin roast
- ½ teaspoon low-sodium salt
- ¼ teaspoon pepper
- 1 tablespoon canola oil
- 3 medium apples, peeled and sliced
- ¼ cup honey
- 1 small red onion, halved and sliced
- 1 tablespoon ground cinnamon

DIRECTION

- Season the pork with salt and pepper.
- Heat the oil in a skillet and brown the pork on all sides.
- Arrange half the apples in the base of a 4 to 6-quart slow cooker.
- Top with the honey and remaining apples.
- Sprinkle with cinnamon and cover.
- Cover and cook on low for 6-8 hours until the meat is tender.

NUTRITIONAL

- calories 290,
- fat 10g, c
- arbs 19g,
- protein 29g,
- fiber 2g,
- potassium 789mg,
- sodium 22mg

Preparation Time: 20 minutes |Cooking Time: 6 hours |Servings: 6

Lemon & herb turkey breasts

INGREDIENTS

- 1 can (14-1/2 ounces) chicken broth
- 1/2 cup lemon juice
- 1/4 cup packed brown sugar
- 1/4 cup fresh sage
- 1/4 cup fresh thyme leaves
- 1/4 cup lime juice
- 1/4 cup cider vinegar
- 1/4 cup olive oil
- 1 envelope low-sodium onion soup mix
- 2 tablespoon dijon mustard
- 1 tablespoon fresh marjoram, minced
- 1 teaspoon paprika
- 1 teaspoon garlic powder
- 1 teaspoon pepper
- ½ teaspoon low-sodium salt
- 2 2lb boneless skinless tur-

DIRECTION

- Make a marinade by blending all the ingredients in a blender.
- Pour over the turkey and leave overnight.
- Place the turkey and marinade in a 4 to 6-quart slow cooker and cover.
- Cover and cook on high for 3-1/2 to 4-1/2 hours or until a thermometer reads 165°.

NUTRITIONAL

- calories 219,
- fat 5g,
- carbs 3g,
- protein 36g,
- fiber 0g,
- potassium 576mg,
- sodium 484mg

Preparation Time: 25 minutes |Cooking Time: 3 1/2 hours |Servings: 12

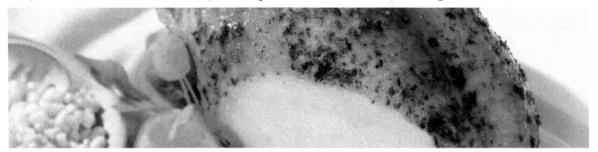

Beef chimichangas

INGREDIENTS

- Shredded beef
- 3lb boneless beef chuck roast, fat trimmed away
- 3 tablespoon low-sodium taco seasoning mix
- 1 10ounce canned low-sodium diced Red bell peppers
- 6ounce canned diced green chilies with the juice
- 3 garlic cloves, minced
- To serve
- 16 medium flour tortillas
- Sodium-free refried beans
- Mexican rice, sour cream, cheddar cheese
- Guacamole, salsa, let-

DIRECTION

- Arrange the beef in a 5-quart or larger slow cooker.
- Sprinkle over taco seasoning and coat well.
- Add Red bell peppers and garlic and cover.
- Cook on low for 10 to 12 hours.
- When cooked remove the beef and shred.
- Make burritos out of the shredded beef, refried beans, Mexican rice, and cheese.
- Bake for 10 minutes at 350° f until brown.
- Serve with salsa, lettuce, and guacamole.

NUTRITIONAL

- calories 249,
- fat 18g,
- carbs 3g,
- protein 33g,
- fiber 5g,
- potassium 633mg, s
- odium 457mg

Preparation Time: 10minutes |Cooking Time: 10-12 hours |Servings: 16

Crockpot peachy pork chops

INGREDIENTS

- 4 large peaches, pitted and peeled
- 1 onion, finely minced
- ¼ cup ketchup
- ¼ cup low-sodium honey barbecue sauce
- 2 tablespoon brown sugar
- 1 tablespoon low sodium soy sauce
- ¼ teaspoon low-sodium garlic salt
- ½ teaspoon ground ginger
- 2lb boneless pork chops
- 3 tablespoon olive oil

DIRECTION

- Puree the peaches with a blender.
- Mix the peach puree with the onion, ketchup, barbecue sauce, brown sugar, soy sauce, salt, garlic salt, and ginger.
- Brown the pork chops in a large skillet then transfer to a 6-quart or larger slow cooker.
- Pour the sauce over the pork chops and cover.
- Cook for 5 to 6 hours on high.

NUTRITIONAL

- calories 252,
- fat 8g,
- carbs 18g,
- protein 26g,
- fiber 1g,
- potassium 710mg,
- sodium 325mg

Preparation Time: 30minutes |Cooking Time: 2-3 hours |Servings: 8

Chicken salad balsamic

INGREDIENTS

- 3 cup diced cold, cooked chicken
- 1 cup diced apple
- 1/2 cup diced celery
- 2 green onions, chopped
- 1/2 cup chopped walnuts
- 3 tablespoons. Balsamic vinegar
- 5 tablespoons. Olive oil
- Salt and pepper to taste

DIRECTION

- Toss together the celery, chicken, onion, walnuts, and apple in a big bowl.
- Whisk the oil together with the vinegar in a small bowl. Pour the dressing over the salad. Then add pepper and salt to taste. Combine the ingredients thoroughly. Leave the mixture for 10-15 minutes. Toss once more and chill.

NUTRITIONAL

- calories: 336
- total fat: 26.8 g
- carbohydrates: 6g
- protein: 19 g
- cholesterol: 55 mg
- sodium: 58 mg

Preparation time 15 minutes |Cooking Time: 15 minutes|Servings: 6

Chicken salad with apples, grapes, and walnuts

INGREDIENTS

- 4 cooked chicken breasts, shredded
- 2 granny smith apples, cut into small chunks
- 2cupchopped walnuts, or to taste
- 1/2 red onion, chopped
- 3 stalks celery, chopped
- 3 tablespoons. Lemon juice
- 1/2cupvanilla yogurt
- 5 tablespoons. Creamy salad dressing (such as miracle whip®)
- 5 tablespoons. Mayonnaise
- 25 seedless red grapes, halved

DIRECTION

- In a big bowl, toss together the shredded chicken, lemon juice, apple chunks, celery, red onion, and walnuts.
- Get another bowl and whisk together the dressing, vanilla yogurt, and mayonnaise. Pour over the chicken mixture. Toss to coat. Fold the grapes carefully into the salad.

NUTRITIONAL

- calories: 307
- total fat: 22.7 g
- carbohydrates: 10.8g
- protein: 17.3 g
- cholesterol: 41 mg
- sodium: 128 mg

Preparation Time: 25 minutes|Cooking Time: 25 minutes|Servings: 12

Chicken strawberry green lettuce salad with ginger-lime dressing

INGREDIENTS

- 2 teaspoons. Corn oil
- 1 skinless, boneless chicken breast half - cut into bite-size pieces
- 1/2 teaspoon garlic powder
- 1 1/2 tablespoons. Mayonnaise
- 1/2 lime, juiced
- 1/2 teaspoon ground ginger
- 2 teaspoons. Milk
- 2cupfresh green lettuce, stems removed
- 4 fresh strawberries, sliced
- 1 1/2 tablespoons. Slivered almonds
- Freshly ground black pepper to taste

DIRECTION

- In a skillet, heat oil over medium heat. Add the chicken breast and garlic powder. Cook the chicken for 10 minutes per side. When the juices run clear, remove from heat and set aside.
- Combine the lime juice, milk, mayonnaise, and ginger in a bowl.
- Place the green lettuce on serving dishes. Top with strawberries and chicken. Then sprinkle with almonds. Drizzle the salad with the dressing. Add pepper and serve.

NUTRITIONAL

- calories: 242
- total fat: 17.3 g
- carbohydrates: 7.5g
- protein: 15.8 g
- cholesterol: 40 mg
- sodium: 117 mg

Preparation Time: 10 minutes|Cooking Time: 30 minutes|Servings: 2

Lemon Pepper Chicken Legs

INGREDIENTS

- ½ tsp. garlic powder
- 2 tsp. baking powder
- 8 chicken legs
- 4 tbsp. salted butter, melted
- 1 tbsp. lemon pepper seasoning

DIRECTION

- In a small container add the garlic powder and baking powder, then use this mixture to coat the chicken legs. Lay the chicken in the basket of your fryer.
- Cook the chicken legs at 375°F for twenty-five minutes. Halfway through, turn them over and allow to cook on the other side.
- When the chicken has turned golden brown, test with a thermometer to ensure it has reached an ideal temperature of 165°F. Remove from the fryer.
- Mix together the melted butter and lemon pepper seasoning and toss with the chicken legs until the chicken is coated all over. Serve hot.

NUTRITIONAL

- Calories: 132
- Fat: 16 g
- Carbs: 20 g
- Protein: 48 g
- Calcium 79mg,
- Phosphorous 132mg,
- Potassium 127mg
- Sodium: 121 mg

Preparation Time: 5 minutes |Cooking Time: 25 minutes |Servings: 4

Turkey Broccoli Salad

INGREDIENTS

- 8 cups broccoli florets
- 3 cooked skinless, boneless chicken breast halves, cubed
- 6 green onions, chopped
- 1 cup mayonnaise
- ¼ cup apple cider vinegar
- ¼ cup honey

DIRECTION

- Combine broccoli, chicken and green onions in a large bowl.
- Whisk mayonnaise, vinegar, and honey together in a bowl until well blended.
- Pour mayonnaise dressing over broccoli mixture; toss to coat.
- Cover and refrigerate until chilled, if desired. Serve

NUTRITIONAL

- Calories 133,
- Sodium 23mg,
- Dietary Fiber 1.6g,
- Total Sugars 7.7g,
- Protein 6.2g,
- Calcium 24mg,
- Potassium 157mg
- Phosphorus 148 mg

Preparation Time: 10 minutes |Cooking Time: 00 minutes|Servings: 4

Gnocchi and chicken dumplings

INGREDIENTS

- Chicken breast – 2 pounds
- Gnocchi – 1 pound
- Light olive oil – ¼ cup
- Better than bouillon® chicken base – 1 table-spoon
- Chicken stock (re-duced-sodium) – 6 cups
- Fresh celery (diced finely) – ½ cup
- Fresh onions (diced finely) – ½ cup
- Fresh carrots (diced finely) – ½ cup
- Fresh parsley (chopped) – ¼ cup
- Black pepper – 1 teaspoon
- Italian seasoning – 1 tea-spoon

DIRECTION

- Start by placing the stock over a high flame. Add in the oil and let it heat through.
- Add the chicken to the hot oil and shallow-fry until all sides turn golden brown.
- Toss in the carrots, onions, and celery and cook for about 5 minutes. Pour in the chicken stock and let it cool on a high flame for about 30 minutes.
- Reduce the flame and add in the chicken bouillon, italian seasoning, and black pepper. Stir well.
- Toss in the store-bought gnocchi and let it cook for about 15 minutes. Keep stirring.
- Once done, transfer into a serving bowl. Add parsley and serve hot!

NUTRITIONAL

- protein – 28 g
- carbohydrates – 38 g
- fat – 10 g
- cholesterol – 58 mg
- sodium – 121 mg
- potassium – 485 mg
- calcium – 38 mg
- fiber – 2 g

Preparation Time: 10 minutes|Cooking Time: 40 minutes |Servings: 10

Creamy Turkey

INGREDIENTS

- 4 skinless, boneless turkey breast halves
- Salt and pepper to taste
- ½ teaspoon ground black pepper
- ½ teaspoon garlic pow-der
- 1 (10.75 ounces) can chicken soup

DIRECTION

- Preheat oven to 375 degrees F.
- Clean turkey breasts and season with salt, pepper and garlic powder (or whichever seasonings you prefer) on both sides of turkey pieces.
- Bake for 25 minutes, then add chicken soup and bake for 10 more minutes (or until done). Serve over rice or egg noodles.

NUTRITIONAL

- Calories 160,
- Sodium 157mg,
- Dietary Fiber 0.4g,
- Total Sugars 0.4g,
- Protein 25.6g,
- Calcium 2mg,
- Potassium 152mg,
- Phosphorus 85 mg

Preparation Time: 12 minutes |Cooking Time: 10 minutes|Servings: 4

Fruity Chicken Salad

INGREDIENTS

- 4 skinless, boneless chicken breast halves - cooked and diced
- 1 stalk celery, diced
- 4 green onions, chopped
- 1 Golden Delicious apple - peeled, cored and diced
- 1/3 cup seedless green grapes, halved
- 1/8 teaspoon ground black pepper
- 3/4 cup light mayonnaise

DIRECTION

- In a large container, add the celery, chicken, onion, apple, grapes, pepper, and mayonnaise.
- Mix all together. Serve!

NUTRITIONAL

- Calories 196,
- Sodium 181mg,
- Total Carbohydrate 15.6g,
- Dietary Fiber 1.2g,
- Total Sugars 9.1g,
- Protein 13.2g,
- Calcium 13mg,
- Iron 1mg,
- Potassium 115mg,
- Phosphorus 88 mg

Preparation Time: 10 minutes |Cooking Time: 5 minutes|Servings: 3

Buckwheat Salad

INGREDIENTS

- 2 cups water
- 1 clove garlic, smashed
- 1 cup uncooked buckwheat
- 2 large cooked chicken breasts - cut into bite-size pieces
- 1 large red onion, diced
- 1 large green bell pepper, diced
- 1/4 cup chopped fresh parsley
- 1/4 cup chopped fresh chives
- 1/2 teaspoon salt
- 2/3 cup fresh lemon juice
- 1 tablespoon balsamic vinegar
- 1/4 cup olive oil

DIRECTION

- Bring the water, garlic to a boil in a saucepan. Stir in the buckwheat, reduce heat to medium-low, cover, and simmer until the buckwheat is tender and the water has been absorbed, 15 to 20 minutes.
- Discard the garlic clove and scrape the buckwheat into a large bowl.
- Gently stir the chicken, onion, bell pepper, parsley, chives, and salt into the buckwheat.
- Sprinkle with the olive oil, balsamic vinegar, and lemon juice. Stir until evenly mixed.

NUTRITIONAL

- Calories 199,
- Total Fat 8.3g,
- Sodium 108mg,
- Dietary Fiber 2.9g,
- Total Sugars 2g,
- Protein 13.6g,
- Calcium 22mg,
- Potassium 262mg,
- Phosphorus 188 mg

Preparation Time: 12 minutes |Cooking Time: 20 minutes|Servings: 3

Parmesan and Basil turkey Salad

INGREDIENTS

- 2 whole skinless, boneless turkey breasts
- salt and pepper to taste
- 1 cup mayonnaise
- 1 cup chopped fresh basil
- 2 cloves crushed garlic
- 3 stalks celery, chopped
- 2/3 cup grated Parmesan cheese

DIRECTION

- Season turkey with salt and pepper. Roast at 375 degrees F for 35 minutes, or until juices run clear. Let cool, and chop into chunks.
- In a food processor, puree the mayonnaise, basil, garlic, and celery.
- Combine the chunked turkey, pureed mixture, and Parmesan cheese; toss. Refrigerate, and serve.

NUTRITIONAL

- Calories 303,
- Sodium 190mg,
- Dietary Fiber 0.4g,
- Total Sugars 4.7g,
- Protein 8.5g,
- Calcium 73mg,
- Potassium 121mg,
- Phosphorus 100 mg

Preparation Time: 15 minutes |Cooking Time: 35 minutes|Servings: 4

Cherry Chicken Salad

INGREDIENTS

- 3 cooked, boneless chicken breast halves, diced
- 1/3 cup dried cherries
- 1/3 cup diced celery
- 1/3 cup low-fat mayonnaise
- 1/2 teaspoon ground black pepper
- 1/3 cup cubed apples (optional)

DIRECTION

- In a large bowl, combine the chicken, dried cherries, celery, mayonnaise, and pepper and apple if desired.
- Toss together well and refrigerate until chilled.
- Serve

NUTRITIONAL

- Calories 281,
- Total Fat 11.8g,
- Cholesterol 31mg,
- Sodium 586mg,
- Dietary Fiber 1.4g,
- Total Sugars 2.9g,
- Protein 14.7g,
- Calcium 12mg,
- Potassium 55mg,
- Phosphorus 20 mg

Preparation Time: 15 minutes |Cooking Time: 00 minutes|Servings: 4

Elegant Brunch Chicken Salad

INGREDIENTS

- 1-pound skinless, boneless chicken breast halves
- 1 egg
- 1/4 teaspoon dry mustard
- 2 teaspoons hot water
- 1 tablespoon white wine vinegar
- 1 cup olive oil
- 2 cups halved seedless red grapes

DIRECTION

- Boil water in a large pot. Add the chicken and simmer until cooked thoroughly approximately 10 minutes. Drain, cool and cut into cubes.
- While boiling chicken, make the mayonnaise: Using a blender or hand-held electric mixer, beat the egg, mustard, water and vinegar until light and frothy.
- Add the oil a tablespoon at a time, beating thoroughly after each addition. As the combination starts to thicken, you can add oil more quickly.
- Continue until the mixture reaches the consistency of creamy mayonnaise.
- In a large bowl, toss together the chicken, grapes and 1 cup of the mayonnaise. Stir until evenly coated, adding more mayonnaise if necessary. Refrigerate until serving.

NUTRITIONAL

- Calories 676,
- Sodium 56mg,
- Total Carbohydrate 14.7g,
- Dietary Fiber 1.4g,
- Total Sugars 12.2g,
- Protein 28.1g,
- Calcium 10mg,
- Potassium 183mg,
- Phosphorus 120 mg

Preparation Time: 20 minutes |Cooking Time: 0 minutes|Servings: 4

Oven-Baked Turkey Thighs

INGREDIENTS

- 10 ounces turkey thighs, skin on, bone-in
- 1/3 cup white wine
- 1 lemon
- 1 tablespoon fresh oregano
- 1/4 teaspoon cracked black pepper
- 1 tablespoon olive oil

DIRECTION

- Heat the oven to 350 degrees F.
- Add turkey thighs and white wine to an oven-proof pan. Squeeze half the lemon over turkey. Slice remaining lemon and top turkey with lemon slices.
- Season turkey with fresh oregano, cracked pepper and olive oil.
- Bake turkey for 25 to 30 minutes or until internal temperature reaches 165 degrees F to 175 degrees F.

NUTRITIONAL

- Calories 189,
- Sodium 62mg,
- Dietary Fiber 0.9g,
- Total Sugars 0.6g,
- Protein 20.8g,
- Calcium 34mg,
- Potassium 232mg,
- Phosphorus 180 mg

Preparation Time: 10 minutes |Cooking Time: 30 minutes|Servings: 4

Southern Fried Chicken

INGREDIENTS

- 2 x 6-oz. boneless skinless chicken breasts
- 2 tbsp. hot sauce
- ½ tsp. onion powder
- 1 tbsp. chili powder
- 2 oz. pork rinds, finely ground

DIRECTION

- Chop the chicken breasts in half lengthways and rub in the hot sauce. Combine the onion powder with the chili powder, then rub into the chicken. Leave to marinate for at least a half hour.
- Use the ground pork rinds to coat the chicken breasts in the ground pork rinds, covering them thoroughly. Place the chicken in your fryer.
- Set the fryer at 350°F and cook the chicken for 13 minutes. Turn over the chicken and cook the other side for another 13 minutes or until golden.
- Test the chicken with a meat thermometer. When fully cooked, it should reach 165°F. Serve hot, with the sides of your choice.

NUTRITIONAL

- Calories: 408
- Fat: 19 g
- Carbs: 10 g
- Protein: 35 g
- Calcium 39mg,
- Phosphorous 216mg,
- Potassium 137mg
- Sodium: 153 mg

Preparation Time: 5 minutes |Cooking Time: 26 minutes|Servings: 2

Cilantro Drumsticks

INGREDIENTS

- 8 chicken drumsticks
- ½ cup chimichurri sauce
- ¼ cup lemon juice

DIRECTION

- Coat the chicken drumsticks with chimichurri sauce and refrigerate in an airtight container for no less than an hour, ideally overnight.
- When it's time to cook, pre-heat your fryer to 400°F.
- Remove the chicken from refrigerator and allow return to room temperature for roughly twenty minutes.
- Cook for eighteen minutes in the fryer. Drizzle with lemon juice to taste and enjoy.

NUTRITIONAL

- Calories: 483
- Fat: 29 g
- Carbs: 16 g
- Protein: 36 g
- Calcium 38mg,
- Phosphorous 146mg,
- Potassium 227mg
- Sodium: 121 mg

Preparation Time: 12 minutes |Cooking Time: 18 minutes|Servings: 4

Basil Chicken over Macaroni

INGREDIENTS

- 1 (8 ounces) package macaroni
- 2 teaspoons olive oil
- 1/2 cup finely chopped onion
- 1 clove garlic, chopped
- 2 cups boneless chicken breast halves, cooked and cubed
- 1/4 cup chopped fresh basil
- 1/4 cup Parmesan cheese
- 1/2 teaspoon black pepper

DIRECTION

- In a large pot of boiling water, cook macaroni until it is al dente, about 8 to 10 minutes. Drain, and set aside.
- In a large skillet, heat oil over medium-high heat. Sauté the onions and garlic. Stir in the chicken, basil, and pepper.
- Reduce heat to medium, and cover skillet. Simmer for about 5 minutes, stirring frequently.
- Toss sauce with hot cooked macaroni to coat. Serve with Parmesan cheese.

NUTRITIONAL

- Calories 349,
- Sodium 65mg,
- Dietary Fiber 2.2g,
- Total Sugars 2.1g,
- Protein 28.5g,
- Calcium 44mg,
- Potassium 286mg,
- Phosphorus 280 mg

Preparation Time: 10 minutes |Cooking Time: 30 minutes|Servings: 4

Chicken Saute

INGREDIENTS

- 4 oz. chicken fillet
- 4 Red bell peppers, peeled
- 1 bell pepper, chopped
- 1 teaspoon olive oil
- 1 cup of water
- 1 teaspoon salt
- 1 chili pepper, chopped
- ½ teaspoon saffron

DIRECTION

- Pour water in the pan and bring it to boil.
- Meanwhile, chop the chicken fillet.
- Add the chicken fillet in the boiling water and cook it for 10 minutes or until the chicken is tender.
- After this, put the chopped bell pepper and chili pepper in the skillet.
- Add olive oil and roast the vegetables for 3 minutes.
- Add chopped Red bell peppers and mix up well.
- Cook the vegetables for 2 minutes more.
- Then add salt and a ¾ cup of water from chicken.
- Add chopped chicken fillet and mix up.
- Cook the saute for 10 minutes over the medium heat.

NUTRITIONAL

- Calories 192,
- Fat 7.2 g,
- Fiber 3.8 g,
- Carbs 14.4 g,
- Protein 19.2 g
- Calcium 79mg,
- Phosphorous 216mg,
- Potassium 227mg
- Sodium: 101 mg

Preparation Time: 10 minutes |Cooking Time: 25 minutes |Servings: 2

Grilled Marinated Chicken

INGREDIENTS

- 2-pound chicken breast, skinless, boneless
- 2 tablespoons lemon juice
- 1 teaspoon sage
- ½ teaspoon ground nutmeg
- ½ teaspoon dried oregano
- 1 teaspoon paprika
- 1 teaspoon onion powder
- 2 tablespoons olive oil
- 1 teaspoon chili flakes
- 1 teaspoon salt
- 1 teaspoon apple cider vinegar

DIRECTION

- Make the marinade: whisk together apple cider vinegar, salt, chili flakes, olive oil, onion powder, paprika, dried oregano, ground nutmeg, sage, and lemon juice.
- Then rub the chicken with marinade carefully and leave for 25 minutes to marinate.
- Meanwhile, preheat grill to 385F.
- Place the marinated chicken breast in the grill and cook it for 10 minutes from each side.
- Cut the cooked chicken on the servings

NUTRITIONAL

- Calories 218
- Fat 8.2 g,
- Fiber 0.8 g,
- Carbs 0.4 g,
- Protein 32.2 g
- Calcium 29mg,
- Phosphorous 116mg,
- Potassium 207mg
- Sodium: 121 mg

Preparation Time: 35 minutes |Cooking Time: 20 minutes |Servings: 6

Tasty Turkey Patties

INGREDIENTS

- 14.5-ounces turkey
- 1-ounce cream cheese
- 1 large egg
- 1/8 teaspoon ground sage
- 1/2 teaspoon garlic powder
- 1/2 teaspoon black pepper
- 1 teaspoon onion powder
- 1 teaspoon Italian seasoning
- 3 tablespoons olive oil

DIRECTION

- Set cream cheese out to soften.
- Using a fork, mash turkey with juices in a medium bowl.
- Add the cream cheese, egg, sage, garlic powder, black pepper, onion powder, Italian seasoning and mix well.
- Form 4 patties.
- Heat olive oil on low hotness, in a small skillet.
- Fry patties for 5- to 6 minutes on each side or until crispy on the outside and heated thoroughly.

NUTRITIONAL

- Calories 270,
- Sodium 204mg,
- Dietary Fiber 1.1g,
- Total Sugars 3.5g,
- Protein 13.5g,
- Calcium 17mg,
- Potassium 143mg,
- Phosphorus 100 mg

Preparation Time: 10 minutes |Cooking Time: 12 minutes|Servings: 4

Roasted Citrus Chicken

INGREDIENTS

- 1 tablespoon olive oil
- 2 cloves garlic, minced
- 1 teaspoon Italian seasoning
- 1/2 teaspoon black pepper
- 8 chicken thighs
- 2 cups chicken broth, reduced sodium
- 3 tablespoons lemon juice
- 1/2 large chicken breast for 1 chicken thigh

DIRECTION

- Warm oil in a huge skillet.
- Include garlic and seasonings.
- Include chicken bosoms and dark-colored all sides.
- Spot chicken in the moderate cooker and include the chicken soup.
- Cook on LOW heat for 6 to 8 hours
- Include lemon juice toward the part of the bargain time.

NUTRITIONAL

- Calories 265,
- Fat 19g,
- Protein 21g,
- Carbohydrates 1g

Preparation Time: 20 Minutes |Cooking Time: 60 Minutes |Servings: 8

Chicken with Asian Vegetables

INGREDIENTS

- 2 tablespoons canola oil
- 6 boneless chicken breasts
- 1 cup low-sodium chicken broth
- 3 tablespoons reduced-sodium soy sauce
- 1/4 teaspoon crushed red pepper flakes
- 1 garlic clove, crushed
- 1 can (8ounces) water chestnuts, sliced and rinsed (optional)
- 1/2 cup sliced green onions
- 1 cup chopped red or green bell pepper
- 1 cup chopped celery
- 1/4 cup cornstarch
- 1/3 cup water
- 3 cups cooked white rice
- 1/2 large chicken breast for 1 chicken thigh

DIRECTION

- Warm oil in a skillet and dark-colored chicken on all sides.
- Add chicken to a slow cooker with the remainder of the fixings aside from cornstarch and water.
- Spread and cook on LOW for 6 to 8hours
- Following 6-8 hours, independently blend cornstarch and cold water until smooth. Gradually include into the moderate cooker.
- At that point turn on high for about 15mins until thickened. Don't close the top on the moderate cooker to enable steam to leave.
- Serve Asian blend over rice.

NUTRITIONAL

- Calories 415,
- Fat 20g,
- Protein 20g,
- Carbohydrates 36g

Preparation Time: 10 Minutes , Cooking Time: 20 Minutes , Servings: 8

Chicken and Veggie Soup

INGREDIENTS

- 4 cups cooked and chopped chicken
- 7 cups reduced-sodium chicken broth
- 1-pound frozen white corn
- 1 medium onion diced
- 4 cloves garlic minced
- 2 carrots peeled and diced
- 2 celery stalks chopped
- 2 teaspoons oregano
- 2 teaspoon curry powder
- 1/2 teaspoon black pepper

DIRECTION

- Include all fixings into the moderate cooker.
- Cook on LOW for 8 hours
- Serve over cooked white rice.

NUTRITIONAL

- Calories 220,
- Fat7g,
- Protein 24g,
- Carbohydrates 19g

Preparation Time: 15 Minutes |Cooking Time: 25 Minutes |Servings: 8

Turkey Sausages

INGREDIENTS

- 1/4 teaspoon salt
- 1/8 teaspoon garlic powder
- 1/8 teaspoon onion powder
- 1 teaspoon fennel seed
- 1 pound 7% fat ground turkey

DIRECTION

- Press the fennel seed and in a small cup put together turkey with fennel seed, garlic, and onion powder, and salt.
- Cover the bowl and refrigerate overnight.
- Prepare the turkey with seasoning into different portions with a circle form and press them into patties ready to be cooked.
- Cook at medium heat until browned.
- Cook it for 1 to 2 minutes per side and serve them hot. Enjoy!

NUTRITIONAL

- Calories 55,
- Protein 7 g,
- Sodium 70 mg,
- Potassium 105 mg,
- Phosphorus 75 mg

Preparation Time: 10 Minutes |Cooking Time: 10 Minutes |Servings: 2

Rosemary Chicken

INGREDIENTS

- 2 zucchinis
- 1 carrot
- 1 teaspoon dried rosemary
- 4 chicken breasts
- 1/2 bell pepper
- 1/2 red onion
- 8 garlic cloves
- Olive oil
- 1/4 tablespoon ground pepper

DIRECTION

- Prepare the oven and preheat it at 375°F (or 200°C).
- Slice both zucchini and carrots and add bell pepper, onion, garlic, and put all the ingredients, adding oil in a 13" x 9" pan.
- Spread the pepper on the pan and roast for about 10 minutes.
- Meanwhile, lift the chicken skin and spread black pepper and rosemary on the flesh.
- Remove the vegetable pan from the oven and add the chicken, returning the pan to the oven for about 30 more minutes. Serve and enjoy!

NUTRITIONAL

- Calories 215,
- Protein 28 g,
- Sodium 105 mg,
- Potassium 580 mg,
- Phosphorus 250 mg

Preparation Time: 10 Minutes |Cooking Time: 10 Minutes |Servings: 2

Smokey Turkey Chili

INGREDIENTS

- 12-ounce lean ground turkey
- 1/2 red onion, chopped
- 2 cloves garlic, crushed and chopped
- 1/2 teaspoon of smoked paprika
- 1/2 teaspoon of chili powder
- 1/2 teaspoon of dried thyme
- 1/4 cup reduced-sodium beef stock
- 1/2 cup of water
- 11/2 cups baby green lettuce leaves, washed
- 3 wheat tortillas

DIRECTION

- Brown the ground beef in a dry skillet over medium-high heat.
- Add in the red onion and garlic.
- Sauté the onion until it goes clear.
- Transfer the contents of the skillet to the slow cooker.
- Add the remaining ingredients and simmer on low for 30-45 minutes.
- Stir through the green lettuce for the last few minutes to wilt.
- Slice tortillas and gently toast under the broiler until slightly crispy.
- Serve on top of the turkey chili.

NUTRITIONAL

- Calories 93.5,
- Protein 8g,
- Carbohydrates 3g,
- Fat 5.5g,
- Cholesterol 30.5mg,
- Sodium 84.5mg,
- Potassium 142.5mg,
- Phosphorus 92.5mg,
- Calcium 29mg,
- Fiber 0.5g

Preparation Time: 5 Minutes |Cooking Time: 45 Minutes |Servings: 8

Herbs and Lemony Roasted Chicken

INGREDIENTS

- 1/2 teaspoon ground black pepper
- 1/2 teaspoon mustard powder
- 1/2 teaspoon salt
- 1 3-lb whole chicken
- 1 teaspoon garlic powder
- 2 lemons
- 2 tablespoons. olive oil
- 2 teaspoons. Italian seasoning

DIRECTION

- In a small bowl, mix black pepper, garlic powder, mustard powder, and salt.
- Rinse chicken well and slice off giblets.
- In a greased 9 x 13 baking dish, place chicken on it. Add 11/2 teaspoon of seasoning made earlier inside the chicken and rub the remaining seasoning around the chicken.
- In a small bowl, mix olive oil and juice from 2 lemons. Drizzle over chicken.
- Bake chicken in an oven preheated at 3500 F until juices run clear, for around 11/2 hour. Occasionally, baste the chicken with its juices.

NUTRITIONAL

- alories per Serving 190,
- Carbohydrates 2g,
- protein 35g, fats 9g,
- phosphorus 341mg,
- potassium 439mg,
- sodium 328mg

Preparation Time: 15 Minutes |Cooking Time: 1 Hour and 30 Minutes |Servings: 8

Ground Chicken and Peas Curry

INGREDIENTS

- For Marinade:
- 3 tablespoons essential olive oil
- 2 bay leaves
- 2 onions, ground to some paste
- 1/2 tablespoon garlic paste
- 1/2 tablespoon ginger paste
- 2 Red bell peppers, chopped finely
- 1 tablespoon ground cumin
- 1 tablespoon ground coriander
- 1 teaspoon ground turmeric
- 1 teaspoon red chili powder
- Salt, to taste
- 1-pound lean ground chicken
- 2 cups frozen peas
- 11/2 cups water
- 1-2 teaspoons garam masala powder

DIRECTION

- In a deep skillet, heat oil on medium heat.
- Add bay leaves and sauté for approximately half a minute.
- Add onion paste and sauté for approximately 3-4 minutes.
- Add garlic and ginger paste and sauté for around 1-11/2 minutes.
- Add Red bell peppers and spices, and cook, stirring occasionally for about 3-4 minutes.
- Stir in chicken and cook for about 4-5 minutes.
- Stir in peas and water and bring to a boil on high heat.
- Reduce the heat to low and simmer approximately 5-8 minutes or till desired doneness.
- Stir in garam masala and remove from heat. Serve hot.

NUTRITIONAL

- Calories 450,
- Fat 10g,
- Carbohydrates 19g,
- Fiber 6g,
- Protein 38g

Preparation Time: 15 Minutes |Cooking Time: 6 to 10 Minutes |Servings: 3-4

White Bean, Chicken & Apple Cider Chili

INGREDIENTS

- 3 cups chopped cooked chicken (see Basic "Rotisserie" Chicken)
- 2 (15-ounce) cans white navy beans, rinsed well and drained
- 1 medium onion, chopped
- 1 (15-ounce) can diced tomatoes
- 3 cups Chicken Bone Broth or store-bought chicken broth
- 1 cup apple cider
- 2 bay leaves
- 1 tablespoon extra-virgin oil
- 2 teaspoons garlic powder
- 1 teaspoon chili powder
- 1 teaspoon salt
- ½ teaspoon ground cumin
- ¼ teaspoon ground cinnamon
- Pinch cayenne pepper
- Freshly ground black pepper
- ¼ cup apple cider vinegar

DIRECTION

- In your slow cooker, combine the chicken, beans, onion, tomatoes, broth, cider, bay leaves, oil, garlic powder, chili powder, salt, cumin, cinnamon cayenne, and season with black pepper.
- Cover the cooker and set to low. Cook for 7 to 8 hours.
- Remove and discard the bay leaves. Stir in the apple cider vinegar until well blended and serve.

NUTRITIONAL

- Calories: 469
- Total Fat: 8g
- Total Carbs: 46g
- Sugar: 13g
- Fiber: 9g
- Protein: 51g
- Sodium: 147mg

Preparation Time: 15 minutes |Cooking Time: 7 to 8 hours|Servings: 4

Buffalo Chicken Lettuce Wraps

INGREDIENTS

- 1 tablespoon extra-virgin oil
- 2 pounds boneless, skinless chicken breast
- 2 cups Vegan Buffalo Dip
- 1 cup water
- 8 to 10 romaine lettuce leaves
- ½ red onion, thinly sliced

DIRECTION

- Coat the bottom of the slow cooker with oil.
- Add the chicken, dip, and water, and stir to combine.
- Cover the cooker and set to low. Cook for around 7 to 8 hours, or until the internal temperature reaches 165°F on a meat thermometer and the juices run clear.
- Shred the chicken using a fork, then mix it into the dip in the slow cooker.
- Divide the meat mixture among the lettuce leaves.
- serve.

NUTRITIONAL

- Calories: 437
- Total Fat: 18g
- Total Carbs: 18g
- Sugar: 8g
- Fiber: 4g
- Protein: 49g
- Sodium: 13mg

Preparation Time: 15 minutes |Cooking Time: 7 to 8 hours|Servings: 4

Chapter 21.
Dessert Recipes

Baked Apples with Cherries and Walnuts

INGREDIENTS

- 1/3 cup dried cherries, coarsely chopped
- 3 tablespoons chopped walnuts
- 1 tablespoon ground flax-seed meal
- 1 tablespoon firmly packed brown sugar
- 1 teaspoon ground cinnamon
- 1/8 teaspoon nutmeg
- 6 Golden Delicious apples, about 2 pounds total weight, washed and unpeeled
- 1/2 cup 100 percent apple juice
- 1/4 cup water
- 2 tablespoons dark honey
- 2 teaspoons extra-virgin olive oil

DIRECTION

- Preheat the oven to 350°F.
- In a small bowl, toss together the cherries, walnuts, flaxseed meal, brown sugar, cinnamon, and nutmeg until all the ingredients are evenly distributed. Set aside.
- Working from the stem end, core each apple, stopping ¾ of an inch from the bottom. Gently press the cherries into each apple cavity. Arrange the apples upright in a heavy ovenproof skillet or baking dish just large enough to hold them.
- Pour the apple juice and water into the pan. Drizzle the honey and oil evenly over the apples, and cover the pan snugly with aluminum foil. Bake until the apples are tender when pierced with a knife, 35 to 40 minutes.
- Transfer the apples to individual plates and drizzle with the pan juices. Serve warm.

NUTRITIONAL

- Calories: 162;
- Total Fat 5g;
- Saturated Fat: 1g;
- Cholesterol: 0mg;
- Sodium: 4mg;
- Potassium: 148mg;
- Total Carbohydrate: 30g;
- Fiber: 4g; Protein: 1g

Preparation Time: 10 minutes|Cooking Time: 35 to 40 minutes|Servings: 6

Easy Peach Crumble

INGREDIENTS

- 8 ripe peaches, peeled, pitted and sliced
- 3 tablespoons freshly squeezed lemon juice
- 1/2 teaspoon ground cinnamon
- 1/4 teaspoon ground nutmeg
- 1/2 cup oat flour
- 1/4 cup packed dark brown sugar
- 2 tablespoons margarine, cut into thin slices
- 1/4 cup quick-cooking oats

DIRECTION

- Preheat the oven to 375°F. Lightly coat a 9-inch pie pan with cooking spray. Arrange peach slices in the prepared pie plate and sprinkle with the lemon juice, cinnamon, and nutmeg.
- In a small bowl, whisk together the flour and brown sugar. With your fingers, crumble the margarine into the flour-sugar mixture. Add the uncooked oats and stir to mix. Sprinkle the flour mixture over the peaches.
- Bake until the peaches are soft and the topping is browned, about 30 minutes.
- Cut into 8 even slices and serve warm.

NUTRITIONAL

- Calories: 130;
- Total Fat 4g;
- Saturated Fat: 0g;
- Cholesterol: 0mg;
- Sodium: 42mg;
- Potassium: 255mg;
- Total Carbohydrate: 28g;
- Fiber: 3g;
- Protein: 2g

Preparation Time: 10 minutes|Cooking Time: 30 minutes|Servings: 8

Lemon Thins

INGREDIENTS

- Cooking spray
- 11/4 cups whole wheat pastry flour
- 1/3 cup cornstarch
- 11/2 teaspoons baking powder
- ¾ cup sugar, divided
- 2 tablespoons butter, softened
- 2 tablespoons extra-virgin olive oil
- 1 large egg white
- 3 teaspoons freshly grated lemon zest
- 11/2 teaspoons vanilla extract
- 4 tablespoons freshly squeezed lemon juice

DIRECTION

- Preheat the oven to 350°F. Coat two baking sheets with cooking spray.
- In a mixing bowl, whisk together the flour, cornstarch, and baking powder.
- In another mixing bowl beat 1/2 cup of the sugar, the butter, and olive oil with an electric mixer on medium speed until fluffy.
- Add the egg white, lemon zest, and vanilla and beat until smooth. Beat in the lemon juice.
- Add the dry ingredients to the wet ingredients and fold in with a rubber spatula just until combined.

- Drop the dough by the teaspoonful, 2 inches apart, onto the prepared baking sheets.
- Place the remaining 1/4 cup sugar in a saucer. Coat the bottom of a wide-bottomed glass with cooking spray and dip it in the sugar. Flatten the dough with the glass bottom into 21/2-inch circles, dipping the glass in the sugar each time.
- Bake the cookies until they are just starting to brown around the edges, 8 to 10 minutes. Transfer to a flat surface (not a rack) to crisp.

NUTRITIONAL

- (1 cookie) Calories: 40;
- Total Fat 2g;
- Saturated Fat: 1g;
- Cholesterol: 2mg;
- Sodium: 26mg;
- Potassium: 3mg;
- Total Carbohydrate: 5g;
- Fiber: 1g;
- Protein: 1g

Preparation Time: 15 minutes|Cooking Time: 8 to 10 minutes|Servings: 30 cookies

Snickerdoodle Chickpea Blondies

INGREDIENTS

- 1 (15-ounce) can chickpeas, drained and rinsed
- 3 tablespoons nut butter of choice
- ¾ teaspoon baking powder
- 2 teaspoons vanilla extract
- 1/8 teaspoon baking soda
- ¾ cup brown sugar
- 1 tablespoon unsweetened applesauce
- 1/4 cup ground flaxseed meal
- 21/4 teaspoons cinnamon

DIRECTION

- Preheat the oven to 350°F. Grease an 8-by-8-inch baking pan.
- Blend all ingredients in a food processor until very smooth. Scoop into the prepared baking pan.
- Bake until the tops are medium golden brown, 30 to 35 minutes. Allow the brownies to cool completely before cutting.

NUTRITIONAL

- Calories: 85;
- Total Fat 2g;
- Saturated Fat: 0g;
- Cholesterol: 0mg; Sodium: 7mg;
- Potassium: 62mg;
- Total Carbohydrate: 16g;
- Fiber: 2g;
- Protein: 3g

Servings: 15|Preparation Time: 10 minutes|Cooking Time: 30 to 35 minutes

Chocolate Chia Seed Pudding

INGREDIENTS

- 11/2 cups unsweetened vanilla almond milk
- 1/4 cup unsweetened cocoa powder
- 1/4 cup maple syrup (or substitute any sweetener)
- 1/2 teaspoon vanilla extract
- 1/3 cup chia seeds
- 1/2 cup strawberries
- 1/4 cup blueberries
- 1/4 cup raspberries
- 2 tablespoons unsweetened coconut flakes
- 1/4 to 1/2 teaspoon ground cinnamon (optional)

DIRECTION

- Add the almond milk, cocoa powder, maple syrup, and vanilla extract to a blender and blend until smooth. Whisk in chia seeds.
- In a small bowl, gently mash the strawberries with a fork. Distribute the strawberry mash evenly to the bottom of 4 glass jars.
- Pour equal portions of the blended milk-cocoa mixture into each of the jars and let the pudding rest in the refrigerator until it achieves a pudding like consistency, at least 3 to 5 hours and up to overnight.

NUTRITIONAL

- Calories: 189;
- Total Fat 7g;
- Saturated Fat: 2g;
- holesterol: 0mg;
- Sodium: 60mg;
- Potassium: 232mg;
- Total Carbohydrate: 28g;
- Fiber: 10g;
- Protein: 6g

Preparation Time: 15 minutes, plus 3 to 5 hours or overnight to rest|Cooking Time: 0 minutes|Servings: 4

Chocolate-Mint Truffles

INGREDIENTS

- 14 ounces semisweet chocolate, coarsely chopped
- ¾ cup half-and-half
- 1/2 teaspoon pure vanilla extract
- 11/2 teaspoon peppermint extract
- 2 tablespoons unsalted butter, softened
- ¾ cup naturally unsweetened or Dutch-process cocoa powder

DIRECTION

- Place semisweet chocolate in a large heatproof bowl.
- Microwave in four 15-second increments, stirring after each, for a total of 60 seconds. Stir until almost completely melted. Set aside.
- In a small saucepan over medium heat, heat the half-and-half, whisking occasionally, until it just begins to boil. Remove from the heat, then whisk in the vanilla and peppermint extracts.
- Pour the mixture over the chocolate and, using a wooden spoon, gently stir in one direction.
- Once the chocolate and cream are smooth, stir in the butter until it is combined and melted.
- Cover with plastic wrap pressed on the top of the mixture, and then let it sit at room temperature for 30 minutes.
- After 30 minutes, place the mixture in the refrigerator until it is thick and can hold a ball shape, about 5 hours.
- Line a large baking sheet with parchment paper or a use a silicone baking mat. Set aside.
- Remove the mixture from the refrigerator. Place the cocoa powder in a bowl.
- Scoop 1 teaspoon of the ganache and, using your hands, roll into a ball. Roll the ball in the cocoa powder, the place on the prepared baking sheet. (You can coat your palms with a little cocoa powder to prevent sticking).
- Serve immediately or cover and store at room temperature for up to 1 week.

NUTRITIONAL

- Calories: 21;
- Total Fat 2g;
- Saturated Fat: 1g;
- Cholesterol: 2mg;
- Sodium: 2mg;
- Potassium: 21mg;
- Total Carbohydrate: 2g;
- Fiber: 1g;
- Protein: 0g

Preparation Time: 45 minutes|Cooking Time: 5 hours|Servings: 60 small truffles

Personal Mango Pies

INGREDIENTS

- Cooking spray
- 12 small wonton wrappers
- 1 tablespoon cornstarch
- 1/2 cup water
- 3 cups finely chopped mango (fresh, or thawed from frozen, no sugar added)
- 2 tablespoons brown sugar (not packed)
- 1/2 teaspoon cinnamon
- 1 tablespoon light whipped butter or buttery spread

DIRECTION

- Unsweetened coconut flakes (optional)
- Preheat the oven to 350°F.
- Spray a 12-cup muffin pan with nonstick cooking spray.
- Place a wonton wrapper into each cup of the muffin pan, pressing it into the bottom and up along the sides.
- Lightly spray the wrappers with nonstick spray. Bake until lightly browned, about 8 minutes.
- Meanwhile, in a medium nonstick saucepan, combine the cornstarch with the water and stir to dissolve. Add the mango, brown sugar, and cinnamon and turn heat to medium.
- Stirring frequently, cook until the mangoes have slightly softened and the mixture is thick and gooey, 6 to 8 minutes.
- Remove the mango mixture from heat and stir in the butter.
- Spoon the mango mixture into wonton cups, about 3 tablespoons each. Top with coconut flakes (if using) and serve warm.

NUTRITIONAL

- Calories: 61;
- Total Fat 1g;
- Saturated Fat: 0g;
- Cholesterol: 2mg;
- Sodium: 52mg;
- Potassium: 77mg;
- Total Carbohydrate: 14g;
- Fiber: 1g; Protein: 1g

Preparation Time: 15 minutes|Cooking Time: 14 to 16 minutes|Servings: 12

Grilled Peach Sundaes

INGREDIENTS

- 1 tbsp. toasted un-sweetened coconut
- 1 tsp. canola oil
- 2 peaches, halved and pitted
- 2 scoops non-fat vanilla yogurt, frozen

DIRECTION

- Brush the peaches with oil and grill until tender.
- Place peach halves on a bowl and top with frozen yogurt and coconut

NUTRITIONAL

- Calories: 61;
- carbs: 2g;
- protein: 2g;
- fats: 6g;
- phosphorus: 32mg;
- potassium: 85mg;
- sodium: 30mg

Preparation Time: 15 minutes |Cooking Time: 5 minutes |Servings: 1

Blueberry Swirl Cake

INGREDIENTS

- 1/2 cup margarine
- 1 1/4 cups reduced fat milk
- 1 cup granulated sugar
- 1 egg
- 1 egg white
- 1 tbsp. lemon zest, grated
- 1 tsp. cinnamon
- 1/3 cup light brown sugar
- 2 1/2 cups fresh blue-berries
- 2 1/2 cups self-rising flour

DIRECTION

- Cream the margarine and granulated sugar using an electric mixer at high speed until fluffy.
- Add the egg and egg white and beat for an-other two minutes.
- Add the lemon zest and reduce the speed to low.
- Add the flour with milk alternately.
- In a greased 13x19 pan, spread half of the batter and sprinkle with blueberry on top. Add the remaining batter.
- Bake in a 350-degree Fahrenheit preheated oven for 45 minutes.
- Let it cool on a wire rack before slicing and serving.

NUTRITIONAL

- Calories: 384;
- carbs: 63g;
- protein: 7g;
- fats: 13g;
- phosphorus: 264mg;
- potassium: 158mg;
- sodium: 456mg

Preparation Time: 15 minutes , Cooking Time: 45 minutes , Servings: 9

Peanut Butter Cookies

INGREDIENTS

- 1/4 cup granulated sugar
- 1 cup unsalted peanut butter
- 1 tsp. baking soda
- 2 cups all-purpose flour
- 2 large eggs
- 2 tbsp. butter
- 2 tsp. pure vanilla extract
- 4 ounces softened cream cheese

DIRECTION

- Line a cookie sheet with a non-stick liner. Set aside.
- In a bowl, mix flour, sugar and baking soda. Set aside.
- On a mixing bowl, combine the butter, cream cheese and peanut butter.
- Mix on high speed until it forms a smooth consistency. Add the eggs and vanilla gradually while mixing until it forms a smooth consistency.
- Add the almond flour mixture slowly and mix until well combined.
- The dough is ready once it starts to stick together into a ball.
- Scoop the dough using a 1 tablespoon cookie scoop and drop each cookie on the prepared cookie sheet.
- Press the cookie with a fork and bake for 10 to 12 minutes at 350oF.

NUTRITIONAL

- Calories: 138;
- carbs: 12g;
- protein: 4g;
- fats: 9g;
- phosphorus: 60mg;
- potassium: 84mg;
- sodium: 31mg

Preparation Time: 15 minutes |Cooking Time: 24 minutes |Servings: 24

Deliciously Good Scones

INGREDIENTS

- 1/4 cup dried cranberries
- 1/4 cup sunflower seeds
- 1/2 teaspoon baking soda
- 1 large egg
- 2 cups all-purpose flour
- 2 tablespoon honey

DIRECTION

- Preheat the oven to 3500F.
- Grease a baking sheet. Set aside.
- In a bowl, mix the salt, baking soda and flour. Add the dried fruits, nuts and seeds. Set aside.
- In another bowl, mix the honey and eggs.
- Add the wet ingredients to the dry ingredients. Use your hands to mix the dough.
- Create 10 small round dough and place them on the baking sheet.
- Bake for 12 minutes.

NUTRITIONAL

- Calories: 44;
- carbs: 27g;
- protein: 4g;
- fats: 3g;
- phosphorus: 59mg;
- potassium: 92mg;
- sodium: 65mg

Preparation Time: 15 minutes |Cooking Time: 12 minutes |Servings: 10

Mixed Berry Cobbler

INGREDIENTS

- 1/4 cup coconut milk
- 1/4 cup ghee
- 1/4 cup honey
- 1/2 cup almond flour
- 1/2 cup tapioca starch
- 1/2 tablespoon cinnamon
- 1/2 tablespoon coconut sugar
- 1 teaspoon vanilla
- 12 ounces frozen raspberries
- 16 ounces frozen wild blueberries
- 2 teaspoon baking powder
- 2 teaspoon tapioca starch

DIRECTION

- Place the frozen berries in the slow cooker. Add honey and 2 teaspoons of tapioca starch. Mix to combine.
- In a bowl, mix the tapioca starch, almond flour, coconut milk, ghee, baking powder and vanilla. Sweeten with sugar. Place this pastry mix on top of the berries.
- Set the slow cooker for 4 hours.

NUTRITIONAL

- Calories: 146;
- carbs: 33g;
- protein: 1g;
- fats: 3g;
- phosphorus: 29mg;
- potassium: 133mg;
- sodium: 4mg

Preparation Time: 15 minutes |Cooking Time: 4 hours |Servings: 8

Blueberry Espresso Brownies

INGREDIENTS

- 1/4 cup organic cocoa powder
- 1/4 teaspoon salt
- 1/2 cup raw honey
- 1/2 teaspoon baking soda
- 1 cup blueberries
- 1 cup coconut cream
- 1 tablespoon cinnamon
- 1 tablespoon ground coffee
- 2 teaspoon vanilla extract
- 3 eggs

DIRECTION

- Preheat the oven to 3250F.
- In a bow mix together coconut cream, honey, eggs, cinnamon, honey, vanilla, baking soda, coffee and salt.
- Use a mixer to combine all ingredients.
- Fold in the blueberries
- Pour the batter in a greased baking dish and bake for 30 minutes or until a toothpick inserted in the middle comes out clean.
- Remove from the oven and let it cool.

NUTRITIONAL

- Calories: 168;
- carbs: 20g;
- protein: 4g;
- fats: 10g;
- phosphorus: 79mg;
- potassium: 169mg;
- sodium: 129mg

Preparation Time: 15 minutes |Cooking Time: 30 minutes |Servings: 12

Coffee Brownies

INGREDIENTS

- 3 eggs, beaten
- 2 tablespoons cocoa powder
- 2 teaspoons Erythritol
- 1/2 cup almond flour
- 1/2 cup organic almond milk

DIRECTION

- Place the eggs in the mixing bowl and combine them with Erythritol and almond milk.
- With the help of the hand mixer, whisk the liquid until homogenous.
- Then add almond flour and cocoa powder.
- Whisk the mixture until smooth.
- Take the non-sticky brownie mold and transfer the cocoa mass inside it.
- Flatten it gently with the help of the spatula. The flattened mass should be thin.
- Preheat the oven to 365F.
- Transfer the brownie in the oven and bake it for 20 minutes.
- Then chill the cooked brownies at least till the room temperature and cut into serving bars.

NUTRITIONAL

- calories 78,
- fat 5.8,
- fiber 1.3,
- carbs 2.7,
- protein 5.5

Preparation Time: 15 minutes |Cooking Time: 20 minutes |Servings: 4

Keto Marshmellow

INGREDIENTS

- 1/4 cup water, boiled
- 4 tablespoons Erythritol
- 2 tablespoons gelatin powder
- 1 fl. oz. water

DIRECTION

- Line the baking tray with the baking paper.
- Pour 1 floozy of water in the shallow bowl and add gelatin. Stir it. Leave the gelatin.
- Pour a 1/4 cup of water in the saucepan and bring it to boil.
- Then add Erythritol and stir.
- Bring the liquid to boil and keep cooking for 3 minutes over the medium-low heat.
- Then switch off the heat.
- Start to add gelatin mixture in the sweet water. Whisk it with the help of the hand mixer. Use the maximum speed.
- When the mixture changes the color into white, whisk it for 1-2 minutes more or until you get strong peaks.
- Very fast transfer the whisked mixture in the tray and flatten it.
- Leave the marshmallow for 20 minutes to stabilize.
- Then make the sharp knife wet and cut the marshmallow into the cubes.

NUTRITIONAL

- calories 7,
- fat 0, fiber 0,
- carbs 6.9,
- protein 1.7

Preparation Time: 15 minutes |Cooking Time: 5 minutes |Servings: 7

Fragrant Lava Cake

INGREDIENTS

- 1 teaspoon baking powder
- 1 teaspoon vanilla extract
- 2 eggs, whisked
- 4 tablespoons cocoa powder
- 2 tablespoons Erythritol
- 8 tablespoons heavy cream
- 4 teaspoon almond flour
- Cooking spray

DIRECTION

- Whisk the eggs together with heavy cream.
- Then add vanilla extract, Erythritol, cocoa powder, and almond flour.
- Mix the mixture until smooth.
- Spray the mini cake molds with the cooking spray.
- Preheat the oven to 350F.
- Pour the cake mixture into the cake molds and place in the oven.
- Bake the cakes for 15 minutes.
- Then remove the lava cakes from the oven and discard from the cake molds.
- Serve the lava cakes only hot.

NUTRITIONAL

- calories 218,
- fat 19.1,
- fiber 3.7,
- carbs 8.3,
- protein 8.1

Preparation Time: 10 minutes |Cooking Time: 15 minutes |Servings: 5

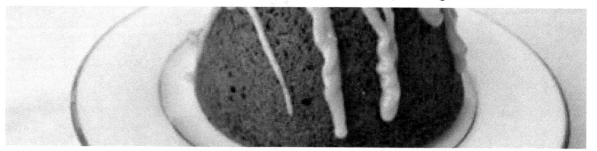

Almond Butter Mousse

INGREDIENTS

- 2 strawberries
- 1 cup of coconut milk
- 1/2 teaspoon vanilla extract
- 2 teaspoon Erythritol
- 4 tablespoons almond butter
- ¾ teaspoon ground cinnamon

DIRECTION

- Pour coconut milk in the food processor.
- Add vanilla extract, Erythritol, almond butter, and ground cinnamon.
- Blend the mixture until smooth.
- Ten transfer it in the saucepan and start to preheat it over the medium heat.
- Stir it all the time.
- When the mousse starts to be thick, remove it from the heat and stir.
- Pour the mousse into the serving glasses.
- Slice the strawberries.
- Top the mousse with the strawberries.

NUTRITIONAL

- calories 321,
- fat 31.1,
- fiber 4.4,
- carbs 9.6,
- protein 6.4

Preparation Time: 7 minutes |Cooking Time: 7 minutes |Servings: 3

Keto Panna Cotta

INGREDIENTS

- 1 cup heavy cream
- 1 teaspoon vanilla extract
- 2 teaspoons Erythritol
- 2 teaspoon blackberries
- 1 tablespoon gelatin powder
- 5 tablespoons water

DIRECTION

- Pour heavy cream in the saucepan and bring it to boil.
- Meanwhile, mix up together water with gelatin powder. Let gelatin powder to soak water.
- When the heavy cream is boiling, remove it from the heat, add vanilla extract.
- Chill the heavy cream to the 104F.
- Mash the blackberries with Erythritol.
- Mix up together soaked gelatin and chilled heavy cream. When the mixture is smooth pour it into the pannacotta glasses.
- Chill the mixture in the fridge for 20 minutes.
- After this, top Pannacotta with the mashed blackberries.
- Chill the dessert in the fridge until it is solid (appx.20 minutes).

NUTRITIONAL

- calories 226.
- Fat 22.2,
- fiber 0.2,
- carbs 2.2,
- protein 4.3

Preparation Time: 10 minutes |Cooking Time: 10 minutes |Servings: 2

Almond Truffles

INGREDIENTS

- 1/2 cup almond flour
- 2 teaspoons almond butter
- ¾ teaspoon ground cinnamon
- 1 teaspoon liquid stevia
- 1 oz. dark chocolate
- 1 tablespoon heavy cream

DIRECTION

- Mix up together almond flour and almond butter.
- Add ground cinnamon and liquid stevia.
- Mix up the mixture until smooth.
- Then make 5 truffles and place them on the baking paper.
- Freeze them for 15 minutes in the freezer.
- Meanwhile, preheat dark chocolate and heavy cream.
- When the mixture is homogenous, the chocolate batter is cooked.
- Remove the truffles from the freezer and sprinkle them with the chocolate batter.
- Let the cooked truffles chill.

NUTRITIONAL

- calories 98,
- fat 8.1,
- fiber 1.5,
- carbs 5.4,
- protein 2.2

Preparation Time: 15 minutes |Cooking Time: 5 minutes |Servings: 5

Blueberry Cheesecake

INGREDIENTS

- 2 tablespoons butter
- 1 teaspoon of cocoa powder
- 1/2 cup almond flour
- 2 cups cream cheese
- 1 tablespoon blueberry
- 2 tablespoons Erythritol
- 4 eggs, beaten
- 1 teaspoon vanilla extract

DIRECTION

- Make the cheesecake crust: mix up together butter, cocoa powder, and almond flour and knead the dough.
- Then place the dough into the 9-inch springform pan and flatten to get the shape of pie crust.
- Freeze it in the freezer.
- Meanwhile, blend the cream cheese until it is a soft and little bit fluffy.
- Then add eggs, Erythritol, blueberries, and vanilla extract.
- Blend the mixture until smooth.
- Remove the pie crust from the freezer.
- Put the cream cheese mixture over the pie crust and flatten it well.
- Preheat the oven to 355F and place the cheesecake inside.
- Cook the cheesecake for 55 minutes.
- Then switch off the oven and let the cake sit for 25 minutes more. The perfect texture of the cheesecake will be reached after 7 hours of chilling.
- Slice the cheesecake into the servings.

NUTRITIONAL

- calories 272,
- fat 26.2,
- fiber 0.3,
- carbs 2.5,
- protein 7.6

Preparation Time: 20 minutes |Cooking Time: 55 minutes |Servings: 8

Chapter 12.
Side Dishes

Ginger Cauliflower Rice

INGREDIENTS

- 5 cups cauliflower florets
- 3 tablespoons coconut oil
- 4 ginger slices, grated
- 1 tablespoon coconut vinegar
- 3 garlic cloves, minced
- 1 tablespoon chives, minced
- A pinch of sea salt
- Black pepper to taste

DIRECTION

- Put cauliflower florets in a food processor and pulse well.
- Heat up a pan with the oil over medium-high heat, add ginger, stir and cook for 3 minutes.
- Add cauliflower rice and garlic, stir and cook for 7 minutes.
- Add salt, black pepper, vinegar, and chives, stir, cook for a few seconds more, divide between plates and serve.
- Enjoy!

NUTRITIONAL

- Calories 125,
- fat 10,4,
- fiber 3,2,
- carbs 7,9,
- protein 2,7
- Phosphorus: 110mg
- Potassium: 117mg
- Sodium: 75mg

Preparation Time: 10 minutes |Cooking Time: 10 minutes |Servings: 4

Basil Zucchini Spaghetti

INGREDIENTS

- 1/3 cup coconut oil, melted
- 4 zucchinis, cut with a spiralizer
- ¼ cup basil, chopped
- A pinch of sea salt
- Black pepper to taste
- ½ cup walnuts, chopped
- 2 garlic cloves, minced

DIRECTION

- In a bowl, mix zucchini spaghetti with salt and pepper, toss to coat, leave aside for 1 hour, drain well and put in a bowl.
- Heat up a pan with the oil over medium-high heat, add zucchini spaghetti and garlic, stir and cook for 5 minutes.
- Add basil and walnuts and black pepper, stir and cook for 3 minutes more.
- Divide between plates and serve as a side dish
- Enjoy!

NUTRITIONAL

- Calories 287,
- fat 27,8,
- fiber 3,3,
- carbs 8,7,
- protein 6,3
- Phosphorus: 110mg
- Potassium: 117mg
- Sodium: 75mg

Preparation Time: 1 hour and 10 minutes |Cooking Time: 10 minutes |Servings: 4

Braised Cabbage

INGREDIENTS

- 1 small cabbage head, shredded
- 2 tablespoons water
- A drizzle of olive oil
- 6 ounces shallots, cooked and chopped
- A pinch of black pepper
- A pinch of sweet paprika
- 1 tablespoon dill, chopped

DIRECTION

- Heat up a pan with the oil over medium heat, add the cabbage and the water, stir and sauté for 5 minutes.
- Add the rest of the ingredients, toss, cook for 5 minutes more, divide everything between plates and serve as a side dish!
- Enjoy!

NUTRITIONAL

- Calories 91,
- fat 0,5,
- fiber 5,8,
- carbs 20,8,
- protein 4,1
- Phosphorus: 120mg
- Potassium: 127mg
- Sodium: 75mg

Preparation Time: 10 minutes |Cooking Time: 10 minutes |Servings: 4

Cauliflower and Leeks

INGREDIENTS

- 1 and ½ cups leeks, chopped
- 1 and ½ cups cauliflower florets
- 2 garlic cloves, minced
- 1 and ½ cups artichoke hearts
- 2 tablespoons coconut oil, melted
- Black pepper to taste

DIRECTION

- Heat up a pan with the oil over medium-high heat, add garlic, leeks, cauliflower florets and artichoke hearts, stir and cook for 20 minutes.
- Add black pepper, stir, divide between plates and serve.
- Enjoy!

NUTRITIONAL

- Calories 192,
- fat 6,9,
- fiber 8,2,
- carbs 35,1,
- protein 5,1
- Phosphorus: 110mg
- Potassium: 117mg
- Sodium: 75mg

Preparation Time: 10 minutes |Cooking Time: 20 minutes |Servings: 4

Eggplant and Mushroom Sauté

INGREDIENTS

- 2 pounds oyster mushrooms, chopped
- 6 ounces shallots, peeled, chopped
- 1 yellow onion, chopped
- 2 eggplants, cubed
- 3 celery stalks, chopped
- 1 tablespoon parsley, chopped
- A pinch of sea salt
- Black pepper to taste
- 1 tablespoon savory, dried
- 3 tablespoons coconut oil, melted

DIRECTION

- Heat up a pan with the oil over medium high heat, add onion, stir and cook for 4 minutes.
- Add shallots, stir and cook for 4 more minutes.
- Add eggplant pieces, mushrooms, celery, savory and black pepper to taste, stir and cook for 15 minutes.
- Add parsley, stir again, cook for a couple more minutes, divide between plates and serve.
- Enjoy!

NUTRITIONAL

- calories 1013,
- fat 10,9,
- fiber 35,5,
- carbs 156,5,
- protein 69,1
- Phosphorus: 210mg
- Potassium: 217mg
- Sodium: 105mg

Preparation Time: 10 minutes |Cooking Time: 30 minutes |Servings: 4

Mint Zucchini

INGREDIENTS

- 2 tablespoons mint
- 2 zucchinis, halved lengthwise and then slice into half moons
- 1 tablespoon coconut oil, melted
- ½ tablespoon dill, chopped
- A pinch of cayenne pepper

DIRECTION

- Heat up a pan with the oil over medium-high heat, add zucchinis, stir and cook for 6 minutes.
- Add cayenne, dill and mint, stir, cook for 1 minute more, divide between plates and serve.
- Enjoy!

NUTRITIONAL

- Calories 46,
- fat 3,6,
- fiber 1,3,
- carbs 3,5,
- protein 1,3
- Phosphorus: 120mg
- Potassium: 127mg
- Sodium: 75mg

Preparation Time: 10 minutes |Cooking Time: 7 minutes |Servings: 4

Celery and Kale Mix

INGREDIENTS

- 2 celery stalks, chopped
- 5 cups kale, torn
- 1 small red bell pepper, chopped
- 3 tablespoons water
- 1 tablespoon coconut oil, melted

DIRECTION

- Heat up a pan with the oil over medium-high heat, add celery, stir and cook for 10 minutes.
- Add kale, water, and bell pepper, stir and cook for 10 minutes more.
- Divide between plates and serve.
- Enjoy!

NUTRITIONAL

- Calories 81,
- fat 3,5,
- fiber 1,8,
- carbs 11,3,
- protein 2,9
- Phosphorus: 120mg
- Potassium: 147mg
- Sodium: 75mg

Preparation Time: 10 minutes |Cooking Time: 20 minutes |Servings: 4

Kale, Mushrooms and Red Chard Mix

INGREDIENTS

- ½ pound brown mushrooms, sliced
- 5 cups kale, roughly chopped
- 1 and ½ tablespoons coconut oil
- 3 cups red chard, chopped
- 2 tablespoons water
- Black pepper to taste

DIRECTION

- Heat up a pan with the oil over medium high heat, add mushrooms, stir and cook for 5 minutes.
- Add red chard, kale and water, stir and cook for 10 minutes.
- Add black pepper to taste, stir and cook 2 minutes more.
- Divide between plates and serve.
- Enjoy

NUTRITIONAL

- Calories 97,
- fat 3,4,
- fiber 2,3,
- carbs 13,3,
- protein 5,4
- Phosphorus: 110mg
- Potassium: 117mg
- Sodium: 75mg

Preparation Time: 10 minutes |Cooking Time: 17 minutes |Servings: 4

Bok Choy and Beets

INGREDIENTS

- 1 tablespoon coconut oil
- 4 cups bok choy, chopped
- 3 beets, cut into quarters and thinly sliced
- 2 tablespoons water
- A pinch of cayenne pepper

DIRECTION

- Put water in a large saucepan, add the beets, bring to a boil over medium heat, cover, and cook for 20 minutes and drain.
- Heat up a pan with the oil over medium high heat, add the bok choy and the water, stir and cook for 10 minutes.
- Add beets and cayenne pepper, stir, cook for 2 minutes more, divide between plates and serve as a side dish!
- Enjoy!

NUTRITIONAL

- Calories 71, fat 3,7, fiber 2,2, carbs 9, protein 2,3
- Phosphorus: 110mg
- Potassium: 117mg
- Sodium: 75mg

Preparation Time: 10 minutes |Cooking Time: 30 minutes |Servings: 4

Broccoli and Almonds Mix

INGREDIENTS

- 1 tablespoon olive oil
- 1 garlic clove, minced
- 1 pound broccoli florets
- 1/3 cup almonds, chopped
- Black pepper to taste

DIRECTION

- Heat up a pan with the oil over medium-high heat, add the almonds, stir, cook for 5 minutes and transfer to a bowl,
- Heat up the same pan again over medium-high heat, add broccoli and garlic, stir, cover and cook for 6 minutes more.
- Add the almonds and black pepper to taste, stir, divide between plates and serve.
- Enjoy!

NUTRITIONAL

- Calories 116,
- fat 7,8, fiber 4,
- carbs 9,5,
- protein 4,9
- Phosphorus: 110mg
- Potassium: 117mg
- Sodium: 75mg

Preparation Time: 10 minutes |Cooking Time: 11 minutes |Servings: 4

Squash and Cranberries

INGREDIENTS

- 1 tablespoon coconut oil
- 1 butternut squash, peeled and cubed
- 2 garlic cloves, minced
- 1 small yellow onion, chopped
- 12 ounces coconut milk
- 1 teaspoon curry powder
- 1 teaspoon cinnamon powder
- ½ cup cranberries

DIRECTION

- Spread squash pieces on a lined baking sheet, place in the oven at 425 degrees F, bake for 15 minutes and leave to one side.
- Heat up a pan with the oil over medium high heat, add garlic and onion, stir and cook for 5 minutes.
- Add roasted squash, stir and cook for 3 minutes.
- Add coconut milk, cranberries, cinnamon and curry powder, stir and cook for 5 minutes more.
- Divide between plates and serve as a side dish!
- Enjoy!

NUTRITIONAL

- Calories 518,
- fat 47,6,
- fiber 7,3,
- carbs 24,9,
- protein 5,3
- Phosphorus: 110mg
- Potassium: 117mg
- Sodium: 75mg

Preparation Time: 10 minutes |Cooking Time: 30 minutes |Servings: 2

Creamy Chard

INGREDIENTS

- Juice of ½ lemon
- 1 tablespoon coconut oil
- 12 ounces coconut milk
- 1 bunch chard
- A pinch of sea salt
- Black pepper to taste

DIRECTION

- Heat up a pan with the oil over medium-high heat, add chard, stir and cook for 5 minutes.
- Add lemon juice, a pinch of salt, black pepper, and coconut milk, stir and cook for 5 minutes more.
- Divide between plates and serve as a side.
- Enjoy!

NUTRITIONAL

- Calories 453,
- fat 47,4, fiber 4,
- carbs 10,1,
- protein 4,2
- Phosphorus: 130mg
- Potassium: 1127mg
- Sodium: 85mg

Preparation Time: 10 minutes |Cooking Time: 10 minutes |Servings: 2

Dill Carrots

INGREDIENTS

- 1 tablespoon coconut oil, melted
- 2 tablespoons dill, chopped
- 1 pound baby carrots
- 1 tablespoon coconut sugar
- A pinch of black pepper

DIRECTION

- Put carrots in a large saucepan, add water to cover, bring to a boil over medium-high heat, cover and simmer for 30 minutes.
- Drain the carrots, put them in a bowl, add melted oil, black pepper, dill, and the coconut sugar, stir very well, divide between plates and serve.
- Enjoy!

NUTRITIONAL

- Calories 85,
- fat 3,6,
- fiber 3,5,
- carbs 13,4,
- protein 1
- Phosphorus: 140mg
- Potassium: 147mg
- Sodium: 65mg

Preparation Time: 10 minutes |Cooking Time: 30 minutes |Servings: 4

Chapter 23.
Broths, Condiment and Seasoning Mix

Spicy Herb Seasoning

INGREDIENTS

- ¼ cup celery seed
- 1 tablespoon dried basil
- 1 tablespoon dried oregano
- 1 tablespoon dried thyme
- 1 tablespoon onion powder
- 2 teaspoons garlic powder
- 1 teaspoon freshly ground black pepper
- ½ teaspoon ground cloves

DIRECTION

- Mix the celery seed, basil, oregano, thyme, onion powder, garlic powder, pepper, and cloves in a small bowl. Store for up to 1 month.

NUTRITIONAL

- Calories: 7
- Fat: 0g
- Sodium: 2mg
- Carbohydrates: 1g
- Phosphorus: 9mg
- Potassium: 27mg
- Protein: 0g

Preparation Time: 10 minutes |Cooking Time: 0 minutes|Servings: ½ cup

Phosphorus-Free Baking Powder

INGREDIENTS

- ¾ cup cream of tartar
- ¼ cup baking soda

DIRECTION

- Mix the cream of tartar plus baking soda in a small bowl. Sift the mixture together several times to mix thoroughly. Store the baking powder in a sealed container in a cool, dark place for up to 1 month.

NUTRITIONAL

- Calories: 6
- Fat: 0g
- Sodium: 309mg
- Carbohydrates: 1g
- Phosphorus: 0g
- Potassium: 341mg
- Protein: 0g

Preparation Time: 5 minutes |Cooking Time: 0 minutes|Servings: 1

Basil Oil

INGREDIENTS

- 2 cups olive oil
- 2½ cups fresh basil leaves patted dry

DIRECTION

- Put the olive oil plus basil leaves in a food processor or blender, and pulse until the leaves are coarsely chopped.
- Transfer these to a medium saucepan, and place over medium heat. Heat the oil, occasionally stirring, until it just starts to simmer along the edges, about 4 minutes. Remove, then let it stand until cool, about 2 hours.
- Pour the oil through a fine-mesh sieve or doubled piece of cheesecloth into a container. Store the basil oil in an airtight glass container in the refrigerator for up to 2 months.
- Before using for dressings, remove the oil from the refrigerator and let it come to room temperature, or for cooking, scoop out cold spoonsful.

NUTRITIONAL

- Calories: 40
- Fat: 5g
- Sodium: 0g
- Carbohydrates: 0g
- Phosphorus: 0g
- Potassium: 0g
- Protein: 0g

Preparation Time: 15 minutes |Cooking Time: 4 minutes|Servings: 3

Basil Pesto

INGREDIENTS

- 2 cups gently packed fresh basil leaves
- 2 garlic cloves
- 2 tablespoons pine nuts
- ¼ cup olive oil
- 2 tablespoons freshly squeezed lemon juice

DIRECTION

- Pulse the basil, garlic, plus pine nuts using a food processor or blender within about 3 minutes. Drizzle the olive oil into this batter, and pulse until thick paste forms.
- Put the lemon juice, and pulse until well blended. Store the pesto in a sealed glass container in the refrigerator for up to 2 weeks.

NUTRITIONAL

- Calories: 22
- Fat: 2g
- Sodium: 0mg
- Carbohydrates: 0g
- Phosphorus: 3mg
- Potassium: 10mg
- Protein: 0g

Preparation Time: 15 minutes |Cooking Time: 0 minutes|Servings: 1 ½ cups

Sweet Barbecue Sauce

INGREDIENTS

- 1 teaspoon olive oil
- ½ sweet onion, chopped
- 1 teaspoon minced garlic
- ¼ cup honey
- ¼ cup apple cider vinegar
- 2 tablespoons low-sodium tomato paste
- 1 tablespoon Dijon mustard
- 1 teaspoon hot sauce
- 1 teaspoon cornstarch

DIRECTION

- Warm-up olive oil in a medium saucepan over medium heat. Add the onion and garlic and sauté until softened, about 3 minutes.
- Stir in ¾ cup water, the honey, vinegar, tomato paste, mustard, and hot sauce. Cook within 6 minutes.
- In a small cup, stir together ¼ cup of water and the cornstarch. Whisk the cornstarch into the sauce and continue to cook, stirring, until the sauce thickens about 2 minutes. Cool. Pour the sauce into a sealed glass container and store in the refrigerator for up to 1 week.

NUTRITIONAL

- Calories: 14
- Fat: 0g
- Sodium: 10mg
- Carbohydrates: 3g
- Phosphorus: 3mg
- Potassium: 17mg
- Protein: 0g

Preparation Time: 15 minutes|Cooking Time: 11 minutes|Servings: 2 cups

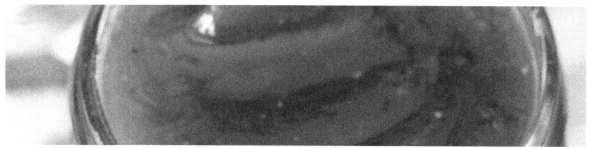

Low-Sodium Mayonnaise

INGREDIENTS

- 2 egg yolks
- 1 teaspoon Dijon mustard
- 1 teaspoon honey
- 2 tablespoons white vinegar
- 2 tablespoons freshly squeezed lemon juice
- 2 cups olive oil

DIRECTION

- Mix the egg yolks, mustard, honey, vinegar, and lemon juice in a large bowl. Mix in the olive oil in a thin stream. You can store this in a glass container in the refrigerator for up to 2 weeks.

NUTRITIONAL

- Calories: 83
- Fat: 9g
- Sodium: 2mg
- Carbohydrates: 0g
- Phosphorus: 2mg
- Potassium: 3mg
- Protein: 0g

Preparation Time: 15 minutes |Cooking Time: 0 minutes|Servings: 3

Citrus and Mustard Marinade

INGREDIENTS

- ¼ cup freshly squeezed lemon juice
- ¼ cup freshly squeezed orange juice
- ¼ cup Dijon mustard
- 2 tablespoons honey
- 2 teaspoons chopped fresh thyme

DIRECTION

- Mix the lemon juice, orange juice, mustard, honey, and thyme until well blended in a medium bowl. Store the marinade in a sealed glass container in the refrigerator for up to 3 days. Shake before using it

NUTRITIONAL

- Calories: 35
- Fat: 0g
- Sodium: 118mg
- Carbohydrates: 8g
- Phosphorus: 14mg
- Potassium: 52mg
- Protein: 1g

Preparation Time: 15 minutes|Cooking Time: 0 minutes|Servings: ¾ cup

Fiery Honey Vinaigrette

INGREDIENTS

- 1/3 cup freshly squeezed lime juice
- ¼ cup honey
- ¼ cup olive oil
- 1 teaspoon chopped fresh basil leaves
- ½ teaspoon red pepper flakes

DIRECTION

- Mix the lime juice, honey, olive oil, basil, and red pepper flakes in a medium bowl, until well blended. Store the dressing in a glass container, and store it in the fridge for up to 1 week.

NUTRITIONAL

- Calories: 125
- Fat: 9g
- Sodium: 1mg
- Carbohydrates: 13g
- Phosphorus: 1mg
- Potassium: 24mg
- Protein: 0g

Preparation Time: 15 minutes|Cooking Time: 0 minutes|Servings: ¾ cup

Buttermilk Herb Dressing

INGREDIENTS

- ½ cup skim milk
- ½ cup Low-Sodium Mayonnaise
- 2 tablespoons apple cider vinegar
- ½ scallion, green part only, chopped
- 1 tablespoon chopped fresh dill
- 1 teaspoon chopped fresh thyme
- ½ teaspoon minced garlic
- Freshly ground black pepper

DIRECTION

- Mix the milk, mayonnaise, and vinegar until smooth in a medium bowl. Whisk in the scallion, dill, thyme, and garlic. Season with pepper. Store.

NUTRITIONAL

- Calories: 31
- Fat: 2g
- Sodium: 19mg
- Carbohydrates: 2g
- Phosphorus: 13mg
- Potassium: 26mg
- Protein: 0g

Preparation Time: 15 minutes|Cooking Time: 0 minutes|Servings: 1 ½ cup

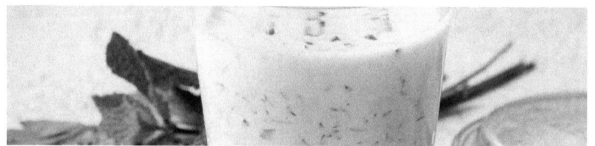

Poppy Seed Dressing

INGREDIENTS

- ½ cup apple cider or red wine vinegar
- 1/3 cup honey
- ¼ cup freshly squeezed lemon juice
- 1 tablespoon Dijon mustard
- 1 cup olive oil
- ½ small sweet onion, minced
- 2 tablespoons poppy seeds

DIRECTION

- Mix the vinegar, honey, lemon juice, and mustard in a small bowl. Whisk in the oil, onion, and poppy seeds. Store the dressing in a sealed glass container in the refrigerator for up to 2 weeks.

NUTRITIONAL

- Calories: 151
- Fat: 14g
- Sodium: 12mg
- Carbohydrates: 7g
- Phosphorus: 13mg
- Potassium: 30mg
- Protein: 0g

Preparation Time: 15 minutes, Cooking Time: 0 minutes, Servings: 2 cups

Mediterranean Dressing

INGREDIENTS

- ½ cup balsamic vinegar
- 1 teaspoon honey
- ½ teaspoon minced garlic
- 1 tablespoon dried parsley
- 1 tablespoon dried oregano
- ½ teaspoon celery seed
- Pinch freshly ground black pepper
- ½ cup olive oil

DIRECTION

- Mix the vinegar, honey, garlic, parsley, oregano, celery seed, and pepper in a small bowl. Whisk in the olive oil until emulsified. Store the dressing in a sealed glass container in the refrigerator for up to 1 week.

NUTRITIONAL

- Calories: 100
- Fat: 11g
- Sodium: 1mg
- Carbohydrates: 1g
- Phosphorus: 1mg
- Potassium: 10mg
- Protein: 0g

Preparation Time: 15 minutes|Cooking Time: 0 minutes|Servings: 1 cup

Fajita Rub

INGREDIENTS

- 1½ teaspoons chili powder
- 1 teaspoon garlic powder
- 1 teaspoon roasted cumin seed
- 1 teaspoon dried oregano
- ½ teaspoon ground coriander
- ¼ teaspoon red pepper flakes

DIRECTION

- Put the chili powder, garlic powder, cumin seed, oregano, coriander, and red pepper flakes in a blender, pulse until ground and well combined. Transfer the spice mixture and store for up to 6 months.

NUTRITIONAL

- Calories: 1
- Fat: 0g
- Carbohydrates: 0g
- Phosphorus: 2mg
- Potassium: 7mg
- Sodium: 7mg
- Protein: 0g

Preparation Time: 15 minutes |Cooking Time: 0 minutes|Servings: ¼ cup

Dried Herb Rub

INGREDIENTS

- 1 tablespoon dried thyme
- 1 tablespoon dried oregano
- 1 tablespoon dried parsley
- 2 teaspoons dried basil
- 2 teaspoons ground coriander
- 2 teaspoons onion powder
- 1 teaspoon ground cumin
- 1 teaspoon garlic powder
- 1 teaspoon paprika
- ½ teaspoon cayenne pepper

DIRECTION

- Put the thyme, oregano, parsley, basil, coriander, onion powder, cumin, garlic powder, paprika, and cayenne pepper in a blender, and pulse until the ingredients are ground and well combined. Transfer the rub to a small container with a lid. Store in a cool, dry area for up to 6 months.

NUTRITIONAL

- Calories: 3
- Fat: 0g
- Carbohydrates: 1g
- Phosphorus: 3mg
- Potassium: 16mg
- Sodium: 1mg
- Protein: 0g

Preparation Time: 15 minutes |Cooking Time: 0 minutes|Servings: 1/3 cup

Mediterranean Seasoning

INGREDIENTS

- 2 tablespoons dried oregano
- 1 tablespoon dried thyme
- 2 teaspoons dried rosemary, chopped finely or crushed
- 2 teaspoons dried basil
- 1 teaspoon dried marjoram
- 1 teaspoon dried parsley flakes

DIRECTION

- Mix the oregano, thyme, rosemary, basil, marjoram, and parsley in a small bowl until well combined. Transfer then store.

NUTRITIONAL

- Calories: 1
- Fat: 0g
- Carbohydrates: 0g
- Phosphorus: 1mg
- Potassium: 6mg
- Sodium: 0mg
- Protein: 0g

Preparation Time: 15 minutes |Cooking Time: 0 minutes|Servings: 1

Hot Curry Powder

INGREDIENTS

- ¼ cup ground cumin
- ¼ cup ground coriander
- 3 tablespoons turmeric
- 2 tablespoons sweet paprika
- 2 tablespoons ground mustard
- 1 tablespoon fennel powder
- ½ teaspoon green chili powder
- 2 teaspoons ground cardamom
- 1 teaspoon ground cinnamon
- ½ teaspoon ground cloves

DIRECTION

- Pulse the cumin, coriander, turmeric, paprika, mustard, fennel powder, green chili powder, cardamom, cinnamon, plus cloves using a blender, until the fixing is ground and well combined. Transfer it to a small container, put in a cool, dry place for up to 6 months.

NUTRITIONAL

- Calories: 19
- Fat: 1g
- Carbohydrates: 3g
- Phosphorus: 24mg
- Potassium: 93mg
- Sodium: 5mg
- Protein: 1g

Preparation Time: 15 minutes |Cooking Time: 0 minutes|Servings: 1 ¼ cup

Cajun Seasoning

INGREDIENTS

- ½ cup sweet paprika
- ¼ cup garlic powder
- 3 tablespoons onion powder
- 3 tablespoons freshly ground black pepper
- 2 tablespoons dried oregano
- 1 tablespoon cayenne pepper
- 1 tablespoon dried thyme

DIRECTION

- Pulse the paprika, garlic powder, onion powder, black pepper, oregano, cayenne pepper, and thyme in a blender until the fixing is ground and well combined.

NUTRITIONAL

- Calories: 7
- Fat: 0g
- Carbohydrates: 2g
- Phosphorus: 8mg
- Potassium: 40mg
- Sodium: 1mg
- Protein: 0g

Preparation Time: 15 minutes|Cooking Time: 0 minutes|Servings: 1 ¼ cup

Apple Pie Spice

INGREDIENTS

- ¼ cup ground cinnamon
- 2 teaspoons ground nutmeg
- 2 teaspoons ground ginger
- 1 teaspoon allspice
- ½ teaspoon ground cloves

DIRECTION

- Mix the cinnamon, nutmeg, ginger, allspice, and cloves in a small bowl. Store for up to 6 months.

NUTRITIONAL

- Calories: 6
- Fat: 0g
- Carbohydrates: 1g
- Phosphorus: 2mg
- Potassium: 12mg
- Sodium: 1mg
- Protein: 0g

Preparation Time: 15 minutes |Cooking Time: 0 minutes|Servings: 1/3 cup

Ras El Hanout

INGREDIENTS

- 2 teaspoons ground nutmeg
- 2 teaspoons ground coriander
- 2 teaspoons ground cumin
- 2 teaspoons turmeric
- 2 teaspoons cinnamon
- 1 teaspoon cardamom
- 1 teaspoon sweet paprika
- 1 teaspoon ground mace
- 1 teaspoon freshly ground black pepper
- 1 teaspoon cayenne pepper
- ½ teaspoon ground allspice
- ½ teaspoon ground

DIRECTION

- Mix the nutmeg, coriander, cumin, turmeric, cinnamon, cardamom, paprika, mace, black pepper, cayenne pepper, allspice, and cloves in a small bowl. Store.

NUTRITIONAL

- Calories: 5
- Fat: 0g
- Carbohydrates: 1g
- Phosphorus: 3mg
- Potassium: 17mg
- Sodium: 1mg
- Protein: 0g

Preparation Time: 5 minutes |Cooking Time: 0 minutes|Servings: ½ cup

Poultry Seasoning

INGREDIENTS

- 2 tablespoons ground thyme
- 2 tablespoons ground marjoram
- 1 tablespoon ground sage
- 1 tablespoon ground celery seed
- 1 teaspoon ground rosemary
- 1 teaspoon freshly ground black pepper

DIRECTION

- Mix the thyme, marjoram, sage, celery seed, rosemary, and pepper in a small bowl. Store for up to 6 months.

NUTRITIONAL

- Calories: 3
- Fat: 0g
- Carbohydrates: 0g
- Phosphorus: 3mg
- Potassium: 10mg
- Sodium: 1mg
- Protein: 0g

Preparation Time: 15 minutes |Cooking Time: 0 minutes|Servings: ½ cup

Berbere Spice Mix

INGREDIENTS

- 1 tablespoon coriander seeds
- 1 teaspoon cumin seeds
- 1 teaspoon fenugreek seeds
- ¼ teaspoon black peppercorns
- ¼ teaspoon whole allspice berries
- 4 whole cloves
- 4 dried chilis, stemmed and seeded
- ¼ cup dried onion flakes
- 2 tablespoons ground cardamom
- 1 tablespoon sweet paprika
- 1 teaspoon ground ginger
- ½ teaspoon ground nutmeg
- ½ teaspoon ground cinnamon

DIRECTION

- Put the coriander, cumin, fenugreek, peppercorns, allspice, and cloves in a small skillet over medium heat. Lightly toast the spices, swirling the skillet frequently, for about 4 minutes or until the spices are fragrant.
- Remove the skillet, then let the spices cool for about 10 minutes. Transfer the toasted spices to a blender with the chilis and onion, and grind until the mixture is finely ground.
- Transfer the ground spice mixture to a small bowl and stir together the cardamom, paprika, ginger, nutmeg, and cinnamon until thoroughly combined. Store the spice mixture in a small container with a lid for up to 6 months.

NUTRITIONAL

- Calories: 8
- Fat: 0g
- Carbohydrates: 2g
- Phosphorus: 7mg
- Potassium: 37mg
- Sodium: 14mg
- Protein: 0g

Preparation Time: 15 minutes |Cooking Time: 4 minutes|Servings: ½ cup

Creole Seasoning Mix

INGREDIENTS

- 1 tablespoon sweet paprika
- 1 tablespoon garlic powder
- 2 teaspoons onion powder
- 2 teaspoons dried oregano
- 1 teaspoon cayenne pepper
- 1 teaspoon ground thyme
- 1 teaspoon freshly ground black pepper

DIRECTION

- Mix the paprika, garlic powder, onion powder, oregano, cayenne pepper, thyme, and black pepper in a small bowl. Store for up to 6 months.

NUTRITIONAL

- Calories: 7
- Fat: 0g
- Carbohydrates: 2g
- Phosphorus: 8mg
- Potassium: 35mg
- Sodium: 1mg
- Protein: 0g

Preparation Time: 15 minutes|Cooking Time: 0 minutes|Servings: ¼ cup

Adobo Seasoning Mix

INGREDIENTS

- 4 tablespoons garlic powder
- 4 tablespoons onion powder
- 4 tablespoons ground cumin
- 3 tablespoons dried oregano
- 3 tablespoons freshly ground black pepper
- 2 tablespoons sweet paprika
- 2 tablespoons ground chili powder
- 1 tablespoon ground turmeric
- 1 tablespoon ground coriander

DIRECTION

- Mix the garlic powder, onion powder, black pepper, cumin, oregano, paprika, chili powder, turmeric, and coriander in a small bowl. Transfer these to a container and store in a cool, dry place for up to 6 months.

NUTRITIONAL

- Calories: 8
- Fat: 0g
- Carbohydrates: 2g
- Phosphorus: 9mg
- Potassium: 38mg
- Sodium: 12mg
- Protein: 0g

Preparation Time: 15 minutes|Cooking Time: 0 minutes|Servings: 1 ¼ cup

Herbes De Provence

INGREDIENTS

- ½ cup dried thyme
- 3 tablespoons dried marjoram
- 3 tablespoons dried savory
- 2 tablespoons dried rosemary
- 2 teaspoons dried lavender flowers
- 1 teaspoon ground fennel

DIRECTION

- Put the thyme, marjoram, savory, rosemary, lavender, and fennel in a blender and pulse a few times to combine. Store for up to 6 months.

NUTRITIONAL

- Calories: 3
- Fat: 0g
- Carbohydrates: 1g
- Phosphorus: 2mg
- Potassium: 9mg
- Sodium: 0mg
- Protein: 0g

Preparation Time: 15 minutes|Cooking Time: 0 minutes|Servings: 1 cup

Lamb and Pork Seasoning

INGREDIENTS

- ¼ cup celery seed
- 2 tablespoons dried oregano
- 2 tablespoons onion powder
- 1 tablespoon dried thyme
- 1½ teaspoons garlic powder
- 1 teaspoon crushed bay leaf
- 1 teaspoon freshly ground black pepper
- 1 teaspoon ground allspice

DIRECTION

- Pulse the celery seed, oregano, onion powder, thyme, garlic powder, bay leaf, pepper, and allspice in a blender a few times. Transfer the herb mixture to a small container; then, you can store it in a cool, dry place for up to 6 months.

NUTRITIONAL

- Calories: 8
- Fat: 0g
- Carbohydrates: 1g
- Phosphorus: 9mg
- Potassium: 29mg
- Sodium: 2mg
- Protein: 0g

Preparation Time: 15 minutes|Cooking Time: 0 minutes|Servings: ½ cup

Asian Seasoning

INGREDIENTS

- 2 tablespoons sesame seeds
- 2 tablespoons onion powder
- 2 tablespoons crushed star anise pods
- 2 tablespoons ground ginger
- 1 teaspoon ground all-spice
- ½ teaspoon cardamom
- ½ teaspoon ground cloves

DIRECTION

- Mix the sesame seeds, onion powder, star anise, ginger, allspice, cardamom, and cloves in a small bowl. Transfer the spice mixture to a container with a cover. Store for up to 6 months.

NUTRITIONAL

- Calories: 10
- Fat: 0g
- Carbohydrates: 1g
- Phosphorus: 11mg
- Potassium: 24mg
- Sodium: 5mg
- Protein: 0g

Preparation Time: 5 minutes|Cooking Time: 0 minutes|Servings: ½ cup

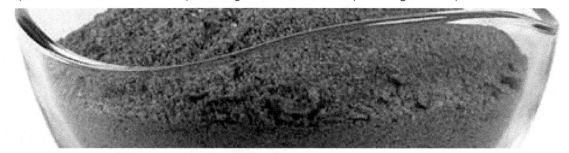

Onion Seasoning Blend

INGREDIENTS

- 2 tablespoons onion powder
- 1 tablespoon dry mustard
- 2 teaspoons sweet paprika
- 2 teaspoons garlic powder
- 1 teaspoon dried thyme
- ½ teaspoon celery seeds
- ½ teaspoon freshly ground black pepper

DIRECTION

- Mix the onion powder, mustard, paprika, garlic powder, thyme, celery seeds, and pepper until well combined in a small bowl. Store for up to 6 months.

NUTRITIONAL

- Calories: 5
- Fat: 0g
- Carbohydrates: 1g
- Phosphorus: 6mg
- Potassium: 17mg
- Sodium: 1mg
- Protein: 1g

Preparation Time: 15 minutes|Cooking Time: 0 minutes|Servings: ½ cup

Everyday No-Salt Seasoning Blend

INGREDIENTS

- 1 teaspoon dried thyme leaves
- 1 teaspoon dried marjoram leaves
- 1 teaspoon dried basil leaves
- 1 teaspoon dried oregano leaves
- ½ teaspoon onion powder
- ½ teaspoon garlic powder
- ½ teaspoon ground mustard
- ¼ teaspoon freshly ground black pepper
- ¼ teaspoon paprika

DIRECTION

- Combine the thyme, marjoram, basil, oregano, onion powder, garlic powder, ground mustard, pepper, and paprika. Transfer and store at room temperature for up to 6 months.

NUTRITIONAL

- Calories: 4
- Fat: 0g
- Sodium: 0mg
- Potassium: 17mg
- Phosphorus: 4mg
- Carbohydrates: 1g
- Protein: 0g

Preparation Time: 15 minutes |Cooking Time: 0 minutes|Servings: 2 tbsp.

Thai-Style Seasoning Blend

INGREDIENTS

- 1½ teaspoons turmeric
- 1½ teaspoons paprika
- 1 teaspoon ground coriander
- 1 teaspoon ground ginger
- 1 teaspoon dry mustard
- 1 teaspoon ground cumin
- 1 teaspoon dried mint leaves, crushed
- 1 teaspoon red pepper flakes

DIRECTION

- Combine the turmeric, paprika, coriander, ginger, dry mustard, cumin, mint, and red pepper flakes and store for up to 6 months.

NUTRITIONAL

- Calories: 5
- Fat: 0g
- Sodium: 1mg
- Potassium: 30mg
- Phosphorus: 6mg
- Carbohydrates: 1g
- Protein: 0g

Preparation Time: 15 minutes |Cooking Time: 0 minutes|Servings: 3 tbsp.

Tex-Mex Seasoning Mix

INGREDIENTS

- 1 tablespoon chili powder
- ½ teaspoon ground cumin
- ½ teaspoon dried oregano leaves
- ½ teaspoon garlic powder
- ½ teaspoon onion powder
- ½ teaspoon cayenne pepper
- ½ teaspoon red pepper flakes

DIRECTION

- Combine the chili powder, cumin, oregano, garlic powder, onion powder, cayenne pepper, and red pepper flakes. Store for up to 6 months.

NUTRITIONAL

- Calories: 7
- Fat: 0g
- Sodium: 39mg
- Potassium: 38mg
- Phosphorus: 7mg
- Carbohydrates: 1g
- Protein: 0g

Preparation Time: 10 minutes |Cooking Time: 0 minutes|Servings: 2 tbsp.

Duxelles

INGREDIENTS

- 1 (8-ounce) package sliced cremini mushrooms
- scallions, white and green parts
- garlic cloves
- 1 tablespoon olive oil
- 1 tablespoon unsalted butter
- 1 teaspoon freshly squeezed lemon juice
- Pinch salt

DIRECTION

- Finely chop the mushrooms, scallions, and garlic in a food processor or blender. Put the mushroom batter in the middle of a kitchen towel. Gather up the ends to create a pouch, and squeeze the pouch over the sink to remove some of the mushrooms' liquid.
- Heat-up olive oil and butter in a large skillet over medium-high heat. Add the drained mushroom mixture to the skillet and sprinkle with the lemon juice and salt.
- Sauté for 8 to 12 minutes, stirring frequently, or until the mushrooms are browned. This mixture can be refrigerated up to 4 days or frozen up to 1 month.

NUTRITIONAL

- Calories: 37
- Fat: 3g
- Sodium: 22mg
- Potassium: 141mg
- Phosphorus: 37mg
- Carbohydrates: 2g
- Protein: 1g

Preparation Time: 15 minutes|Cooking Time: 15 minutes|Servings: 8

Chicken Stock

INGREDIENTS

- 1 tablespoon olive oil
- 1 bone-in skin-on chicken breast (3 to 4 ounces)
- Pinch salt
- 1 onion, unpeeled, sliced
- 1 carrot, unpeeled, sliced
- 1 bay leaf
- 5 cups of water

DIRECTION

- Heat-up olive oil in a large saucepan over medium-high heat. Sprinkle the chicken with salt and add to the pan, skin-side down. Brown for 2 minutes.
- Put the onion plus carrot and cook within 1 minute longer. Add the bay leaf and water and bring to a boil. Adjust the heat to medium-low and simmer within 20 to 22 minutes, stirring occasionally. Remove the scum that pops to the surface.
- Drain or strain the stock through a fine-mesh colander into a bowl. You can reserve the chicken breast for other recipes, although it may be tough after cooking. Discard the remaining solids.
- Fridge the broth and skim off any fat that rises to the top. You can freeze this stock in 1-cup measures to use in recipes. Store freezer up to 3 months.

NUTRITIONAL

- Calories: 37
- Fat: 2g
- Sodium: 22mg
- Potassium: 85mg
- Phosphorus: 30mg
- Carbohydrates: 2g
- Protein: 3g

Preparation Time: 15 minutes|Cooking Time: 25 minutes |Servings: 4

Vegetable Broth

INGREDIENTS

- 1 tablespoon olive oil
- 1 unpeeled onion, sliced
- 2 unpeeled garlic cloves, crushed
- 2 unpeeled carrots, sliced
- 2 celery stalks, cut into 2-inch pieces
- 1 bay leaf
- 1 teaspoon dried basil leaves
- 5 cups of water

DIRECTION

- Heat-up olive oil in a large saucepan over medium-high heat. Sauté the onion, garlic, carrot, and celery for 5 minutes, stirring frequently or lightly browned.
- Add the bay leaf, basil, and water to the saucepan and bring to a boil. Adjust the heat to medium-low, then simmer for 20 to 22 minutes, stirring occasionally. Skim off and discard any scum that rises to the surface.
- Strain the stock to a fine-mesh colander into a bowl. Discard the solids. Fridge the broth and remove any fat that rises to the top. You can freeze this broth in 1-cup measures to use in recipes.

NUTRITIONAL

- Calories: 31
- Fat: 2g
- Sodium: 21mg
- Potassium: 110mg
- Phosphorus: 14mg
- Carbohydrates: 4g
- Protein: 0g

Preparation Time: 15 minutes |Cooking Time: 27 minutes|Servings: 4

Powerhouse Salsa

INGREDIENTS

- 8 grape Red bell peppers, chopped
- 1 yellow bell pepper, chopped
- 1 red bell pepper, chopped
- ¼ cup minced red onion
- 3 scallions, white and green parts, chopped
- 1 garlic clove, minced
- 1 jalapeño pepper, minced
- 2 tablespoons chopped fresh cilantro
- 2 teaspoons chili powder
- 2 tablespoons freshly squeezed lime juice

DIRECTION

- Combine the Red bell peppers, yellow bell pepper, red bell pepper, red onion, scallions, garlic, jalapeño, cilantro, chili powder, lime juice in a medium bowl mix. Use immediately or cover and store in the refrigerator for up to 4 days.

NUTRITIONAL

- Calories: 20
- Fat: 0g
- Sodium: 22mg
- Potassium: 148mg
- Phosphorus: 19mg
- Carbohydrates: 5g
- Protein: 1g
- Sugar: 3g

Preparation Time: 15 minutes|Cooking Time: 0 minutes|Servings: 8

Pesto

INGREDIENTS

- 2 cups fresh basil leaves
- ½ cup flat-leaf parsley
- 2 garlic cloves, sliced
- 3 tablespoons olive oil, + more for drizzling
- 2 tablespoons grated Parmesan cheese
- 2 tablespoons chopped walnuts
- 2 tablespoons water
- 1 tablespoon freshly squeezed lemon juice

DIRECTION

- Process the basil, parsley, garlic, olive oil, cheese, walnuts, water, and lemon juice in a blender or food processor. Put the pesto in a bowl and drizzle more olive oil on top to prevent browning. Store.

NUTRITIONAL

- Calories: 34
- Fat: 3g
- Sodium: 16mg
- Potassium: 35mg
- Phosphorus: 13mg
- Carbohydrates: 1g
- Protein: 1g

Preparation Time: 15 minutes|Cooking Time: 0 minutes|Servings: 16

Ranch Seasoning Mix

INGREDIENTS

- 2 tablespoons dried buttermilk powder
- 1 tablespoon cornstarch
- 1 tablespoon dried parsley
- 1 teaspoon dried dill weed
- 1 teaspoon dried chives
- ½ teaspoon garlic powder
- ½ teaspoon onion powder
- ¼ teaspoon freshly ground black pepper

DIRECTION

- Combine the buttermilk powder, cornstarch, parsley, dill weed, chives, garlic powder, onion powder, and pepper and keep in a small jar with a tight lid at room temperature for up to 6 months.

NUTRITIONAL

- Calories: 8
- Fat: >1g
- Sodium: 1mg
- Potassium: 27mg
- Phosphorus: 4mg
- Carbohydrates: 1g
- Protein: >1g

Preparation Time: 15 minutes|Cooking Time: 0 minutes|Servings: 1/3 cup

Poultry Seasoning Mix

INGREDIENTS

- 2 teaspoons dried thyme leaves
- 2 teaspoons dried basil leaves
- 1½ teaspoons dried marjoram leaves
- ¼ teaspoon onion powder
- ¼ teaspoon garlic powder
- 1/8 teaspoon freshly ground black pepper

DIRECTION

- Combine the thyme, basil, marjoram, onion powder, garlic powder, and pepper in a small bowl and mix. Store at room temperature. You can grind all of these ingredients together to make a more like commercial poultry seasoning.

NUTRITIONAL

- Calories: 21
- Fat: >1g
- Sodium: 23mg
- Potassium: 132mg
- Phosphorus: 17mg
- Carbohydrates: 5g
- Protein: 1g

Preparation Time: 15 minutes|Cooking Time: 0 minutes|Servings: 2 tbsp.

Homemade Mustard

INGREDIENTS

- ¼ cup dry mustard
- 3 tablespoons mustard seeds
- 3 tablespoons apple cider vinegar
- 3 tablespoons water
- 2 tablespoons freshly squeezed lemon juice
- ½ teaspoon turmeric

DIRECTION

- Combine the dry mustard, mustard seeds, vinegar, water, lemon juice, and turmeric in a jar with a tight-fitting lid and stir to combine.
- Refrigerate the mustard for 3 days, stirring once a day and adding a bit more water every day if necessary.
- After three days, the mustard is ready to use. You can process the mixture in a food processor or blender if you'd like smoother mustard. Refrigerate up to 2 weeks.

NUTRITIONAL

- Calories: 9
- Fat: 0g
- Sodium: 0mg
- Potassium: 16mg
- Phosphorus: 13mg
- Carbohydrates: 1g
- Protein: 0g

Preparation Time: 15 minutes|Cooking Time: 0 minutes|Servings: ½ cup

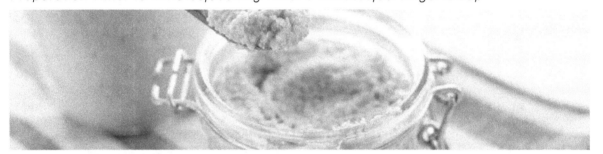

Cranberry Ketchup

INGREDIENTS

- 2 cups fresh cranberries
- 1 1/3 cups water
- 3 tablespoons brown sugar
- Juice of 1 lemon
- 2 teaspoons yellow mustard
- ¼ teaspoon onion powder
- Pinch salt
- Pinch ground cloves

DIRECTION

- Stir together the cranberries, water, brown sugar, lemon juice, mustard, onion powder, salt, and cloves in a medium saucepan on medium heat, then boil.
- Reduce the heat to low and simmer until the cranberries have popped, about 15 minutes. Mash using an immersion blender the ingredients right in the saucepan.
- After mashing, simmer the ketchup for another 5 minutes until thickened. Let the ketchup cool for 1 hour in the saucepan, then put it into an airtight container and store.

NUTRITIONAL

- Calories: 13
- Fat: 0g
- Sodium: 19mg
- Potassium: 17mg
- Phosphorus: 3mg
- Carbohydrates: 3g
- Protein: 0g

Preparation Time: 15 minutes|Cooking Time: 20 minutes|Servings: 1 cup

Barbecue Sauce

INGREDIENTS

- 1 can no-salt-added diced Red bell peppers, with juice
- 1 cup cherry Red bell peppers, cut in half
- 1/3 cup shredded carrots
- 3 tablespoons ketchup
- 2 tablespoons freshly squeezed lemon juice
- 1 tablespoon honey
- 2 teaspoons mustard
- 1 teaspoon paprika
- ½ teaspoon dried oregano
- ¼ teaspoon onion powder
- 1/8 teaspoon cayenne pepper

DIRECTION

- Combine the diced Red bell peppers, cherry Red bell peppers, carrots, ketchup, lemon juice, honey, mustard, paprika, oregano, cayenne, and onion powder. Then boil over medium heat in a saucepan.
- Adjust the heat to low and simmer within 10 to 12 minutes or until the vegetables are tender. Purée the batter using a blender or food processor, or right in the saucepan using an immersion blender or a potato masher.
- Return the mixture to the saucepan if using a blender or food processor. Bring to a simmer again. Simmer the sauce within 5 minutes or until slightly thickened.
- Cool the sauce for 1 hour in the saucepan. Then store in the refrigerator in a container with a lid for up to 2 weeks.

NUTRITIONAL

- Calories: 15
- Fat: 0g
- Sodium: 38mg
- Potassium: 94mg
- Phosphorus: 10mg
- Carbohydrates: 4g
- Protein: 0g

Preparation Time: 15 minutes|Cooking Time: 17 minutes|Servings: 2 cups

Romesco Sauce

INGREDIENTS

- 1 (16-ounce) jar roasted red peppers, drained
- ¼ cup slivered almonds
- 2 tablespoons extra-virgin olive oil
- 2 tablespoons freshly squeezed lemon juice
- 1 garlic clove, peeled
- ½ teaspoon paprika
- Pinch salt

DIRECTION

- Process the red peppers, almonds, olive oil, lemon juice, garlic, paprika, and salt in a food processor or blender. Store.

NUTRITIONAL

- Calories: 67
- Fat: 5g
- Sodium: 245mg
- Phosphorus: 32mg
- Potassium: 155mg
- Carbohydrates: 4g
- Protein: 1g

Preparation Time: 5 minutes |Cooking Time: 5 minutes|Servings: 2 cups

Grainy Mustard

INGREDIENTS

- ¼ cup dry mustard
- ¼ cup mustard seeds
- ¼ cup apple cider vinegar
- 3 tablespoons water
- 2 tablespoons freshly squeezed lemon juice
- ½ teaspoon ground turmeric
- 1/8 teaspoon salt

DIRECTION

- Mix the mustard, mustard seeds, vinegar, water, lemon juice, turmeric, and salt in a jar with a tight-fitting lid.
- Refrigerate the mustard for 5 days, stirring once a day and adding a bit more water every day, as the mustard will thicken as it stands. After 5 days, the mustard is ready to use. Fridge for up to 2 weeks.

NUTRITIONAL

- Calories: 22
- Fat: 2g
- Sodium: 13mg
- Phosphorus: 9mg
- Potassium: 13mg
- Carbohydrates: 1g
- Protein: 1g

Preparation Time: 15 minutes |Cooking Time: 0 minutes|Servings: ½ cup

Salsa Verde

INGREDIENTS

- 2 cups halved tomatillos or 1 can tomatillos, drained
- 3 scallions, chopped
- 1 jalapeño pepper, chopped
- 2 tablespoons extra-virgin olive oil
- 1/3 cup cilantro leaves
- 2 tablespoons freshly squeezed lime juice
- 1/8 teaspoon salt

DIRECTION

- Preheat the oven to 400°F. Mix the tomatillos, scallions, and jalapeño pepper on a rimmed baking sheet.
- Drizzle using the olive oil, then toss to coat. Roast the vegetables for 12 to 17 minutes or until the tomatillos are soft and light golden brown around the edges.
- Blend the roasted vegetables with the cilantro, lime juice, and salt in a blender or food processor. Blend until smooth. Store.

NUTRITIONAL

- Calories: 22
- Fat: 2g
- Sodium: 20mg
- Phosphorus: 8mg
- Potassium: 55mg
- Carbohydrates: 1g
- Protein: 0g

Preparation Time: 20 minutes |Cooking Time: 15 minutes|Servings: 2 cups

Grape Salsa

INGREDIENTS

- 1 cup coarsely chopped red grapes
- 1 cup coarsely chopped green grapes
- ½ cup chopped red onion
- 2 tablespoons freshly squeezed lime juice
- 1 tablespoon honey
- 1/8 teaspoon salt
- ¼ teaspoon freshly ground black pepper

DIRECTION

- Mix the grapes, onion, lime juice, honey, salt, and pepper in a medium bowl. Chill within 1 to 2 hours before serving or serve immediately.

NUTRITIONAL

- Calories: 51
- Fat: 0g
- Sodium: 53mg
- Phosphorus: 14mg
- Potassium: 121mg
- Carbohydrates: 14g
- Protein: 1g

Preparation Time: 15 minutes|Cooking Time: 0 minutes|Servings: 2 cups

Apple and Brown Sugar Chutney

INGREDIENTS

- 3 Granny Smith apples, peeled and chopped
- 1 onion, chopped
- 1 cup of water
- 1/3 cup brown sugar
- 2 teaspoons curry powder
- 1/8 teaspoon salt
- 1/8 teaspoon freshly ground black pepper

DIRECTION

- In a medium saucepan, combine the apples, onion, water, brown sugar, curry powder, and salt, plus pepper, then boil over medium-high heat.
- Adjust the heat to low, then simmer, occasionally stirring, for 45 to 55 minutes. Cool, then decant into jars or containers. Store.

NUTRITIONAL

- Calories: 27
- Fat: 0g
- Sodium: 11mg
- Phosphorus: 6mg
- Potassium: 48mg
- Carbohydrates: 7g
- Protein: 0g

Preparation Time: 15 minutes|Cooking Time: 60 minutes|Servings: 2 cups

Classic Spice Blend

INGREDIENTS

- 1 tablespoon whole black peppercorns
- 2 teaspoons caraway seeds
- 2 teaspoons celery seeds
- 1 teaspoon dill seeds
- 1 teaspoon cumin seeds

DIRECTION

- Grind the peppercorns, caraway seeds, celery seeds, dill seeds, and cumin in a spice blender or a mortar and pestle. Grind until the seeds are broken down, and the mixture almost becomes a powder.

NUTRITIONAL

- Calories: 2
- Fat: 0g
- Sodium: 0mg
- Phosphorus: 3mg
- Potassium: 8mg
- Carbohydrates: 0g
- Protein: 0g

Preparation Time: 10 minutes|Cooking Time: 0 minutes|Servings: 2 tbsp.

Basil Pesto Sauce

INGREDIENTS

- 2/3 cup of nutritional yeast
- .5 of a fresh lemon
- 6 tsp oil (olive)
- 3 garlic cloves
- 1 tsp of pepper
- 6 tsp of flax oil
- 16 oz. basil leaves
- 8 oz. of pine nuts

DIRECTION

- Extract juice out of lemon and put all of the items into a food processor except olive and flax oil.
- Mix the oils and pour them into the processor through the top to evenly distribute them while blending all of the ingredients.
- Stir from the bottom of the blender as needed. Store prepared pesto sauce in a jar or covered container until ready to use.

NUTRITIONAL

- Calories 122
- Phosphorus 99 mg
- Protein 4 g
- Carbohydrates 4 g
- Sodium 7 g
- Potassium 158 mg
- Fat 10 g

Preparation Time: 15 minutes |Cooking Time: 0 minutes|Servings: 1

Seafood Seasoning

INGREDIENTS

- 5 tsp of fennel seeds
- 4 tsp of dried parsley
- 5 tsp of dried basil
- 1 tsp of dried lemon peel

DIRECTION

- Crush up the fennel seeds and put the rest of the items into a jar, shaking to mix. Keep sealed until ready to coat fish or seafood.

NUTRITIONAL

- Calories 10
- Phosphorus 13 mg
- Protein 0 g
- Carbohydrates 2 g
- Sodium 4 mg
- Potassium 65 mg
- Fat 0 g

Preparation Time: 15 minutes |Cooking Time: 0 minutes|Servings: 1

Pizza Sauce

INGREDIENTS

- 1 tsp of oregano
- 6 oz. of tomato paste
- 1 tsp parsley flakes
- 6 tsp basil (fresh)
- 6 tsp of water
- 6 tsp of oil (olive)

DIRECTION

- Mix all of the ingredients. Add the water slowly, continuously stirring until there is nice spreadable consistency to the sauce. Makes enough for two pizzas.

NUTRITIONAL

- Calories 68
- Phosphorus 2 mg
- Protein 1 g
- Potassium 409 mg
- Carbohydrates 9 g
- Sodium 131 mg

Preparation Time: 15 minutes |Cooking Time: 0 minutes|Servings: 1

Chicken and Turkey Seasoning

INGREDIENTS

- 6 tsp sage
- 6 tsp thyme
- 1 tsp of ground pepper
- 2 tsp of dried marjoram

DIRECTION

1. Mix all the spices and keep in an airtight container. Good for up to one year.

NUTRITIONAL

- Calories 3
- Phosphorus 1 mg
- Protein 0 g
- Potassium 8 mg
- Carbohydrates 0 g
- Sodium 0 mg

Preparation Time: 5 minutes|Cooking Time: 0 minutes|Servings: 1

Garlicky Sauce

INGREDIENTS

- 6 tsp of lemon juice
- .25 tsp salt
- 1 head garlic
- 8 oz. of olive oil

DIRECTION

- Peel apart the cloves of garlic and clean them. Place the garlic, half a tablespoon of lemon juice, and salt in the bottom of a blender. Pour the olive oil slowly in a thin stream while blending.
- The mixture should become thick and white, resembling salad dressing. Add the remaining lemon juice and continue to blend. Keeps in a container for fourteen days.

NUTRITIONAL

- Calories 103
- Phosphorus 3 mg
- Protein 0 g
- Carbohydrates 1 g
- Sodium 30 mg
- Potassium 11 mg
- Fat 11 g

Preparation Time: 15 minutes|Cooking Time: 0 minutes|Servings: 1

Conclusion

You likely had little knowledge about your kidneys before. You probably didn't know how you could take steps to improve your kidney health and decrease the risk of developing kidney failure. However, through reading this book, you now understand the power of the human kidney and the prognosis of chronic kidney disease. While over thirty-million Americans are being affected by kidney disease, you can now take steps to be one of the people who is actively working to promote your kidney health.

These stats are alarming, so it is necessary to take proper care of your kidneys, starting with a kidney-friendly diet. These recipes are ideal for whether you have been diagnosed with a kidney problem or want to prevent any kidney issue.

As for your well-being and health, it's a good idea to see your doctor as often as possible to make sure you don't have any preventable problems you don't need to have. The kidneys are your body's channel for toxins (as is the liver), cleaning the blood of unknown substances and toxins removed from things like preservatives in the food and other toxins. The moment you eat without control and fill your body with toxins, food, drink (liquor or alcohol, for example), or even the air you inhale in general, your body will also convert several things that appear to be benign until the body's organs convert them to things like formaldehyde, due to a synthetic response and transformation phase.
One such case is a large part of the dietary sugars used in diet sodas - for example, aspartame is converted to formaldehyde in the body. These toxins must be excreted, or they can cause disease, renal (kidney) failure, malignant growth, and various other painful problems

This isn't a condition that occurs without any forethought it is a dynamic issue and in that it very well may be both found early and treated, diet changed, and settling what is causing the issue is conceivable. It's conceivable to have partial renal failure yet, as a rule; it requires some time (or downright poor diet for a short time) to arrive at absolute renal failure. You would prefer not to reach total renal failure since this will require standard dialysis treatments to save your life.

Dialysis treatments explicitly clean the blood of waste and toxins in the blood utilizing a machine in light of the fact that your body can no longer carry out the responsibility. Without treatments, you could die a very painful death. Renal failure can be the consequence of long-haul diabetes, hypertension, unreliable diet, and can stem from other health concerns.

A renal diet is tied in with directing the intake of protein and phosphorus in your eating routine. Restricting your sodium intake is likewise significant. By controlling these two variables you can control the vast majority of the toxins/waste made by your body and thus this enables your kidney to 100% function. In the event that you get this early enough and truly moderate your diets with extraordinary consideration, you could avert complete renal failure. If you get this early, you can take out the issue completely.

Conversion Tables

Volume Equivalents (Liquid)

US STANDARD	US STANDARD (OUNCES)	METRIC (APPROXIMATE)
2 tablespoons	1 fl. oz.	30 mL
¼ cup	2 fl. oz.	60 mL
½ cup	4 fl. oz.	120 mL
1 cup	8 fl. oz.	240 mL
1½ cups	12 fl. oz.	355 mL
2 cups or 1 pint	16 fl. oz.	475 mL
4 cups or 1 quart	32 fl. oz.	1 L
1 gallon	128 fl. oz.	4 L

Volume Equivalents (Dry)

US STANDARD	METRIC (APPROXIMATE)
¼ teaspoon	1 mL
½ teaspoon	2 mL
1 teaspoon	5 mL
1 tablespoon	15 mL
¼ cup	59 mL
cup	79 mL
½ cup	118 mL
1 cup	177 mL

Oven Temperatures

FAHRENHEIT (F)	CELSIUS (C) (APPROXIMATE)
250°F	120 °C
300°F	150°C
325°F	165°C
350°F	180°C
375°F	190°C
400°F	200°C
425°F	220°C
450°F	230°C

Weight Equivalents

US STANDARD	METRIC (APPROXI-MATE)
½ ounce	15 g
1 ounce	30 g
2 ounces	60 g
4 ounces	115 g
8 ounces	225 g
12 ounces	340 g
16 ounces or 1 pound	455 g
450°F	230°C

Chapter 24.
Meal Plan

Days	Breakfast	Lunch	Dinner
1	Breakfast Salad from Grains and Fruits	Dolmas Wrap	Baked Pork Chops
2	French toast with Applesauce	Salad al Tonno	Beef Kabobs with Pepper
3	Bagels Made Healthy	Arlecchino Rice Salad	One-Pot Beef Roast
4	Cornbread with Southern Twist	Sauteed Chickpea and Lentil Mix	Cabbage and Beef Fry
5	Grandma's Pancake Special	Crazy Japanese Potato and Beef Croquettes	Mushroom and Olive Sirloin Steak
6	Pasta with Indian Lentils	Traditional Black Bean Chili	California Pork Chops
7	Pineapple Bread	Green Palak Paneer	Caribbean Turkey Curry
8	Parmesan Zucchini Frittata	Cucumber Sandwich	Chicken Fajitas
9	Garlic Mayo Bread	Pizza Pitas	Chicken Veronique
10	Strawberry Topped Waffles	Lettuce Wraps with Chicken	Chicken and Apple Curry
11	Cheese Spaghetti Frittata	Turkey Pinwheels	London Broil
12	Shrimp Bruschetta	Chicken Tacos	Sirloin with Squash and Pineapple
13	Strawberry Muesli	Tuna Twist	Slow-Cooked BBQ Beef
14	Yogurt Bulgur	Ciabatta Rolls with Chicken Pesto	Lemon Sprouts
15	Mozzarella Cheese Omelet	Marinated Shrimp Pasta Salad	Lemon and Broccoli Platter
16	Sun-Dried Tomato Frittata	Peanut Butter and Jelly Grilled Sandwich	Chicken Liver Stew
17	Italian Breakfast Frittata	Grilled Onion and Pepper Jack Grilled Cheese Sandwich	Simple Lamb Chops
18	Sausage Cheese Bake Omelet	Crispy Lemon Chicken	Chicken and Mushroom Stew
19	Greek Egg Scrambled	Mexican Steak Tacos	Baked Pork Chops
20	Feta Mint Omelet	Beer Pork Ribs	Beef Kabobs with Pepper
21	Sweet pancakes	Grilled Chicken	One-Pot Beef Roast

Recipes Index

Recipes Index

Recipes Index

Recipes Index

Recipes Index

Recipes Index

Recipes Index

CPSIA information can be obtained
at www.ICGtesting.com
Printed in the USA
LVHW100022050221
678441LV00016B/497